The Pen
Juliette Rose

Jesse W. Benson

Acknowledgements

A special thanks to Grandma who inspired me to live on, even after her death. I knew you for five years, which equates to only 12% of my existence. But that 12% is proof that time, no matter how short, if impactful can make all the difference!

Thank you Emanuel Lamont Axel my brother who died, but through your death my life was positively changed. Your resurrection through me is eternal!

Thank you Crazy Joe. If it wasn't for your immorality and vile hands around the neck of my impressionable young life, I would not be able to help the many who suffer like me today. You are forgiven, but never forgotten!

Thank you everyone that experienced living life with me during one of the most difficult times for me to happily do so. I am certain the journey was not the most consistent or easiest of paths available for any of us to take. However, your loyalty to my pursuit of perfection is greatly appreciated and will not go unrewarded.

"We are all nothing more than the sum total of all of our experiences. Not as individuals, but humanity as one. So with great care and understanding we must not only acknowledge this truth, but we must breathe it. We must nurture it. And we must live it, together!"

JWB

Chapter 1

a Penniless Soul

Sometimes if I close my eyes I can hear every pounding word grinding against my sanity and my serenity causing them both to abandon me. And even though it is excruciatingly loud inside my head I am silently alone. He still haunts me. I am reluctant to admit it because acknowledgement is a prison that I refuse to die in. So instead I just betray the truth by embracing a lie that ultimately lets me continue to breathe. *How long can I keep bobbing my head above what I portray to be shallow water but impossibly drowning me? I have swum this nightmare as long as I can remember without ever reaching shore. I'm tired of swimming, so tired that I'm not.* I do not understand why God has placed me here. I'm too angry to speak with him and too helpless not to which makes me feel pathetically hopeless. So all of my words stay cowardly but loudly hidden inside my heart where only God and I can hear. And even then there are times when my own words elude me and these times are the most frightening because in such I have no restraint over losing myself. *Why can't I get rid of Him? Am I still afraid of Him? Hell no! That's absurd, or is it?* I don't think I've been afraid of anything other than Him since I've been born but I truly don't know. What I do know is fearing Him now is completely unacceptable. *Who am I kidding? Am I just trying to sell myself here? What is the fear of Him anyway? Am I afraid because my nightmares still awaken me to drenched bed sheets, or does everyone sweat it out at night? Does everyone know what it feels like to share your every day life with a demon? Or am I alone in this?* I've always felt alone. And for as long as I can remember I've always been a penniless soul.

I was only 5 years old when God taught me what a coward was. This being a lesson I wish he would have taught another, but for some reason he selected me. To know pain one must experience great joy. So the first four years of my life were joyous ones. So why is it that the great times I remember the least and the evil ones continue to torment me? When I was three I had a book about a plane that I loved to read. I don't remember what the book was totally about. All I remember is that I loved that book. Wherever I went, the book was sure to follow like Mary's little lamb. Until I lost the book. I was so stupid to lose that book! My family used to throw me birthday parties every year back then. I remember loving those parties until I lost those too. I remember everything until I lost everything and I lost everything when she married that coward. *What sane person marries a coward anyway?* He was more than three hours late on their wedding day. *COWARD!* He didn't have a job. *COWARD!* He beat on small children. *COWARD!* And He said I could always come to Him for anything because He loved me. *COWARD! COWARD! COWARD!* Lord help me to never become what I despise the most. Amen!

I had learned first hand at an early age how fear is the ultimate power of true intimidation. A man can manipulate the greatest of minds with only teaspoons of fear. And everyday that coward would force me to choke on plenty. To truly appreciate the effect you must first understand the cause. Before He came into my life I lived in a very close knit, loving environment. My grandmother, mother, aunt, two cousins and I all lived in the same project apartment complex. In fact, for a few years we all lived in the same two bedroomed apartment like happy sardines. Believe it or not these were the most comfortable accommodations of my life. These were also some of the happiest memories

I can recall. Even though we were extremely poor, I never knew it because our house was always filled with joy and laughter. I was never alone then, the house was too small for that. And there was never a quiet moment. Either me and my cousins were fighting or playing (both one in the same), or my grandma and aunt were loving and teaching us how to be (again both one in the same). But there was never a dull moment that's for sure. Poverty never stopped us from having food on the table, clothes on our backs and joy in our hearts. I know now the glue holding all that happiness together was my Grandma Jessie who I'm actually named after. While she was alive everything seemed to have purpose and meaning. Everything seemed to have an unmentioned order to it then. My mom was just an ordinary mom. She loved me but not enough or too much to discipline me. So she left all of the hard chastising up to my granny and auntie. My Aunt Lorene was young and employed which I'm sure helped out a lot. Her daughter Leslie and son Emanuel kept me very busy each day with their curiosities of life and pursuit of mischief. *A young boy couldn't ask for better cousins.* We had ice cream and cake, cookies and cream, toys and games and all of the above. It was just a wonderful time to be kid. It was these things that had us overlook the rats and roaches, homeless strangers and thieves, and the overall gloom of living in the Projects. One cancelled out the other kind of nicely. And the good times we shared always outweighed the bad. So why would mom change it? Why would she try to add to something already good? It was like trying to add rotten fruit to a basket that's already full of fresh ones. It's asinine. It's repulsive. And it's my past.

To this day I don't even know who my father is. Is that important? I'm not sure how important it is because you certainly can't miss something you've never had. But 36 years after the fact, why has my mother chosen to invoke her right to remain silent and not tell me who he is? Well

I may not know who my father is, but I definitely knew who the devil was and He didn't wear Prada! He wore baggy slacks with tennis shoes and no shirt most of the time. He carried kitchen knives and screwdrivers inside of a black rubber glove, with a dirty sock over the top to hide His weapons of choice inside His back pocket. He was in amazing shape for His age. In fact I would be hard pressed to find a fifty-year-old man in better shape than Him. He would take me to the park often just to intimidate me. I never wanted to go, but He would force me to go. As if walking 5 miles to the park wasn't exercise enough, He would run for miles around the park to boost His cardiovascular wretchedness. I would often sprint ahead of Him while we jogged in hopes of losing Him. But no matter what eventually while I'd be pulled off to the side of the track taking a short breather, there He would be catching back up to me at His own pace. In spite of my young age deep inside I knew that our race was never physical, but yet a men tal one. Some days I would be lucky enough to go to the park with Him and other children would be there. I had to ask permission to go play with them and sometimes He would allow it. This of course was a set up that I eventually figured out later. But though I had figured it out, I would still ask permission to play. Why? Today I realize it as a deep down aggressive will to survive in spite of…that's the only way I can describe it. He would give me permission to play with the other kids just to watch me build up some excitement so that eventually He could get his enjoyment of tearing mine down. At first I didn't know He would be watching as I was too busy playing. But later I recognized His gaze during my triumph, and that look was terrifying.

This was my chance to prove that I was a great football player. None of the kids in the park knew how good I was because I usually wasn't allowed to play with them. I didn't have a football at home. All I had was an old tennis ball that I had found in the mud on the side of the road at the park one day. I hid it in my pocket on the way home and kept it hidden under the porch. I knew if He found out I had it He would beat me, so under the porch it stayed most of the time. But when He was not at home I would go outside and throw the ball up against the wall at weird angles so that it would bounce back awkwardly. I tasked myself with then trying to catch the ball off the wall before it could hit the ground no matter how crazily or fast it bounced back. Often I would have to jump or dive in order to catch it. My goal was 100 throws without dropping the ball one time. If I ever dropped it just once, then I would have to start the count over again. The bricks on the side of the homeless shelter wall had grooves in it so I truly never knew which way the ball would bounce back. I just needed to be swift in making a decision once that ball came off that wall. And swift I was! Sometimes I'd be at 99 catches and for the last throw I would attempt a near impossible angle just to challenge myself. Imagine that! All the way to 99 and then risking it all in the last attempt just to prove my worth. I would often miss catching the last one because of the difficulty of the throw, but no matter what if I missed it, the count would have to start over. *Why? Why would I have to start over? It wasn't like this was a real game being played for real money being observed by a real coach! This was a made up game being watched by only two, my ego and myself. However, cheating was never an option for me. I refused to lie to myself. There were plenty of lies going headstrong in my life as it was, no need for me to add to that bodacious number. When you think about it that's a pretty lonely game to be playing as a kid. Why was I alone when I had Leslie and Emanuel to entertain me you ask? What happened to them and why weren't they playing too? It is because in the biggest game of all games...the game of life, there are no rules, no justice and no rhyme to any reasoning of what could or should be. In that game there is only what is. It too holds winners and losers just like any other game, however the stakes are much higher and the rewards of doing exceptionally well or the penalties of failure have way deeper and more defined lines of expressed consequences overall. In the game of life everyone's a player whether they've earned the right to play or not. And He immediately decided when He joined ours that we couldn't play the game together. But the only one of us that would be penalized for the disobedience of this rule would be me, His stepson. Since they were not His and no longer lived with us Leslie and Manny were protected. I was always jealous of their freedom because it used to be familiar to me. Now it was no more familiar than a language spoken by happiness or an embrace cuddled from kindness, both long forsaken and forgotten by my soul. Is this how spirits die or the hell many speak of? I often wondered, but never pondered. There is a difference!*

The team that picked me up was to say the least not the winning team. It was full of kids who were too short, too small, too slow or just plain too *non-footballish'* to be playing football. The winning team had one more player than mine so picking me up just made sense since we were outnumbered. That may have been the only reason they allowed me to play because I didn't know any of these kids. Most of them belonged to a church across the street from the park and had only come over to play football during the lunchtime of a bible school program that they had been attending for the summer. I didn't care what they were there for. I was just excited that He finally gave me permission to play with some children that were my age for once. At home He only allowed me to have one friend in the neighborhood, John, who He only let me play with because John had autism and He thought John was severely dumb. But John wasn't dumb at all. I never explained that to Him because if I did He might have not allowed me to play with John either. Today I was just happy to be playing period because these moments were basically nonexistent. The sad thing was our team was down by two touchdowns and the game was over once any team scored 10 times. The score was 8 to 6 so the other team only had two more times to score before the game would be completely over with. I couldn't allow this to happen because I just started playing and wanted playtime to be a little longer. I mean, how often would I get this opportunity to make new friends and be impressive? Never! So for me this was more than just a pick up game of football, it was the epitome of an opportunity of a lifetime!

If Mook thinks he's getting this ball, he's sadly mistaken. On my way over to the field I had seen him embarrassing his competitors by faking one direction and cutting back the other way. He had kids slipping and falling all over the place. No one could guard him. In the short period of time of me just walking over and asking the group if I could play too, he had scored two touchdowns, one from a handoff and the other off an interception. I had to admit to myself, he was pretty damn good! So since I needed the game to go on much longer I took it upon myself to accept the challenge of stopping him. Mook was pretty quick. He was an elusive player so I had to be very careful in not allowing his cleverness to get the best of me. The first couple of plays I was just feeling him out. I let him catch the ball one time just so I could figure out the way he moved. That one time could have been costly as he almost broke free and scored. That's when I realized I couldn't procrastinate with completely shutting Mook down or my chance at making new friends would be short lived. He was the most dangerous and arrogant player on their team and I could sense that he had no issues with driving nails in coffins. But today he was in for a rude awakening because as you have it I just so happen to not be a huge fan of handyman tools or caskets! That possession I didn't let Mook catch another ball or his team score at all. My teammates were looking at me with amazement as if I had been summoned from on high. The look in their eyes warmed my insides with feelings of empowerment and self worth. In that moment it felt like my life was suspended in midair hovering high above the deceptive and manipulative terrains of filth that I was so accustomed to groveling in. Down there the muds of smothering disappointment were thick with hatred swallowing my entire being and no matter how hard I tried to keep my head above ground, there was always just one more layer to pull and chin up over. But up here I could breathe a god's breath! I could stay up here for a lifetime floating over adversity and gliding to my true self. This was an out of body experience that I could watch on repeat without once having to change the channel. But unfortunately for me I wasn't the only one watching. I completely forgot He was even there and had I known what would happen next I would have certainly turned off the show.

My head twisted sideways so hard from the slap that my neck tensed up to keep it attached. I was slightly dazed but not enough to stop me from quickly spinning back around to see who had the nerve to hit me after I scored. *First of all, who would hit someone in the face after they had clearly scored a touchdown? Second of all, who would hit someone after they had scored the final touchdown to end the game?* All these thoughts barely had time to sprint through my head before I got a glimpse of the masculine figure standing over me. I knew those stupid pants anywhere! Plain dingy tan khakis slightly wrinkled with no belt keeping them on His oddly defined waist. I knew those shoes, clean yet dirty old brownish grey suede McGregor running shoes that you could tell by the color scheme were no longer in production or stock. Only a dinosaur of a man would have been caught dead wearing those! I knew that breath, the kind that didn't smell but you still didn't want in your face because the warmth of it breathing down your neck simply meant you were definitely about to be in harm's way. He was overbearingly perched over me the way eagles stand over their prey right before they take off dragging them by their neck through the sky to their inevitable death, with His t-shirt half twisted over His neck allowing the front of His chest to be shirtless. And before I could realize anything else familiar about Him, He slapped even harder once more with the hand baring the rubber glove. *Who in the hell would wear a weird ass spooky looking rubber glove to a public park anyway?* I thought. *This fool that's who!* I could have absorbed the second slap no differently than the first but to avoid further embarrassment I let my knees buckle so that the grass could catch my fall. I knew that if I had not buckled a third slap would have been indefinite. I even awkwardly fell forward so that my eyes would fall face first in the dirt in a futile attempt to not allow them to make contact with those of my newly acquired friends. But their gasping sounds of "ahhh" were in poor unison like a badly rehearsed gospel choir, none in sync but with overall good intentions... made me glance up at them while picking my head out of the dirt. They had looks of confusion and disbelief resembling the exact same look I had 6 years ago when it happened to me for the first time. By my calculations this would only be the one thousandth three hundredth and fifth time this had taken place, considering I was due an unwarranted beating at least five out of seven days of every week since we had met. The only thing I wondered was if there were any other 11 years olds out there other than me going through these same types of things. But by the looks and the sounds of the park choir, it wasn't likely. Then I felt my shirt tighten up around my neck as I was being hoisted up from the ground by my collar. He began to drag me away from the crowd as if I were a rabid infected dog that He wanted to protect them from. But I so dearly wanted them to protect me from Him! He was the rabid infected dog! No, He was the vicious monster that swallowed the crazy bear that ate the rabid infected dog as far as I was concerned! But I knew they couldn't help me. They barely even knew me. At this point all they knew was I was the kid that won the game and got his ass beat by some crazy man for making the game winning catch. But I so desperately didn't want to be remembered that way. At that moment I so needed to be back in the air hovering above despair, but all of that was over now. Now all I had was the wins and losses from another day of battle. This was the day I realized I was nothing more than a soldier in a war that I didn't want to fight, but had to dig deep to find a way to survive. My enemy was not foreign, but rather domestic and His mission was to destroy my mind, my body and my soul. While He was dragging, pushing and shoving me down the street He thought He was substantially without a shadow of a doubt accomplishing this feat, but fortunately for me He was doing the exact opposite. Because with every tug He was tugging at strings strumming the sounds of character enabling my soul to continue to dance. With every jerk He was jerking away the jolts of self-pity and the wicked weights of regret, so that my body could withstand and bare the pressures of pure evil. And with every slam He was slamming down a permanent mortar for God to lay bricks of intelligence and sandbags of perseverance upon, so that the desolate storm waters of depression and vile waves of persecution could not flood my mind. The looks of helplessness that those children gave me that day actually saved my life because it was those looks at that moment that took charge and decided for me to never allow anyone, not even Him to ever receive pleasure from people looking at me in that despicable, helpless way ever again. So let it be written, so let it be done!

Chapter 2
the Good Ole' Days

Yeah, I remember that. Those were the good ole days. I was in a trance reminiscing on when my life had love and joy. I just sat there on that rusty old orange and green sofa. Some of the stuffing was missing from the pillows and it was literally hard as a rock. My mom had the couch half covered with dingy sheets in a ridiculous attempt to make our furniture look nicer. There was an end table with uneven legs that had a dusty cracked ivory lamp resting on top of it. The lampshade was so dirty that even if a new bulb sat underneath, it would still look pretty dim. But no worries, there wouldn't be a bulb in it anyway for me to test that theory. There was a bold roach hanging out on the wall today not in a rush to get to his destination. For an instant I wondered what was so important for him to risk his life coming out here during the day. Certainly he knew the lifespan of a roach decreases greatly during the daytime and I knew these guys partied every night. *You'd think he'd be somewhere recuperating but then again maybe that's why he was moving so slowly today.* Whatever the case I'd allow him to make it because I wasn't truly looking at him. I was looking past him. I was looking deep toward where I wanted to be but couldn't return. In that imaginary place my Grandma was making homemade chocolate chip cookies, my favorite! I was waiting patiently on her couch that she kept protected by plastic covers, not dingy bed sheets like my mom. Above my head on the wall hung a masterpiece of an extremely large mirror with shelves comingout of it. On the shelves sat all kinds of different types   of porcelain *knick knacks* of cats and dogs, birds and children arranged in a strange but happy artistic fashion. The entire creation was my Grandma's pride and joy. I knew this from the experience of getting a spanking for trying to play with her precious collection many times in the past. Emanuel was taking turns with me playing his new Pac Man video game. He usually wouldn't let me play with him at all but today he was being extra nice because Grandma was making cookies and he didn't want to ruin his opportunity of getting his share of the chocolate treasure. Leslie was playing with her Barbie dolls trying to entice both of us to join in on something we both greatly despised. Every so often she would purposely act like she was having the greatest of times inside her lonely tea party, trying to make us jealous so that we would join in. It was always a pathetic failed attempt as Emanuel and I knew that trick all too well and wanted nothing to do with her overbearing Barbie doll tea parties. But because cookies were on the line instead of calling her silly names to make her angry we just ignored her for the sake of the treats. Because if Grandma ever heard any arguing the cookies would be made but not eaten, which would be a tragedy to say the least. So for now the sounds of Pac Man dying mixed with the fluttering of tongues sticking out at each other would have to do.

Yeah, I remember that. Those were the good ole days when I thought my life was bad but it really wasn't bad at all. Those were the days when love and I would wake up and have pillow fights. The days when our friends would impatiently wait for us at the playground in anticipation of the neighborhood kickball game and love would lace up her skates for us to hold hands and roll down the hill as fast as our little feet could muster. These were the days of cracker jacks and jumping jacks, monkey bars and sliding boards and they were so vivid I could smell them. I could inhale the happiness. I could breathe the sweet air of belonging to something delightfully lighter than the financial burden of mildewed wood my family always carried. But then I heard keys gently jingling outside the front door, the main one raping the lock as if destiny was trying to keep something sinister out. The door creaked while the first footstep stumbled down through the doorway slowly crushing the bubbled memory I'd just created. The sounds of summer began to feverishly seep out from all sides dragging my family and the fun I used to have back into the lake of forgotten dreams from whence they came. I tightly squeezed my eyes to try and plug the holes but there were just too many of them and it was entirely too late. The memories were gone just as quickly as they appeared and what remained in the doorway was the truth, His eyes beading down on me with disgust even though I hadn't done anything to deserve it. I just kept my head down starring at my lap as if I hadn't noticed He was there. This tactic seemed to work best with Him. I learned it from a television special on gorillas, which stated that if you were ever in harms way with one just to look away and to not make eye contact as this could make them angrier, as eye contact is considered by gorillas to be a challenge of strength. This is one gorilla that I was not trying to challenge so both eyes and hands in lap would be the decision I went with. The stare down between us, though only seconds seemed to last for hours. Him staring at me, me staring at my quivering knees. *Why all of sudden did I have to pee?* I frantically thought. *My stupid ass would have to pee at a time like this. Concentrate dumbass before all this twitching gets your head chopped off!* But it was too late. I felt His prison calloused hand wrap around my jaw slamming my head against the wall lips snarling, "You don't know how to speak when someone comes home monkey ass little nigga?!!!" Seeing how the television special lied about eye contact and gorillas I decided to look this monster directly in the eyes, but I didn't say a word. I just needed to know if there was a soul lurking behind those beady little eyes of His and as far as I could tell there was not. So He gripped my face even harder in an attempt to make me answer His rhetorical question. But I didn't want to answer. I didn't want to lie to Him like how my mother lied to me when she told me that everything would be all right because we were children of God and God doesn't make mistakes. She said that God had brought Him and her together and that I needed to respect Him because that's what the Bible said. She said to thank God for all that he had given me and to have faith that things would be better. But I had thanked God for all that he had given me. I also thanked him for all that he had taken away from me. Coincidentally Grandma died as soon as He entered our lives. He had forbid me to see her and she died about one month after that ungodly rule. I know deep down inside that she had died from the heartbreak and loneliness of me not being with her anymore. *Why had God forsaken her when she believed? Why had God forsaken me when I believed as well? Did God not hear me all those days I would lock myself inside the living room closet kneeled facedown in the corner begging for God to allow aliens to abduct Him, murderers to kill Him or for Him to just have a heart attack instead of that other guy?* Mom said that all I needed was the faith of a mustard seed and that God would move on my behalf. *But why wasn't God moving in her behalf? And what the fuck is a mustard seed???* I just wanted this bastard to take His crusty fingers off of me and just let me be! A tear started to roll down the side of my face that I couldn't stop. I wanted to stop it before it slid between His fingers because it was mine and I would never give Him anything that belonged to me. Not my pride. Not my respect. Not my soul. And not even my tears! All He could get was the hell away from me. But I could tell that if I didn't give Him what He truly wanted this entire scene was going to run longer than originally scheduled. So I reluctantly said "Yes sir, sorry daddy!" Then He took His hand off from around my face and walked away. And that's when I took my shoe off and walked over to that roach that was still hanging out on the wall and let him have it!

Chapter 3

Checkers & Grandma

Who am I? Many ask themselves this without ever receiving a truthful or acceptable answer and then die to pass the mystery on to someone else. But I refuse to let it go. I can no longer *zombishly* stumble along unknown paths with the absence of knowing who I am and what I represent. The word on the street is that I'll never know where I'm going if I don't know where I'm from. But where I'm from is clouded by misguided fogs of distrust and betrayal that have skewed my thoughts and prolonged my steps of acceptance of what my true purpose is within this life. So I cannot be concerned with my past, just aware of it. I cannot get lost in the before because afterwards could inevitably have me never found, not even by me. I can only wade in the waters of ago, but never bathe. I can tread, but never swim. So hopefully for my sake to find who I am does not require a great amount of looking backward or living there. Whatever the case I will not accept failure in my search. I am determined to proudly walk upright wherever my steps may lead. If all paths lead to the same place I am now determined to know their names and to make their acquaintances before gracing them with the soles of my feet. For a long time I believed my walk was one of solidarity with the devil but have come to realize how many angels and gods have held hands with me throughout the journey.

The principal of my school had pretty much had enough of my behavior to last her a lifetime. I'm sure she could not fathom how a sixyear-old kid's behavior could be so unruly, but there I was sitting in front of her awaiting her judgment. It was late spring and so far the school year I was having was less than inspiring. At this point I had received a paddle for misbehavior at least once a day every single day of the year, but I didn't believe Mrs. Sanders would entertain paddling me this time. She had already forewarned my mother previously that my next offense would get me removed from the public school system in its entirety. *If that happened how would I continue my education?* We were too poor for me to be instated to a private school or to get home schooled so the only option for me would be to go to a disciplinary school designed for troubled children in and out of juvenile jail. My mom feared this because she knew I would be too young for that fate. "Why'd you do it son?" Mrs. Sanders asked me with the look that adults give children when they're baffled by an occurrence because they truly have zero understanding of the situation since it has never happened to them before. "Why did you leave the school premises without permission?" Now this question was one that I couldn't possibly answer to Mrs. Sander's expectations because I was certain that she was looking for an answer that was short, sweet and to the point. However, the answer that I needed to give that reigned true wouldn't be a short one. It all started a year earlier when I was 5, before Grandma died. She was teaching me who I was to become without me being able to see it at the time, but now it's as clear to me as the sound of a church bell. Grandma would teach me life lessons through life's lessons, which is a form of genius within itself. Checkers is the game that catapulted me into the way I play the game of life I live today. It was going to be hard for me to explain this to Mrs. Sanders because I was too young at the time to understand it myself, let alone explain it to someone else. I looked down at the office floor and began to explain:

"Ahh ha...whatcha' gonna do now Grandma!" I yelled triumphantly as I moved another black checker

piece forward on the checkerboard. Black was my favorite color so I always chose to be the black pieces when I played against her. Grandma had decided to play a game of Checkers with me after she yelled at me for not picking up the garbage I had dropped on the ground earlier. She told me that I was the reason why our neighborhood had rats and roaches. I thought to myself (since I didn't dare speak such things aloud in fear of being smacked in the mouth) Grandma has no idea what she's talking about...I don't even like rats and roaches so why would they come here to be friends with me! I don't know why I was playing her in Checkers anyway. She would religiously beat me every time we'd play. She would wipe out all of my pieces with her three or four kings. I never got far enough across the board to even get a king. I promised her that if I ever got a king, even one, that I would surely beat her. She would just laugh and tell me to shut up and lose. This was probably the only time I truly disliked her. She would never have mercy on me and let me win like my mom would some games. She would beat me the same way with the same intensity every single time. Even when we played simple games like Tic Tac Toe she wouldn't let me win. But today I felt like I could win. But then again I always felt like I could win. Every time Grandma would take one of my pieces I would cry out "You're cheating!" She would just laugh and again tell me to shut up and lose. Every game I felt like she was badly embarrassing me. She would beat me so bad that I would cry. And every time I cried after losing she would yell at me and tell me that we would never play checkers again because she and the world doesn't play with crybabies. But every day, the very next day we would play again and she would beat me again. This would happen over and over and over. However, today was not like the other days. Today I had just as many pieces left on the board as she did. And today I had done the unseen, the impossible, and the unimaginable (at least to me that is). I had finally retrieved my beloved king piece! And oh how I gracefully and cautiously moved him across the board in an attempt to destroy her right where she sat. I wanted to be able to tell her to shut up and lose. Of course even if I won I knew better than to try and say something like that to her. If I ever did I would need dentures, like the ones she would keep in a coffee cup on the kitchen counter. But that's just it, I was winning this time...and distinctively so. Finally Grandma moved her last piece and I swallowed it up as if my pieces were alive and hadn't eaten for weeks. She was dead meat no matter which way she moved and I knew it. "It's over! It's over! Down goes Frazier! Down goes Frazier!" I yelled out emphatically imitating someone that   I had heard on TV earlier. Grandma just sat there quiet for a moment. She had a look on her face that I had never seen before. It was a look of passion and pride. Tears began to roll down her face and I knew that she wasn't crying the same way that I would after I lost games. These were tears of joy and accomplishment. And then she stood up tall, taller than I have ever noticed before and said "Boy, that's who ya are and that's who ya always been...a winner, and don't yas forget it!" *And I wouldn't forget it either. Grandma had instilled in me something that no one could undo. Pride!* This pride would ultimately save my life but currently was the same pride that had me in Mrs. Sander's office. I looked up at her while telling the story expecting her to intervene and stop me from ranting, but she never did so I just continued:

"So we all piled into the car to take a trip to the grocery store. I never even knew we had a car to pile up in, but we did. In fact this would be my first trip to the grocery store as all the other times my mom would go without me and leave me at home with Grandma. And what would Grandma and I be doing while everyone else was at the store? Of course, playing Checkers! But this time we were all going to the store together, me-Grandma-Leslie-Emanuel-Mom   and   Auntie

Lorene. For me this was an exciting thing because at this point in my life I hadn't been anywhere outside of the Projects where we lived. This would be my first encounter with the outside world and I was more than eager to have it. In route to the store we began to pass homes that were different than where we stayed. These were individually owned places with front and backyards with white picket fences and doghouses. The grass was cut to perfection as if the lawns had received very nicely groomed haircuts. The sprinklers were running happily giving the yards their daily baths. And the porches were full of spirited families drinking lemonade poured from pitchers made of the best porcelain glass. I had never before seen the likes of these homes because I had never ventured outside of the confines of the Projects. We didn't have any of these things. We didn't have front or back yards, just spaces that we hoped the neighbors would believe belonged to us. We didn't have sprinklers, as the maintenance men would only use hoses to spray mud from off the bottom of their boots. We did have a bunch of stray cats, but they didn't need houses because they lived on top of the sewers where they chased rats all day. So as you can imagine I was pretty impressed with the houses we were passing on our way to the grocer. So as we passed I asked aloud "What are those?" pointing at the houses. "What are these nice places with the children playing and the big ole porches?" I asked again as everyone was looking around confused as if I were speaking a foreign tongue. My mom just shook her head in annoyance while my cousins laughed and told me to shut up. Auntie Lorene answered me and said "those are houses boy, what of it?" I could tell by her tone that she wasn't aggravated yet so I still had time to get my curiosity out of the way before she snapped on me. So I asked with spirit "Why don't we live in one of those? They're awfully nice, way nicer than where we live!" That's when Leslie shouted "shut up boy!" Auntie Lorene looked at Leslie in dismay and said to me "You have to have money to stay in those dear and we just don't have enough money to stay there. But be thankful for what we do have because it's more than what others will ever get." As nice as my aunt responded to me you'd think I would have just left good enough alone but that's not the type of boy Grandma raised me to be. In my mind this was just another Checkers game and I needed to get my pieces to the other side of the board of understanding so I sarcastically asked "Whose fault is it that we don't have enough money to move where we all definitely deserve to be?" My mom's head just flopped down as if I had just said a bad word. Aunt Lorene joined in with my cousins while they laughed and everyone except Grandma yelped out "Shut up boy!" But Grandma had other plans than squashing my questions and immediately pulled the car over to the side of the road. I could tell that she was upset and that was the last thing that I wanted to happen. I loved Grandma so much and the thought of me upsetting her brought tears to my eyes. She quickly looked at me through the rearview mirror and then she turned to my mom and Auntie Lorene and gave them the same look she gave me that one time I took one of her famous knick knacks outside to play in the dirt. That's when I realized that she wasn't upset with me. Obviously Leslie and Emanuel had seen this from Grandma before because all of a sudden they were sitting up straight in the backseat as if we were in school taking an important test. "Don'ts yous tells that boy tas shut up when he's asking questions thats matters most! Sometimes God's speakin' and we're just too fars into our own selves to even hear him!" she scolded mommy and auntie. And the way she spoke reminded me why Grandma was big mama and also the head of the household. It was as if time itself had stopped just to hear her speak and it wouldn't dare move again until she finished speaking. Then she turned to me and said "Baby, if yous wants ta

live in one of those houses yous gone' need tas makes lots of money when yous grows up. And if you wants tas makes lots of money when yous grows up, yous gone needs ta becomes an engineer. And tas becomes an engineer yous gone needs ta gets straights A's on yas reports cards and tests in that there schools yous bouts to start goings ta in the fall, ya hears me son?" When Grandma asked any questions in the tone she was speaking in I already knew I had to answer whether I understood or not. But I did understand because she always explained things to me in a language that fit my soul. So I with dignity for her coming to my rescue said "Yes mama, to get a nice house I'm going to need a lot of money and to get a lot of money I'm going to need to become an engineer. But to become an engineer I can't get grades like Leslie and Emanuel because the grades they get are the types that put us where we currently live now! You can count on me Grandma!"

I couldn't read the look on Mrs. Sanders' face because I hadn't seen it before. It was a look of astonishment mixed with sympathy, which in turn gave me a sort of frightened mixed with relief type of feeling that I had not encountered before either. I didn't know whether to keep talking or not because I was still waiting for Mrs. Sanders to intervene. But she never did. I had totally forgotten that my mom had coached me before we got to Mrs. Sanders' office to basically be quiet, listen to Mrs. Sanders, say yes ma'am and no ma'am and to speak politely only when Mrs. Sanders asked me to. The look of "OMG here we go again" on my mom's face quickly reminded me of her request of my silence, but because Mrs. Sanders was silent I thought that was my queue to continue on, so that's what I did:

"I never realized how popular my Grandma was until the day of her funeral. There were hundreds of people there many of which I had never seen before. There were even some white people in attendance, which excited me because I only got to see them on

television or in front of the classroom teaching me, but never in person outside of those two areas. Everyone's attire seemed so important, so special because they were well kept and ironed. The funeral hall reminded me of our church, except more grand in appearance and size. My Grandma was asleep in some wooden bed and all I could think about was how could she sleep with all this commotion going on? We were all sitting together in the front row. I was so excited because I was finally getting to spend some time with my cousins, if you can call sitting next to them on a hard wooden bench spending time. I wanted to play hide & go seek in the funeral home but Leslie called me a fool and said we couldn't. Manny just looked at me in disbelief sort of the same way he looked at me that day when he tripped over the yard chain and busted his mouth wide open and I was laughing, except this look was colder, nastier, and sadder. As a matter of fact everyone seemed sad. I may have been the only happy person in the building! I mean at five years old I was only concerned with the gathering of family that Crazy Joe had cut me off from. Crazy Joe... that was the devil's name now! At least that's what the entire neighborhood (all except me) was calling Him. I however was calling Him yes sir and no sir, all day every day in fear of receiving the belt. Thank goodness He wasn't at this funeral!

Everyone was crying and crying. They would go up to the wooden bed, look at Grandma and release the rivers. I just didn't understand it. Why was everyone so sad and how could Grandma sleep for so long with all the noise? Leslie and Manuel were crying too. I asked Leslie why she was crying and she said because Grandma would be sleeping forever. I didn't believe her. She lied often and she probably was trying to trick me again. Just to keep up with everyone else I would cry from time to time, but truthfully I didn't know what was going on. Every time I would cry Leslie would hug me and say "It's ok!" That's why I thought she was full of it because if Grandma was going to be sleeping forever, then that wouldn't be ok! After the funeral service was over we all got into these long cars and drove in a long line out to a field somewhere. I remember not having to stop at any streetlights when they turned red and thought that was cool. When we got to the field we had another boring service around a huge hole in the ground. After the service was over workmen started lowering Grandma's wooden bed into the hole. I asked Leslie where Grandma was and why were they putting her new bed into that hole? Before calling me a moron she said that Grandma was in the box and that we wouldn't see her anymore because Grandma's dead and when people die…we bury them. I started looking around in the crowd of people for Grandma to make sure that Leslie wasn't telling me a fib. I didn't see her anywhere so Leslie must have been telling the truth. The workmen had lowered Grandma into the hole and people began to throw flowers on her box. Then everyone started to walk away back to where we parked the long cars, except me. You see, I had buried things before many of times in the dirt outside our house. Most of the time when I did it well I couldn't remember where I had buried the stuff the following day. I just couldn't sit there while the workmen threw dirt on my Grandma's bed. The hole that they put her in was bigger than any hole I have ever dug, and that's when I realized Leslie was right. If we left Grandma in that hole, she would be sleep forever! So I started screaming at the workmen to stop throwing dirt on Grandma's bed, but they didn't stop. So I screamed louder and picked up some stones to throw at them. I got to throw only two rocks before my mom had grabbed my one arm and my aunt had grabbed the other. I was crying and screaming louder than I ever had, pleading with my mom and aunt to not let them throw dirt on Grandma's bed! But they didn't stop the workmen, no one did. No one seemed to care except me that Grandma was in that hole. I cried all the way home and for the rest of the day. Mom put me to bed and tried to read me a bedtime story. I told her that I wanted to play checkers with Grandma instead. Mom promised me that everything would be ok and that she'd play checkers with me tomorrow. I told her that she could never play checkers like Grandma so why would I play with her? I could tell that comment made my mom very sad. She left my room in tears, which actually made me feel better. Serves her right for allowing those workmen to bury the most important person in my life, I thought to myself. Then I screamed out "Serves you right!" And before I knew it I had fell fast asleep.

So when I got my report card I was devastated. There was not one A' on it and that was all I cared about. If Grandma was awake she'd be so upset because I had not kept my promise to her before she went into her deep sleep. This was one of the few times I was happy she was asleep, but then again I'd do anything to wake her up again including allowing her to be disappointed in this ridiculous report card. School had let out and I took the long way home because I was sad. I was so embarrassed about not having straight A's that I just wanted to slide my report card down in between the iron sewer bars outside our apartment and watch my grades just float away like a paper boat in a dirty stream. But I knew I had to show my mom my report card. I wished Grandma was there because she would have already been waiting for me on the porch since today was the big day, but my mom would have to do for now. By the time I got inside my house the tears were flooding down my face. My mom came running over to see if I was badly hurt and quickly found out that I was crying about the poor results on my report card. I reluctantly gave it to her and buried my head into one of our worn out sofa cushions. The stuffing was hanging out so I knew it'd be the perfect rendition of a pillow to console my soaked face. My mom asked me "What's all the hysteria for?" I told her that "I had promised Grandma that I would get all A's on my report card, so that I could become an engineer, so that I could move us all to the neighborhood with the super big houses and somehow I had failed because there was not a single A' on my card! All I see on my card is stupid E's and U's and that's not what Grandma told me to get. She clearly stated to get straight A's and now we'll never get to the nice neighborhood!" The barely understandable words sobbed through gritted teeth and slobbery lips. And then I heard something that I hadn't heard in awhile. My mom busted out laughing. She was laughing so hard that she started crying right along with me. I didn't think this was a laughing matter at all so the more she laughed the angrier I became. "It isn't funny mom! Stop laughing! When Grandma wakes up I'm going to tell her that you laughed at me for getting bad grades!" I screamed at her as loud as I could. I guess the scream worked because she immediately stopped laughing. Then she came and sympathetically sat by me on the couch. She grabbed my hand and said "Son you actually did get straight A's. See...because you're in the 1st grade you don't get A's, you get E's. E' in this case stands for excellent and is the highest grade that you can get at your level. If you were Leslie's or Emanuel's age you would have gotten all A's, but your school gives younger kids E's instead of A's... but they're both the same thing. Everything on your report card for all of your subjects you've received an E' for excellent. Reading – E', Math – E', Science – E', and Social Studies – E'. So for every subject that can get us into that nicer neighborhood, you did exactly what Grandma asked. The only thing that would disappoint Grandma about this report card are the U's. U's mean unsatisfactory and that means you didn't do a good enough job. You have U's in everything to do with your behavior. Your teacher has even written here that you're the smartest child in the class but you just won't shut up! She says she has to give you a paddle at least once a day just for you to stay in line. Why are you talking so much in class?" But at this point I was no longer paying attention to my mom to even answer. I was so happy that I had not broken my promise to Grandma that everything else my mom said just went in one ear and out the other. I started to do a happy dance celebrating the success of knowing that the dream was alive again. "You put your left foot in. You put your left foot out. You put your report card in and you shake it all about…" I sang with extreme pride while doing my little victory dance. I hadn't noticed the large shadow that suddenly stood tall over me because if I had I would have stopped my victory dance and sat my hyper ass down. I felt a rubber glove slide around my throat choking off the last of my happy song lyrics. As I gasped for air my report card was snatched out of my hand so hard I got a deep paper cut. Then He pushed my face into the floor the way you'd push a dog's face into it's own feces after it mistakenly shit all over your brand new carpet. The only difference here is I wasn't a dog and we didn't have any carpet so my head bounced off the hard tile floor like the tennis ball I'd bounce off the wall when I played outside. Dazed I looked up just in time to see Him look at my report card with a devious face of disgust and then He ripped it up into tiny little pieces and threw it over His head like New Year's confetti. Then He slid His large leather belt off from around His waist and commenced to beat me." "Maybe this'll teach you how to keep your mouth shut at home and in school you monkey ass little dumbass nigga!" He shouted with every swing of that belt. "But I'm gone' make sure your dumbass gets it right though. Imma' rightcha dumbass!"

Finally I could tell that Mrs. Sanders had heard enough to make her want to jump in and get a turn to speak. It was as if she was waiting no differently than how the girls in the neighborhood would wait to get a chance to jump in when playing jump rope. Her head was sticking out just like that waiting for the right moment to jump and this I guess was it. Before she could let the words fly she stood up and took a deep breath. It was as if she was getting ready to plunge off a diving board at the Olympic trials. "All of this young man is very interesting to me and I'm glad that you've told me all these things, but what does all of this have to do with the reason why you walked off of school grounds without permission the other day? I still have no idea why you left and you have yet to explain it to me. That was a very bad thing to do. You had the police, the entire school along with myself looking for you. Where did you go and why did you leave?" This was the second time Mrs. Sanders had asked the question but it wasn't as abrupt as the first. I could see what I believed to be empathetic glances coming from her to me, so I decided right then to get to the reasoning behind my leaving school the day before: **"It was the day after I got beat for having a good/ bad report card. I had made a promise to myself   to not do anything wrong toward getting a beating ever again, even in school. The daily paddling was now a nuisance to my butt and me, so I decided that day that I would be on my best behavior and not receive a paddle going forward. I was so proud of myself because usually I'd receive a spanking by lunchtime, but today I was focused and managed to break my own record of not being paddled. I never made it past lunch before without getting one. After lunch however was a different story. There was a girl in class that I sat next to named Tiffany. Tiffany was my friend. Her and I also came to the conclusion that we were cousins. In my neighborhood if you are cousins then you really have to have each other's backs because cousins are family and family is everything. So I had told Tiffany that I would have her back against a boy who was bothering her every now and then named Wellington. Wellington is a bully in our class. He supposedly takes karate lessons daily after school, which he ensures we're all aware as he boasts he's a** black belt to anyone who will listen every chance he gets. Many children are afraid of Wellington for this reason, however I think Wellington is too small for anything to work in his favor that has to do with fighting. Even if he is practicing karate every day as a black belt... his blackest belt is not black enough to worry me. But coincidently Wellington was sitting right on the other side of Tiffany that day and she had just grew tired of his bothersome shenanigans. Tiffany had brought some new markers to class with her that day and she was using them to color in her coloring book. Most of us can't afford crayons, so markers are a big commodity. The teacher left the classroom to do something. She told us she'd be right back and to be on our best behavior. Obviously Wellington had not heard her directive because as soon as she stepped out of the classroom he reached over and took one of Tiffany's markers. That's when I heard Tiffany scream out "give it back Wellington! It's not yours, it's mine!" If Wellington had just given Tiffany her marker back the rest of the day's events would have probably never taken place. But that would have been asking too much of karate kid so of course Wellington just ignored Tiffany as if she wasn't even in the room. Then in reference to me Tiffany told Wellington that he had till the count of five to give her marker back to her or she'd have her cousin kick his thieving butt! Wellington laughed "who him? He ain't gone' do nothin' but get his head cracked if he even look at me!" And that was all it took for me to stand up and commence the count myself. Once I started counting Wellington stood up and got into some type of weird low karate stance. He was already short, so this pathetic stance just made him look tinier than ever. And because he did that I decided not to count to five, but to three instead which surprised Wellington completely and threw him off guard. I ran towards him and he half balanced kicked a timid foot at my knee. I just caught his foot and spun him to the ground and sat on his back.

I twisted his arm behind him and yanked Tiffany's marker out his hand. By this time the entire class was on their feet and in a uproar over the fight. Tiffany was clapping her hands in relief along with a few other kids Wellington had bullied often. Desk were pushed out of place. School papers and writing utensils were spilled all over the floor. Wellington was struggling, squirming and doing some type of backwards leg bent kick to try and hoist me off his back. And just when I was about to use Tiffany's marker to write my name on Wellington's face the teacher pulled me up off of him. She stood in between us with her eyes bugging out of her head and shouted "what in tarnation is going on here???!!!" Wellington was back in his crouching tiger hidden skills karate stance and I was pointing at him telling her that if she didn't get him and if he tried to kick me again that we would be back on the floor, and I would pick up right where we just left off. To spare Wellington anymore embarrassment she grabbed him by the arm and started to pull him towards the exit. She turned around and told everyone in the class to take their seats. We all knew what was about to happen. She was taking Wellington down the hall to the paddle room. She glared at me with squinted eyes and yelled "don't worry, you're next!" Then she whisked Wellington out the door while her heels clanked down the hall. When I could no longer hear her walking I knew that meant she was in the paddle room. So I turned and threw Tiffany her marker and said "no I'm not! I said I wasn't getting a paddle today and that's what I meant!" I grabbed my members only jacket out of my locker, ran down the main hallway and out the school's front doors! I ran all the way home but no one was there. Moments later I saw from a distance your car along with some police cars circling my neighborhood. We all know your car because it is the only sports car in the school parking lot and you have a space labeled "Principal." But the police cars scared me. If they were with you that meant

they were coming for me and I figure I'm too young to go to jail. I still have some A's to get on my future report cards and jail would ruin that so I ran a little ways down from my apartment and hid in the bushes. I watched the police and you knock on my door to no avail. I thought to myself I already tried that and they're not home stupid! **You seemed very anxious. The police just looked impatient and clearly didn't want to stick around, so they looked at their wrist and then motioned for everyone to get back in their vehicles to leave. Once everyone left I felt relieved, but not relieved enough to go back to my porch. I just sat in the bushes for hours waiting for my mom to get back home."**

Mrs. Sanders' mouth dropped open the way mine did at the circus a year earlier during the high-flying trapeze act. I guess she couldn't believe what she was hearing the same way I couldn't believe what I was seeing when those guys were flipping each other high above the crowd. Even though her mouth was open no words would proceed from it. She motioned for me to sit outside her office in the hallway while she shut the door to privately talk to my mom. I assumed Mrs. Sanders was angry because her face was so red, so this could only mean that she was getting ready to tell my mom that she would be kicking me out of the public school system as promised. Her office door closed hard enough to not be considered an actual slam, but to still exude disappointment in what had just transpired. I could feel my heart drop into my stomach in spite of it rapidly beating inside my chest. Why was I so afraid? Well, I knew I didn't want to be kicked out of school. I liked my school friends. In fact I loved going to school. It was the only place where He couldn't get to me. I dreaded going home. Every time the school bell for dismissal rang I'd almost pee my pants. If He found out that I got kicked out of school He'd kill me for sure. All of a sudden I felt the urge of having to severely pee burning in my lower gut. I started to swing my legs back and forth in my chair for comfort. The tone of Mrs. Sanders coming from her office was not helping the situation any. The louder she got the more I felt the need to pee. I couldn't make out what she was saying but at the bare minimum I knew it wasn't positive. Every now and then my mom would pipe something up in a weaker tone, but most of the conversation was being lead by Mrs. Sanders. The office secretary had seen me wiggling so bad that she escorted me down the hallway to use the bathroom. By the time we returned back to the office Mrs. Sanders' door was open and she was waiting for me. *This is it* I thought with my head embarrassingly pointed toward the office floor. *It's all over now and there's nothing you can do about it!* Then I felt a fingernail touch under my chin. Mrs. Sanders lifted my head up and looked me right in the eyes and said, "It's ok son. I'm not going to remove you from the school. Your mother and I had a long talk and I have come to the decision of keeping you here. But you have to promise me that if you ever feel like running away again instead of making a left out the door, you make a right and come see me in my office first. You are a very intelligent young man and you're going to be something great one day, I just know it. Your grandmother knew it and now I know what she knew all along. Just remember whenever you get the urge to do something that you know is not right, think of your grandmother and what she taught you and do the right thing. I'm counting on you just like she is. Make us all proud and stay out of trouble." Then she gave me a hug and told me that I could come back to school tomorrow, business as usual. It was the first time in a long time that I felt important, as if I had a purpose for existing. I always thought Mrs. Sanders was a mean old lady waiting to boil all the students in her witches' stew that she was brewing up in her office. But that day I realized she was just someone trying to do a good job and in the mist of that job she was someone trying to help me. In fact since Grandma's deep sleep she was the only one in my opinion trying to help me achieve what I set out to do in the first place, which was to make Grandma proud. Mrs. Sanders had given me back my opportunity to do that and for that I thanked her by never receiving another paddle for the rest of my time there!

Chapter 4
Cinnamon with an S'

Summer time for most children was the best time of the year because the next school year wouldn't start up again until fall season. That meant that they would be away from all the heartache of routinely missed homework assignments and random detentions being handed out to them by teachers that barely understood who they were and what their minds truly needed. But for me it would be a threemonth prison sentence where I would be a captive in my own home being punished for my mere existence. At least when school was in I was free. Summer vacations were some of the worst times of my life. There would be no outlets of freedom, no friends to make me feel good, no teachers to purposely annoy and no lunch recess time to help stretch both legs and imagination. For the next three months there would only be beating upon beating and screaming upon screaming without cause. There needed to be cause. There needed to be some type of reasoning behind why He was so crazy. Other people in life had reasons for their insanity usually tied to some type of drug or alcohol addiction. If He had one of these it would have made me feel a little better because then it would have been still unacceptable, but within reason. However He was drug and alcohol free. In fact He despised all drugs, not a drop made it to our house ever. So His craziness was imbedded deep inside some dark place within His own mind and heart that He repeatedly wanted me exposed to. As I think back these were the beginning years dedicated to the struggle of finding my own identity. I believe all of us at some point or another in our lives ask that death-defying question of who we are and what our purpose is for being alive? These questions come piercingly fast to us on wings of cultural flight but the answers to these questions often seem to avoid us like positive news stories or dry paint. I've lived separate lives for almost as long as I can remember. My home life was one of solidarity being held captive in a prison with Him holding me hostage and my mom providing Him sanctuary to do so. My school life was a place where I could get away from all the darkness of home and hang out with children like myself. At school I could be me without having to look over my shoulder worried if my actions were about to cause myself physical harm. But I started having problems being able to keep the two lives separated or knowing when to be my carefree self vs. when to be on guard. So I decided to be on guard most of the time because that was the safest thing for me to do. It was literally a matter of life and death and I was choosing to live. We both couldn't realistically live in the same home but neither of us had anywhere else to go. I figured I was here first anyway so why should I leave. Besides, I was only in the second grade and still had a long way to go before I could become an engineer so if anyone should go it should be Him. They were officially married now and my mom said it was my Christian duty to obey Him since He was now my father. He didn't feel like a father. From what I had seen on television shows and in school not only was He the furthest thing from being a father to me, but our family was nowhere close to being a family either. I had a family before so I knew what that felt like and this wasn't it. My mom had never divulged to me who my biological father was so it never crossed my mind as a child as being something of any importance. My mom would tell me daily, "God said to honor thy father and mother so that your days can be long upon the earth." But there were so many times when He was beating me or trying to destroy my self worth that I wanted my days to be

34

short, not long! One day He came home with a present He had bought me from the store. I was very surprised because He had never bought anything for me before so this was a first. He had recently just threw away a helicopter book that meant so much to me because I believe it was from my real father. I had the book since as long as I could remember until He ripped it up and trashed it. So it was very surprising to me that the gift He had brought home for me was a toy helicopter. I remember thinking to myself *maybe this guy's not going to be so bad after all.* But a snake is a snake is a snake is a snake! It's like that story where the farmer takes a frozen snake that was near death into his bosom to warm it while traveling across the lake and then halfway across the lake the snake warms up. It bites the farmer and they both end up dying from drowning, or something like that. Anyway, a snake is a snake is a snake and a monster of a snake is He! I could hear His keys slightly jingling at the door as if He was trying to sneak into His own home. The jingling was the few seconds of warning that I had to get prepared for whatever craziness was about to occur. But today was different. He was in a jolly mood and had a package in His hand. It was a toy helicopter and He told me that He loved me while giving it to me, so this was His first kind act to me ever. I didn't know what to do because this was as foreign to me as Venus or Mars, but the feeling of being loved by the man my mother loved was certainly desired. Then He went upstairs to His room as if to call it a day for the evening. My mom was giving me a look of "I told you he wasn't so bad…" with her eyes. She smiled at me and walked into the kitchen to finish cooking some meal that would only be for survival, not taste. But I was so excited to have my new gift. I immediately ripped open the package and started to play with the helicopter. It wasn't anything fancy, but it was mine and it was the first toy I had ever received from a guy that I thought hated my guts. *Maybe I was wrong about Him. Maybe my mother did know things that I just couldn't understand as a child. Maybe, just maybe she was on to something great and I just was too young to see the greatness of it?* I began to spin the propellers with my fingers, taking flight from the couch and pretending that the sofa was my helipad and the living room was a world full of adventurous places for me to fly to. But once again in all of my excitement I failed to pay attention to my surroundings and didn't notice that He had never went upstairs to His room at all. Instead He was hiding behind the wall of the stairs watching me with hatred the entire time. This whole situation was a set up; no differently than setting a bear trap up in the woods, He set this trap up for me! It had not even been more than five minutes before I just barely saw the shadow of Him looming over me as He snatched the helicopter out of my hands and pushed me to the floor. It was as if He had waited until the moment He saw that I had fully invested my whole heart into the idea of enjoying the toy before He jumped in to destroy any chance of me being happy from it. His hands in a bullish manner began to crush the helicopter snapping it in half. Pieces of propeller and shaft fell to the floor while He yelled out "I knew I shouldn't have bought you anything. All you're trying to do is scratch up the walls with this stupid ass shit!" From His tone anyone would have thought He was very angry which is probably what made my mom come back into the room. But what I saw in His eyes wasn't anger. Deep inside past the iris, past the pupil I could see what was in those eyes and it wasn't anger. It was glee, a gleaming glee! The type of gleam that you get when you've accomplished something sinister that you've planned out meticulously for a very long time. There was a sparkling smirk of deep routed evil acknowledged achievement within those eyes proudly seeping out the sides as tears of joy swelling up ready to spill over His lashes. I tried to hold back mine but it was way too late for that. I tried to tell them to go back in but they were already streaming down my face the way rain would slowly but surely roll down a window at the beginning of a storm. I was so disappointed in myself for allowing Him to trap me this way. "Now pick this shit up off the floor and throw it in the trash before I gut your dumbass like a filthy pig!" The words snarled out of His lips but I couldn't truly hear them. I was so broken that I just stared at Him like the last staring of a house fire when it has engulfed the entire home but still burns bright. There would be no picking up of anything by me that day and it wouldn't have mattered what the consequences were. My eyes said *pick that shit up yourself bitch!* And my mom must have read them loud and clear because she immediately started picking up pieces of broken toy in her quick attempt to keep peace between us. And in being pleased with Himself and all that He had accomplished, He turned and marched back upstairs to His lair. Then I heard my mom say to me, "You have to be careful not to scratch up the walls when you play with your toys boy!" Her words pierced my heart like a two edged sword carved from injustice. What could I have possibly done in a previous life to deserve such stupidity in this one, is the reply my face gave her. And somehow deep down inside I knew right then this would not be her last time defending the beast! It's up for ever lasting debate between my heart and mind who hurt me most that day, Him or her?

Though I am now an adult and completely understand the difference between a good childhood upbringing and a bad one, the one that I had was not all gloom. There were so many great memories that I'd never take back if given the chance. He tried to isolate me from anyone and everyone that could have any kind of positive impact on my life but those attempts were all in vain because I have the type of character that analyzes everything that happens to me. Because of this I am constantly learning and growing and this is how it's always been. So any time spent large or small, positive or not in the end becomes lessons well learned and received, which in the end ultimately becomes a positive experience for me. My cousin Reggie was my best friend at the time. Reggie and I were friends well before He became my stepfather so we had great history before the storm. I guess this was one of the reasons why Reggie lasted longer than some of my other friends. Some of my other friends just couldn't handle the pressure that came along with being my friend, but Reggie was different. Reggie never really cared about the backlash that came with that territory. Reggie was the type of kid that would always have a bad experience at things that normally everyone else would have a good experience with. But Reggie had a good heart and I loved him for that. I also appreciated how much fun we would have playing and exploring the Projects together because it certainly wasn't easy growing up there. We basically had to use our imaginations for everything because all things were truly in bad shape. But we turned the entire Projects into an adventurous regime of excitement and exploration. As dead as the place was when Reggie and I would step on the scene the entire Projects would come to life. Like the time when we were at his house all alone trying to make cinnamon toast. Neither of us were old enough to spell good yet, but we thought we were old enough to use the stove. We didn't have toasters or toaster ovens like normal homes had. All we had was the bottom of the stove that we used to put bread in that in the end would only toast on one side. The bottom of that oven would get hot really fast and since our stoves didn't have timers we constantly had to pull the bottom open to check on the toast to ensure we didn't burn it. There's nothing worse than bottom of the oven burnt cinnamon toast! Except there was something worse than that which is bottom of the oven, half burnt, sage toast. Let me explain. Because neither of us could spell the word cinnamon when looking through the spices drawer we picked a spice that we thought was cinnamon because the word cinnamon starts off with the letter "S" sound. And because sage and cinnamon look just alike when Reggie grabbed the sage and said "This is what we're looking for right here!" I actually believed him because I couldn't spell either and it all made good sense to me. Boy, were we wrong! Not only had we wasted 8 pieces of bread (which when you're poor is an immortal sin) but that toast no matter how much sugar we put on top of it was the worst cinnamon (or sage) toast I had ever eaten! So to take our minds off of our hunger and our blunder we decided to go outside and play. Today we would be scientists and conduct our continued study on the world of bees which basically meant that we were going to catch some bees in some jars and watch them eventually die from a lack of air. So to increase their lifespan we decided to punch some small holes in the tops of the lids of the jars we would use to catch the bees. I decided to use a fork to punch four tiny holes in the lid of my jar, but Reggie decided to use a knife to punch holes in his because a knife punched holes easier than a fork. The rules of our games were always competitive and for this particular one the objective was to catch more bees than the other person. This was not one of our more simple games to play because bees weren't easy to catch and they also didn't like being cooped up in hot ass jars all day. On top of that the repercussions of making a misstep in catching bees would usually result in someone being stung, which would always end the game prematurely. And depending on the type of bee the mishap could also be a health risk. But these risks were also the types of things that Reggie and I looked forward to each and every afternoon. We loved the risks and we loved the challenges. But before we could get started Reggie would have to go outside and check to see if He was out there looking for me. He had already banned me from playing with Reggie, so every time He caught me a beating was sure to follow. So when Reggie informed me that the coast was clear we eagerly went off to the backfields to start our adventure. On the way to the field was this row of metal dumpsters that were to be picked up every so often to replace the other ones in the neighborhood when they were full of trash. We used these huge empty metal dumpsters as landing strips no differently than logs on a riverbed. When the tops of the dumpsters were closed we would jump from one to another like some type of cool Project obstacle course. The dumpsters were spaced differently so some were easier to jump to than others. There had to be at least 15 dumpsters lined up on our way to the fields so the entire trip was pretty fun and strenuous. There was a small abandoned playground in the field that we used to stop at and play. The ground was covered with lots of dark colored broken glass from old beer bottles, but that never stopped us from having a good time because it was the only playground we had. There wasn't much in the playground besides an old rusted sliding board, merry go round and monkey bars. All of these were made of very hard, old iron bars and all had different dangers attached to them. You could only slide down the right side of the sliding board because that was the smooth side. The left side had sharp metal pieces sticking out of it that if you were lucky would only snag or tear your clothes, best-case scenario. The merry go round was so lopsided that giving it a good old spin with someone on it would most likely injure everyone involved. And the monkey bars had so much broken glass underneath that if you were hanging on them and accidentally slipped you could not only break a bone hitting iron bars on your way down, but you'd most likely cut some primary artery once you reached the bottom. But in spite of all these dangers we loved it because the playground and the field belonged to us. We were the Kings of Dumpville and we knew our kingdom like the backs of our own hands! We played on the playground for quite some time and then decided it was well time for us to do what we set out to do in the first place, catch some bees.

The technique of bee catching in a jar goes as follows: first you had to have the keen eye of seeing the bees perched on the head of a flower. Once spotted, then you would need to unscrew the lid of your bottle and use the lid and the bottle together to quickly scoop the bee (flower head and all) into your jar quickly screwing the lid back on top of your bottle in almost one clean motion before the angry bee could fly out and sting you for disturbing its day! Reggie and I had perfected the craft from days and days of continued practice, so we thought we had nothing to worry about.

The idea was to capture more bees than the next guy and that day I was on a roll. I screamed out "Four bees baby," with excitement in an attempt to get Reggie all pumped up. He had just screamed out that he had caught number 2. Neither of us had ever caught more than four because the more bees you caught the harder it was to keep them in the jar the next time you opened it up to scoop up another bee. And no matter how intense the competition was neither of us was willing to risk a bee sting. And that's when I heard Reggie cry out with horror "Oooouuwwwww....ouch.... ouuuuwwwww!" I turned around anxiously to see what all the commotion was about and saw Reggie jumping up and down shaking his hand. He was crying and howling at the same time, which is never a good sign. I immediately ran over to him and understood exactly what had taken place because it was about to take place again. Reggie had been stung by a bee right on his finger! He had used a knife to make the holes in his jar lid for his bees to breathe, but unfortunately he had made the holes entirely too large and his bees were starting to crawl out the top of his jar. One had already got out and stung Reggie in his finger and another was also getting free. I yelled out in fear for Reggie's other hand, "It's your jar dummy! They're crawling out the top of your jar!" Reggie was so afraid that he just threw his jar up in the air. We weren't standing in the grass any longer so that was an even bigger mistake. His jar came down and shattered on the ground freeing all the angry bees inside. I backed up and watched in terror as Reggie just started screaming and running back up the road. Then mid way through his run I saw him jump up and down grabbing his back in pain. Another bee had stung him in the back while he was trying to flee. At first it wasn't funny but the way Reggie was hopping around shaking his hand and holding his back made him look like he was doing some weird type of cultural rain dance, so I just busted out laughing. And as soon as I started laughing that's when I heard my name being yelled out thunderously as the clouds of depression immediately swarmed in my head. I could feel a sudden chill of darkness swallow my entire body as I froze in fear. Reggie darted into his house as he too knew that this was even more dangerous than the bee stings he had just received. This was an encounter that neither of us wanted or was prepared for. *I could make a run for it but where would I go? Eventually I would have to come back to face an even deadlier fate than what was coming now. Or I could just turn around and handle whatever consequences came with the territory.* At that moment I felt like a jungle gazelle faced with the decision of running through a crocodile infested river to get away from a pride of lions. No matter the choice the odds of getting away completely unscathed was highly unlikely. So I just turned around to face the pride, but this pride was a pride of one. Knowing that the situation was about to turn very ugly, very quickly, I placed my bee jar on the ground to ensure that Reggie's fate didn't become my own. I lowered my head and began the walk of death toward the sounds of disappointment spewing from His lips. The walk was only a minute but it seemed like days. One scared foot in front of the other my shaking knees could barely support my tiny body. I stopped in front of Him with my head lowered not willing to lift it. I could feel His anger bearing down on me, the fierceness weighing down on my shoulders causing sweat beads to erupt from my forehead. We just stood there for a moment, frozen and still, as time did the same. I refused to give Him what He wanted and He refused to move forward until I did. I don't know how long it was but it seemed like we stood there for hours. I was standing still out of fear but He was not. He was hovering over me like a vulture hovers over a dead carcass before the inevitable plunge. The suspense was killing me so I just gave in. I lifted my head to look into the eyes of a demon and as soon as our eyes locked He slapped me in the face so hard that snot came out of my nose. " I saw you up there with that bad little boy. I told you to stay away from him, didn't I? I saw you two breaking glass and tearing up the neighborhood. Two destructive monkey ass Negros tearin' up everything they can, but can't fix a got' damn thang!" He just bellowed on and on shaking and slapping me throughout His entire speech. Then He grabbed me by the neck and shoved me all the way home and I realized once again that this was going to be a very long and disappointing summer break.

Chapter 5
God's Closet

His wish was granted. If His wish was for me to be terrified of Him every single moment of every single day, then He had surely succeeded and that wish had come true. Each one of my days was riddled with fear and desolation. I was afraid to go to sleep at night and I was afraid to wake up in the morning as well. There were so many rules that I had to follow that I couldn't possibly keep up with them all and many of them He was making up as time went along. I wasn't allowed to get up in the morning and go downstairs until He and my mom were awake. That meant that I wouldn't get to come out of my room until well into the afternoon. My mom loved watching soap operas every day on television. Hearing soap opera theme music was my daily queue that it was ok for me to go downstairs and start my day. Though I would already be awake, the soaps became my daily alarm clock to knowing that the coast was clear for me to be alive and active. I would always hear their infamous phrases "like sands through an hour glass" or "these are the young and the…" which would be my signals that it was ok for me to come down to eat breakfast! I never had to do regular chores that other children complained about having to do like laundry or cleaning my room. I guess that was because I didn't really have a lot of clothes and the few I did have I would have to wash by hand in our bathtub on my own. Like normal children I did have to empty the trash though. If He ever woke up and saw that there was trash in the bathroom or kitchen, "Your ass is grass," as He would put it. So every morning for hours I would just lay in my bed counting the grooves on the ceiling waiting to hear the soaps come on. When I'd finally hear them I would jump up out of the bed and run to the bathroom to bathe. I would always take my clothes that I was going to wear that day into the bathroom with me so that I could bathe, put on my clothes, grab the trash on my way out the bathroom, run downstairs, grab the trash from the kitchen, run outside to the dumpster, run back into the house and sit down on the couch to watch the soap operas (which I really hated watching) while patiently waiting for my mother to finish cooking breakfast, which often meant that breakfast would be ready around 2:00pm in the afternoon. I had the entire routine down to a science because any mistakes on my end could result in me being physically beaten or at this point even killed. The beatings I received were no different than the ones I would see on old slavery movies or read about in black history books. He would use an extension cord to punish me time and time again. The cord would cut through my skin leaving welts and marks just like the backs of the slaves I saw on television. The only difference was that their skin never healed and was full of scars while mine would heal within a few days and normally never left any scars, just scabs that I would peel from time to time. So I began to thank God for not receiving permanent scars from the constant beatings I got. And I also wanted to help God out by not giving my stepfather a reason to beat me in the first place. That was hard because He would always find some reason to beat me no matter how well I did. He beat me once for using the handrail to go down the steps because He said I was too young to have to use the rail. He beat another time for my feet making too much noise going down the steps stating that I was purposely trying to step loudly to wake up the neighbors next door. We only had one bathroom upstairs and He beat me once for having to use the restroom at the exact same time that He had to use it. At that point I was so afraid to use the restroom that I decided to start peeing in the corner of the floor of our downstairs closet because that was safer than taking the risk of going upstairs and running into Him. At that time I was so young that I didn't know urine would start to smell after time. Luckily for me He didn't use the downstairs closet enough to notice the pissy, mildewed smell because if He had I'm not sure I'd be alive today to tell anyone about the entire experience.

The next few years of my life passed by very slowly yet somehow impossibly quick. It was as if my soul was being aggressively pulled simultaneously in opposite directions by two completely different forces. The love I used to know was desperately trying to hold on to me, struggling with worn fingers and calloused hands while the hate that was currently too familiar was locked onto my heart like the jaws of a great white shark ripping away everything that was pure and true while it dragged me to the bottom of the darkest abyss! Everything I loved about life was disappearing, but everything I hated was slowly sliding along like a sluggish load getting larger and larger by the day. In school I was doing extremely well because of the promise I made my grandmother to succeed, but my behavior was still the reflection of a broken mirror smeared with the blood of someone I didn't want to be, but was surely becoming. This battle within myself would become an everlasting war to no end. One moment everything would be ok and then the next I'd be fighting with myself or someone else. Most of my school teachers throughout my childhood could never understand it, but there were a few special ones that could partially see beyond the dusty clothes and rugged hair. One of the first ones to see hope inside of my defeated eyes was my second grade teacher Mrs. Wiggins. Where others had seen a lost cause she saw a profound gift and made it her mission to unleash it to the world. I cherished the small amount of time we spent together in class each day. Even though there were about 20 other students in her class, for some reason I believed that she was my teacher and mine alone. She treated me as if my life had meaning and actually mattered. Everyone else to this point treated me like a household chore that you hated doing but knew had to be done like toilet cleaning. Mrs. Wiggins however was kind and interested in teaching her students more than just letters and numbers, she was teaching them how to live and love life fully for what it truly was, and to be kind to everyone no matter who they were or where they were from. She taught us to be courteous, not because we had to but because it just felt better than to not be. And she taught us lessons in humility every single day. These are things that I hold dear to my heart even now. I remember that there was a program that she loved keeping us engaged in called "Book It." I'll never forget the program because it helped teach me a valuable lesson in humility. The program was owned by a pizza company and the idea was to get children to read more books. Every week the students in Mrs. Wiggins' class had to read books and write a report on the book that they had read. At the end of the week whichever student wrote the best report on their book would get to go to the pizza restaurant with Mrs. Wiggins for lunch and their lunch would be free. At my house we usually never got the opportunity to order pizza. In fact our neighborhood was too dangerous for anyone to deliver anything to our door, not even pizza or taxi service. The only person that would deliver anything to us was the mailman and sometimes he wouldn't even come! So I was determined to win the "Book It" contest every single week. Not only did I want to win because of the pizza, but I also loved my one on one talks with Mrs. Wiggins. Sometimes our lunches would be short, just half an hour. But often we would sit, eat and talk for more than an hour…maybe even two. Many of our conversations would end with her crying. She would tell me that she was shedding tears of joy and understanding, but at that time I truly didn't understand what those were because any tears that fell from my eyes were always the result of me being hurt. I noticed that Mrs. Wiggins would look at me with such sympathetic, yet confused eyes. It was as if she was a great scientist well known for her amazing studies and accomplished formulas but was struggling with being able to solve the simple puzzle of my impossible life. All I understood was that free pizza and lunch with Mrs. Wiggins every week was something I majorly enjoyed. Then one Friday Mrs. Wiggins came to me with a request. She told me that every week her and I both knew that no matter what book anyone read (most of the students in my class wouldn't read a book a week, not even for pizza) and no matter how hard they tried to win, that no one would be able to write a book report as well as me. With that being said she asked my permission for her to pick another student as the book report winner just so another student could experience a free pizza lunch with the teacher. At first I thought this was highly unacceptable. "Why should I have to suffer because other students don't read or write well?" I emphatically begged Mrs. Wiggins to come up with a more suitable solution. This idea of taking a backseat is not one that I was familiar with because Grandma never mentioned this concept to me during Checkers. Grandma would just obliterate me with no remorse! But Mrs. Wiggins was teaching me "True strength is a child of humility!" Which basically means "It is sometimes more impressive to take a backseat when you know the front seat is already yours!" When I agreed to let someone else win the contest in spite of their inabilities, I could see the joy in Mrs. Wiggins' eyes as if she was getting closer to solving the puzzle of me.

My relationship with Mrs. Wiggins was getting stronger and stronger by the day. In fact, this was the best school year I had thus far. This was the only year I had great behavior to go along with my exceptional grades. Mrs. Sanders thought it was a miracle and even announced my name in recognition one day over the loudspeaker during her morning announcements. I used to get in fights with students during recess or on the walks home from school, but not anymore. During recess I'd be at lunch with Mrs. Wiggins and she started driving me home from school every day so I wouldn't get into fights anymore. I would just help Mrs. Wiggins prepare for her class the next day after school by washing the chalkboard and straightening up the chairs. Mrs. Wiggins and I would talk for hours and I'd get home from school pretty late. I was expecting to be banned from this relationship no differently than any others that I had developed, but for some reason He never tried to physically beat me out of this one. However my mom was not a fan of Mrs. Wiggins. She told me that I was spending too much time with her and that I was getting too big for my britches! This would make me automatically reply with, "I know I'm too big for my Britches because you won't buy me any new clothes!" My mom also had my uncle (who later I came to understand was a crazy man) speak to me about the entire matter and he told me that white people are the devil and they bleed blue blood so no matter what you do don't ever trust them, ever! The whole thing was starting to freak me out but my experiences with Mrs. Wiggins were simply so much better than my experiences at home that I truly didn't care what anyone thought except for her. My mom became so jealous of my relationship with Mrs. Wiggins that she started making up ridiculous excuses as to why I had to stop hanging around her like, "You're starting to smell like a wet dog and starting to pick up a European accent...before you know it you'll be whiter than Michael Jackson!" I never told Mrs. Wiggins about all the negative publicity I was getting at home because of our friendship, as I knew it would really crush her no differently than it was starting to crush me. But finally my mother had enough and gave me a directive that I was fretting to hear the entire time, which was I was no longer allowed to be around Mrs. Wiggins except in class. I was not allowed to go with her to lunch. I couldn't stay after school with her. I was no longer allowed to enjoy the company of the only person (besides my mother) that truly loved me and I knew this would be a directive that I wouldn't be able to follow. She stated to me that if she caught me riding home from school with Mrs. Wiggins ever again that I would get the spanking of a lifetime. My mom never really spanked me often at all and the times she did I might as well had been spanking myself, that's how soft the smacks would be. But this time the tone in her voice alluded to the assumption that she was not playing around, and would surely beat me good if I disobeyed her. She also started picking me up when school let out just to ensure that Mrs. Wiggins would not get to drive me home. I could tell that someone had also gotten to Mrs. Wiggins because she didn't suggest for me to stay over to help her after class anymore. However she did allow me to stay with her in class during recess. My mom coming up to the school every day to walk me home was short lived. So after about one week I begged Mrs. Wiggins to let me stay after class to help her because I didn't want to get jumped and beat up after school by a couple of nasty bullies. Of course I had lied about the bullies. I was from the Projects and it was practically impossible for anyone to bully us. We were the bullies. I don't think Mrs. Wiggins believed my story anyway but just wanted to have our relationship back to normal, so she agreed.

I gave Mrs. Wiggins a hug before jumping out of her car. I watched her pull away up a concrete hill that we called *"The Black Hill"* by name because of the black tar it was made of. The hill was always longer when we played on it but when Mrs. Wiggins was driving up it, the ride was as short as short could be. For some reason I just stood there waving goodbye even when she was gone as if deep down inside I knew that would be our last intriguing car ride together. Then I turned around to make the long trip (which was less than 20 feet) from the parking lot to my porch. When I got in the house my mom was waiting for me with a look of rage deeply written across her entire face. Her forehead had more lines in it than a diary. I hadn't seen that look since the one time she spanked me for almost getting hit by a car when I inadvertently made a mad dash towards a busy street when I was just 3 years old. I remember that spanking well and something told me that I would remember this one even more. But this spanking was different than the others. This one was not like the time when I had ran away from school, or like the time I got spanked for talking too much during church service. This was one that wasn't justified and I was proud to receive it. This was like the stories I had read about Martin Luther King Jr. and the punishments he received for standing up for what was true and decent. Besides, it was from my mom, which in comparison to the beatings He gave me regularly I'd gladly take any day. But all I could really think about when she whooped me was if this was truly something that she wanted to do, or was this in some diabolical way His idea all along? So once again I was at a crossroads of knowing whether or not this entire symphony was something being orchestrated by Him or her?

My life was really taking a turn for the worse at speeds the lean could not be controlled. It was as if I was looking at the world from the inside out instead of outside in. There is a difference. See, when you're looking at the world from the outside there's a certain type of freedom that automatically comes with that view. Even though you're trying to find a way in, when you can't you just turn around and go home. But when you're looking at the world from the inside out your eyes begin to suffocate so your visions can't breathe. The fishbowl is too small for your mind to swim in so you just walk around hoping to whirlpool your way out. But you need a whirlwind not a whirlpool. So your feelings just keep spinning round and round while you pray the bowl cracks just to allow a slither of light in for you to see a shadow of hope!

I was living my life in two pieces now, the life at home and the life away from home. My life at home was the most dangerous one as these were the times when I never knew what was going to take place. He had completely cut me off from all of my cousins and friends, as His cardinal rule was that I had no communication with anyone outside of school. Leslie, Manual and Reggie were the only family and friends I had at the time so this began to be a very stressful situation for me. It's not easy for an 8 year-old kid to only have 3 people to trust in when those people are children themselves. But that's all I had. Reggie and I weren't even in the same class anymore. Manual was two grades ahead of me so I only saw him when he would monitor our class at lunchtime. And Leslie was in middle school so I never saw her at all. I was alone. But not alone the way most people are. Everyone wanted to be friends with me in school because I was literally a badass! The only time I had good behavior was when I was in Mrs. Wiggins' class and that was over now. In a short period of time I was back to being my devilish, defensive self. And for some reason that type of behavior was always popular and attracted everyone to me like flies to a flame. The girls thought I was instant boyfriend material and the guys thought I was cool, so in my opinion everything was great inside those school walls. But my loneliness was internal. The type of loneliness that grips your mind and heart, slowly tightening and squeezing ever so often like a boa until eventually your mind can't move and your heart can't beat. And that's when the head of depression opens its mouth and swallows you whole! My new teacher was an asshole. All she did was scream at us and tell us how "unruly" we were. She was the type of person that hated their job and was determined to take out all of her frustration on whoever was weak enough to allow her to do so. So teaching children was the perfect fix for her cowardice addiction. She was an adult bully and she hated me the most out of all of her students. She forced me to sit in the back of the class. It was a 3rd/4th split class, which means we had two grades sitting and sharing the same room. The 3rd graders all sitting on her right hand side and the 4th graders sitting on her left. *How absurd is that?!!* The only thing separating the children was an imaginary line she drew down the middle of the classroom stating neither group could cross that line entering into the other grade's territory or they'd be punished. It reminded me of the earth's equator she was teaching us about. Since 3rd and 4th graders typically don't like each other and are ready to pounce on each other at the drop of a dime, that imaginary line was very hot and could explode at any minute. 45 Project students all cramped in a hot, tiny, old room waiting for the right moment to tear each other's heads off. No wonder this lady hated her job. There were no inspirational posters hanging on the walls except Nancy Reagan's "Be Smart, Don't Start" drug prevention slogans that were only there to cover up cracks and holes in the walls that the room had. Half of the florescent lights were out and most of the school desk were either too big or too small for the bodies sitting in them. The entire class looked like somebody's cruel joke to get back at society and the joke was on us! But in spite of everything and in the mist of all this confusion I could only see the huge opportunity hovering in front of me. All I could see was the chance for me to learn double by paying attention to the teacher at all times. She had a system of how she would teach her lesson plans. She would give the 4th graders homework assignments while she used the chalkboard to teach us 3rd graders our lessons and vice versa. I quickly realized that our 3rd grade work was mostly repeats of our second grade lessons that we had already learned, just at a higher and more detailed level. So I decided to take part in both classes thoroughly. While all the other 3rd graders were deep head first into their 3rd grade lessons I would be intently paying close attention to the 4th grade teachings just as passionately as the 3rd grade ones. This taught me a valuable lesson early in life that no matter what anyone else believes your growth capability is, you're going to be as great as whatever you truly believe yourself. I mean, the entire school system believed that for my age I should have been in the 3rd grade, but I believed that I should be in the 4th grade, so that's how I acted. I started stealing 4th grade homework papers and completing them. The teacher would always review the correct answers for homework aloud, so I would check my 4th grade work off of what she reviewed. After a while I just assumed I was in the 4th grade instead of the 3rd. It even got to the point that I would participate in the 4th grade lessons from my side of the room. The teacher would call on 4th grade students to answer questions during class and I started to play a game of how quickly could I answer a question aloud before they could. I usually got the questions right first which not only aggravated my teacher, but also made my 4th grade peers despise me. They didn't take it too well that a 3rd grader was showing them up at their own game so they began to call me names and wanted to fight me after school. This wasn't a problem at first because as far as name calling went I could jive with the best of them. And since I was from the Projects fighting was a regular part of our DNA, so I certainly wasn't a stranger to rumbling and tumbling around in the dirt. But soon the entire 4th grade class hated me. And though I could hold my own on the field of battle, I couldn't fight off 20 students all at the same time so something had to give. I tried to get more 3rd graders in the class to participate in the 4th grade lesson plans but they weren't interested. They could barely understand and complete their own 3rd grade homework let alone handle a 4th grade curriculum. So the plan of adding more people to my numbers to handle the 4th grade mob just backfired.

In particular there were three 4th graders that really wanted to whoop my ass...Johnny, Tony & Tito. They weren't from the Projects but they were from our neighborhood. Actually we were all from the same hood, but the Projects were just in a higher state of emergency than the rest of our neighborhood. We all were poor. It just seemed like the people from the Projects were poorer than everyone else. Johnny seemed to be the ringleader of the trio. Whatever he said the other two would just eagerly oblige, so I nicknamed the crew *Johnny and Them*. Johnny and Them were cool kids. They had cooler clothes and shoes than most of us. They were physically bigger than most of us because though they were in the 4th grade they had most likely flunked the previous year and were repeating that grade over for a second time. They were often rude to our teacher, which I thought was hilarious since she didn't care anything about us anyway. And second to her (sometimes first) they were running our class. I admired them. I wanted to be like them but it was hard for me to play both roles. You just couldn't be smart and unruly at the same time as this went against their code. But I tried my best to be both at all times. Half the time it worked. Sometimes Johnny and Them wanted to whoop my ass and other times they wanted me to be a part of the team. All the time my teacher hated us all so mission accomplished.

The school year was flying by and my life was beginning to have some consistency to it. It didn't matter how hard things were because there's a certain amount of strength that comes with consistency. And with consistency comes a certain amount of peace. It didn't matter that half the time Johnny and Them were my enemies because the other half they were my friends. It didn't matter that my teacher hated me because while she was hating me she still had to take her crooked witch finger and write "Well Done" and "100% Awesome, Keep It Up" on the top of all my tests and completed homework assignments. The only thing that did matter to me besides my grades was my social status. I had to do everything I could to keep up with the Jones' and that was one of the hardest tasks I had. Allowing your social status to become poor in the schools in my city could ruin a child's life, forever. The scarring that your mind could render after being ridiculed by your peers repeatedly could often have serious and permanent damage well into adulthood. And if there was any spirit housed deep inside of my soul it was the spirit of determination. I was determined to be more. I was determined to be better. And I was determined to be recognized, never ignored. My Grandmother had planted the seeds of determination into the soils of my soul in anticipation of the adversities I would have to face. It wouldn't matter who or where these adversities came from as long as I persevered through them. She knew this would be more important than anything else she could ever teach me and she was right. This allowed me to appreciate the light of consistency even in the darkest of hours. Without these seeds I would have surely died well before my time. It was well into the winter and Christmas was right around the corner. Everywhere I turned there were jingles and bells, people dashing through the snow and Santa Clauses on almost every corner. There were plenty of snowmen but none of them were as clean as Frostie. They were all dusty from the dirty snow that drifted in the yards from the highway, but at least someone took the time to roll the snow up into stacked dust balls to keep the festivities on the up and up! The past few days were really tough for me because the school kept having Santa's Workshops and I couldn't participate. Santa's Workshop was on the 2nd floor of the building and in the school library. The workshop was full of small toys, trinkets and gadgets that students could come in and purchase for their friends and families to give away at Christmas time. The gifts were really cheap and for us small children this was just a way for us to get out of class and visit a floor that we were hardly ever allowed on. Most of us would purchase gifts for our families but by lunchtime our curiosity of wanting to play with the gifts would have us open them up and play with them to the amusement of the entire class. For many students having the ability to buy gifts was a social status booster. Not only could you purchase gifts for popular students in the class to buy their affection, but you would also receive status points for being financially endowed enough to have the money to purchase gifts period. Even though all of our families were pretty poor since all of us were either from the Projects or hood homes, economic separation still existed based off of how poor you actually were compared to everyone else. No one in my class wanted to be labeled the "poor kid" because that would be social suicide. There were plenty of tricks you could do to boost your economic status and I was on top of them all. You could wear new clothes but since I didn't have any of those I just had to keep mine clean, which only meant allowing kids to throw me on the ground during recess needed to happen less often…no problem. You could wear the latest name brand tennis shoes but since I couldn't afford those I just needed to ensure that mine didn't have holes in them or grass stains all over them…again no problem. And you could never ever allow yourself to be caught anywhere at anytime with government assisted food stamps in your possession. These were brightly colored forms of government printed money that were given to poor families to help them survive each month by allowing the stamps to be used to purchase food. The bigger the stamp amount, the more colorful the stamp would actually be. On a positive note these stamps often came in handy each month in assisting our families in our quests of not going hungry from day to day. On the first of the month, every month people would just sit on their front porch and religiously wait for the mailman to drop off their food stamps. It was kind of like a monthly Christmas and our mailman was the Projects' Santa Claus himself! The only difference between the two was that Santa Claus passed up the Projects every Christmas and never got any slack from doing so, but if our mailman was ever late delivering our food stamps on the first, he might as well have signed his own death warrant because he literally could be killed for being tardy! That last week of the month was always stressful for everyone in the hood, especially the months with five weeks. I'm sure if anyone was to do a study in my neighborhood on the death count during that time, they would come to conclude that more people lost their lives at the end of the month than any other time because people were rarely good at managing their stamps efficiently enough to have funds left over. In the Projects I used to call the last week of the month freak week because all of the drug addicts used to freak out since they wouldn't have enough food stamps left over to trade in for cash money. I mean the entire Projects was on a 100 dollars in food stamps to get 50 dollars in cash money movement. At the beginning of the month the entire hood was like Black Wall Street except the trade was candy colored paper instead of reliable stocks and bonds! I don't believe there were any families in the Projects not on welfare, but to disclose this information about yourself to your friends in our school environment would be political suicide. The odds of the entire class using you for the brunt of all jokes would be highly probable, so we all knew the rules on this topic. Bill Clinton didn't invent "don't ask, don't tell..." we did. The poor people's society was more of a secret than the Free Masons Masonry Club for crying out loud. As my teacher was lining students up that had money to go to Santa's Workshop, I began to remember that one day my mom sent me to the corner store to get a few things as she normally would throughout the week. The store was about a 30-minute walk from our house so the entire trip would usually take me about an hour to complete, 45 minutes if I ran some of the way. When I got to the store I took out the grocery list my mom had written on the back of a piece of paper she had torn from the envelope of some old junk mail. My mom used her strategic wit to often write information on the backs of old mail envelopes just to justify her laziness in not throwing away junk mail in the trash where it belonged. Half our kitchen table was for eating and the other half was for the storage of multiple *Clearing House* adds that I would beg God daily to bless us to win. I assume most saints prayed for penance while I obviously missed that memo and would crack my knees daily praying for a celebrity with a news crew to knock on our steel riddled door with cameras rolling naming us as their newest winners. That prayer would always come after the one where I'd pray for Him to get lost or mugged on His way home from wherever He ran off to from time to time. He to me was the reason I had to go on these tedious trips to the store in the first place. If He had a job we could buy a car and drive to the store. I promised myself to never follow in His unemployed footsteps, which in turn created inside of me a certain type of repulsion for welfare overall. Basically we needed government assistance and that need made me sick to my stomach. I started grabbing the items my mom had written on the list. I would use the cashier counter to house my goods since corner stores didn't usually have buggies to stroll around and put your items in. Besides, corner stores were not supposed to be used for grocery shopping because their products were usually overpriced and outdated. Everyone knows you have to be careful buying anything from the corner store because you could literally die from eating an expired donut! As I reached over and under dusty shelves to find the stuff my mom wanted I tripped on one of the many broken mildew stained tiles that graced the floor and bumped my head on a bag of half rotten potatoes. *Must be an omen*, I thought as I picked it up and carried it to the counter. It was the last item on the list and I could tell by the look on the cashier's face that she was well ready for me to get all of my items off the counter and out of the store. I took one more look around the store to ensure the coast was clear for me to take out some food stamps and pay for the goods. I had to hurry up because not only was my mom waiting for me to get back home so that she could fix dinner, but the line behind me was starting to get backed up as there was only one cash register and I could tell by the impatient sighs breathing down my neck that the adults wanted me to get my ass out of their way. Just when the cashier was telling me what I owed I heard over the store door's opening bell jingle the mischievous sounds of some kids that I really couldn't afford to run in to. "What up bitch boy! Yeah what up bitch boy!" their voices chimed in awkward unison like fully stuffed hyenas with small sharp pieces of bone from their latest carcass still grossly logged against the back of their vocal chords. Just my luck it was Johnny and Them and their timing couldn't have been worse. Fortunately for me I had not yet pulled out the food stamps to pay the cashier or my life would have been over. I just looked up at the lady and said "I forgot to get something" as I darted away from the counter. I was completely willing to hold up the entire store line just to avoid Johnny and Them seeing me pull out a colorful book of food stamps to pay the cashier with. As soon as I left the counter and started panicking in each isle pretending to look for something else to buy, Johnny and Them were breathing down my neck as if they were rabid dogs and I was a huge steak wearing a pork chop necklace! They were just waiting for something to antagonize me about so I just patiently waited right along with them remembering from time to time to look around for that last product I was supposed to be finding. Eventually my patience overcame theirs and they went to the counter to pay for some bubble gum and cup cakes. After they left I went back to the counter to pay for my stuff. Some of the milk products I had to re-get because the cashier put them back to avoid them from spoiling, that's how long it took for me to get rid of those dudes. I paid for my groceries with the cartoon money and started my long walk home. I even went a different way just in case Johnny and Them had decided that their torture of me was not complete. There was no way I could afford to get my groceries stolen or damaged by a gang of smalltime hoodlums. It was already bad enough that my normal hour journey to the store was turning into a two-hour affair and counting. I was so distracted by the hustle and bustle of what was going on that I didn't realize how much time had passed in-between. Now my walk home was filled with anticipation of what the repercussions would be for my tardiness. *Would He be awake waiting for my return only to kill me as soon as I knocked on the front door? Would He even let me put down the groceries before He delivered his wrath upon my back? Would my mom be so angry that she didn't get a chance to start dinner on time that she too would join in on the festivities? Should I have just stepped up as a man and paid the cashier those food stamps with pride and took on the aftermath of Johnny and Them with a full head of steam? Hell no!* I snapped back out of my corner store daydream as Johnny and Them were already standing in line making jokes because I was still sitting in my seat which was a clear indicator that once again I didn't have any money to buy gifts for my family and friends for Christmas. They were already calling me "bum baby" so I could just imagine what despicable insults would have dripped from their blood sucking lips had they caught me paying for shit with those punk ass food stamps just the other day! The embarrassment would have gone to a whole other level that my reputation may not have been strong enough to carry. Thank God for sensible cowardly ambition, as it came in mighty handy that day. As the entire class laughed at me and the one other kid that couldn't afford to go to Santa's Workshop I just cringed at my desk gripping the sides on my chair so hard that my knuckles were turning white. I could feel myself getting ready to launch out of my seat to fuck up some well deserving kids' day by stabbing them in the throat with a number 2 pencil! But before my anger could reach its peak the class was already marching out the door to go on their second floor expedition. I could still slightly hear Johnny and Them talking shit as the class drifted further and further away until all that was left was my heavy breathing and the faint whimpering of the other kid in the room with me. He was devastated by the ridicule that had taken place and had made the grave mistake of allowing the class to see him cry before they had left the room. Little did he know that once they returned from Santa's Workshop that he'd be the point of interest for the rest of the day simply because he let those assholes see him breakdown in public. "You never let Him see you break down in public," I screamed with purpose at the teary cheeked kid blubbering across the room. "Him?" he asked with a look of extreme confusion running across his face. It was so dirty that his tears were streaming down his cheeks in muddy lines as if he was wearing mascara. In my frustration I hadn't even noticed that I had said "Him" instead of "them" as I had intended. "Never mind dumbass!" I squawked in an attempt to quickly cover up my mistake. I was more concerned that it was only Wednesday and we were going to have to put up with this Santa's Workshop bullshit for two more days. *What in seven fucks was I even going to do?* All I knew was I couldn't take another moment of Johnny and Them's nasty ass insults as the entire class was starting to join in on the fun. *I barely had made it through today's test and tomorrow's would certainly be a fail. I had to think of some way to change things, but what???!!!*

Chapter 6

Grandma's Voice Within

When I got home from school I was less than eager to endure more punishment from my secondary life. My first life (which was my school life) had taken a turn for the worse so having trouble at home could only dampen my spirit more than the norm. But the moment I found out that He wasn't home was the moment my cloudy day was starting to show promise. Wherever He was it was about that time for me to go into the closet, kneel down and pray to God for Him never to return back home to us. I would spend at least an hour feverishly begging God to allow something horrible to happen to Him like a school bus' tire exploding causing the bus to inadvertently run off the road and plow Him over…or that muggers would rob Him for His belongings and when they realized that He had nothing to offer, in a fit of rage they'd just tie Him to a tree and leave His headless body for the rats to eat. My prayers to God that day wouldn't last long because I couldn't take my mind off of what tomorrow's school day would consist of once it was time to go to Santa's Workshop again. Then as if God himself had parted the clouds of heaven, an idea struck me like a comet riding on the back of a lightening bolt! For most of the year I had been crying to my mom to have mercy and buy me a special remote control toy truck. This truck was the truck of all trucks. Though they tried very hard to do it justice, even Saturday morning cartoon commercials couldn't capture all the glory and splendor of this masterpiece of a toy, and they were pretty good at doing so. It was a monster truck that had 8 wheels (four on top and four on the bottom) with tiger claws that would randomly come in and out of them while operating. It had a paint job full of specially designed mean ass colors that when you looked at them you knew they represented something that was a terror to whatever terrain it was created to maneuver. If it came to a wall the claws would come out of its tires and the truck would just half climb the wall, flip upside down and proceed back the opposite direction ready to once again devour the road ahead. At the time it was the most beautiful thing I had ever seen besides the new girl, Sonya who had just joined our class a few days ago. She was a knockout and Johnny and Them were already all over her like flies on the ass of a poopy kid's diaper, so I knew it wouldn't be long before my daydreams of meeting up with her at recess would soon turn into nightmares just like everything else in my life. But one thing that wasn't a nightmare was that toy truck, which by the way was conveniently nicely hidden in my mom's bedroom closet. So finally my mom had gotten me the truck I'd been begging her for. She had gotten it for me for Christmas! I only knew this because she had sent me upstairs to her bedroom closet to fetch her purse and in doing so I discovered a bag with Christmas gifts in it neatly tucked away purposely being hidden by old lady dresses, underwear and pantyhose. The only thing that made me look in the bag in the first place was the Christmas wrapping paper sticking up out of it. And since I already knew Santa Claus wasn't real because he supposedly travelled to children's houses on Christmas Eve sliding down chimneys, but there was no way he was coming to the Projects because not only did we not have chimneys, but if any of our neighborhood thugs ever saw a cherry cheeked white guy with a bag full of toys running around tearing up our rooftops...his ass would have been robbed and killed the minute the first reindeer hoof touched down. So I knew for a long time any gifts I received at Christmas were gifts my mom bought with her hard-earned government assisted checks! Besides, she had already been telling me for the entire year that if I was on my best behavior she'd get me that truck for Christmas that I always wanted. I was just thinking that God had delivered the idea to me to ask my mom if I could have my Christmas present early to help me cope with the recent troubles I was having in school. But before I could ask her that I quickly realized that if I asked her about a toy truck that I wasn't supposed to know about, I would be stupidly informing her of my snooping crime in the first place, which in turn would certainly earn me a beating instead of an early Christmas gift. So I immediately understood that the idea hadn't come from God at all, but instead it had come from the Devil himself no differently than many of the other smart ideas I had that my mom so graciously reminded me of from time to time. So if I couldn't open up a Christmas gift early I'd just have to grow a pair and ask my mom for something she'd probably never agreed to. I'd have to ask her to give me money so I could buy gifts at the next Santa's Workshop. Geez, asking her for money would be no different than asking a starving Gorilla for a banana. That could go bad, real fast. But nothing could be worse than not having any money and sitting around while the entire class laughed at you for being poor. I'd wrestle with a starving Gorilla over a banana before going through that horrid experience again. So I got on my knees and begged and begged my mom to give me some money for Santa's Workshop. The underlined issue here is if I knew my mom then like I know her now I would have never asked her for anything. *My mom's a shark! Better yet, she's a polar bear! Why am I referring to her as a polar bear? Because polar bears when facing starvation will eat their own cubs. So in other words when my mom sees an opening to gain higher ground she'll take it, even if it means hurting her own children.* After an hour of begging her to give me money for Santa's Workshop and her steadfastly telling me no repeatedly, she finally came up with a devilish bargaining chip to flip into my grubby, desperate little paws. She told me that she would give me $5.00 for Santa's Workshop, but if she gave me the money she wasn't going to get me that monster truck I'd been asking her for all year for Christmas. And that's when I became overwhelmed with delight! Oh for once the stars had lined up in my favor. My mom had no idea that I had seen the toy truck in her closet that she had already bought for me. With Christmas being the following week this was a win-win situation! My mom just knew I'd turn down the deal because there was no way I'd give up getting my monster truck over a measly punk ass $5.00. But since she had already purchased my truck this would be one of those few times I'd get to have my cake and eat it too, in spite of the many times she told me this was impossible. So I shook her hand and accepted her terms. But while I was shaking her hand deep down inside I could feel a burning insecurity bubbling up telling me that I had made a bad decision. For now though at least I could sleep easy knowing that tomorrow's school day would be a better one.

For the past few days our class had been full of crossword puzzles and magnetic mazes to the point that our teacher was getting frustrated and started confiscating workshop gifts and holding them hostage until the end of the day. I had been patiently waiting all day for the Workshop Elves to make their daily rounds and come to our class to pick up all the students that had money to visit Santa's Workshop. It was just my luck that today of all days they were fashionably late! *Where the hell are these damn elves when you need them?* I impatiently pondered. Today would be the first day this week that I wouldn't have to be ridiculed by the entire class for being poor so I was really excited. Hopefully this would change their perception overall and I'd be back on track to being a cool kid. Then there was a knock at the door. I could see their little elf ears sticking up right outside the door window. It was finally time to go to Santa's Workshop! When my teacher asked everyone with money for Santa's Workshop to stand up and get into line, I was already standing there. As usual everyone got up and shuffled their way over towards the door except today there was only going to be one person left sitting at their desk, not two! Once the line was established Johnny and Them started their usual bash session except I was in line with them so they couldn't bash me. Charles was the only kid sitting there and I could already tell by the look on his face that at any moment he was about to break. I thought that I would feel really good about not being the kid laughed at by the entire class, but this view from the line looking down at Charles was a view that I didn't want to be a part of. I was so worried about how bad it made me feel to be laughed at that I assumed just getting myself out of the situation would make everything ok, but I was wrong. The feeling of leaving Charles there all alone to endure the class' punishment on his own felt worse than their ridicule could ever feel. In fact I was starting to get angry and just as the class was preparing themselves to enjoy another roast session sponsored by Johnny and Them, I walked over to Charles and whispered in his ear, "You better not start crying and don't look all weird from what I'm about to say. I got you today man. Just get in line cause I got enough money for the both of us! Nobody's going to be sitting down here today. We're all going to Santa's punk ass Workshop!" Charles tried to keep his composure but he couldn't help himself. He jumped up and sprinted over to the line with joy and anticipation oozing out of the large grin pulsating on his face. His look wasn't the only one that I noticed. Johnny and Them were really pissed off that I had ruined their show. In fact I think some of the other students in the class were pissed off as well. But their anger didn't matter to me. The feeling I had just received was one that I'd never forget. It was the first time in my life that I felt in control and proud of what I had done. For a small moment my life had purpose and meaning. But because this was also something I hadn't ever felt before it was a really scary, unforgettable experience. It was the perfect way to end the school quarter before Christmas vacation. When we got back to the classroom from Santa's Workshop we all had magnetic mazes, crossword puzzles and little gadgets for our teacher to get frustrated with and take away. And that was all that mattered to me!

It was only a few days until Christmas and my excitement to open up gifts from Santa was being derailed by my anticipation to get back to school. This Christmas vacation was no different to me than summer vacation except that at least in the summer it wasn't so cold. I hated the wintertime and I believe I hated it because everything looked a lot nicer than it felt. The trees may have been naked but they were laced in white lingerie dancing to the beat of a cold winter's drum. The snow softly draped our houses and cars like white cotton candy. It was truly a beautiful sight to behold. However, it also made every task and commandment He gave me so much harder for me to accomplish than usual. I had to keep the trash cans in the house empty which meant multiple freezing trips outside to the neighborhood dumpster. After every trip I had to mop the floor from the snow I tracked in from taking out the garbage. The long walks to the corner store were dreadful, as my feet would be freezing in my soaked tennis shoes from walking in the wet snow. Most of the time I had to walk in the street where the snow had been plowed away just to stay dry, but sometimes on slightly warmer days the snow would be slushy and when cars would pass they'd splash dirty snow on my already dirty clothes, adding insult to injury. At least when I was in school for eight hours a day I was warm and cozy and couldn't be summoned to go on long grocery shopping adventures! There were three of us children living in this hell of a home now. My mom had managed to get pregnant twice in the past eight years so I had a three year-old sister and a one year-old brother to look after too. For years I thought His craziness was nurtured by the notion that He hated me because I was His stepson, but when my siblings were born I quickly realized that wasn't the case because He treated them just as bad as He treated me…and in many cases He treated them worse. I had been trying to find some reasoning to explain His madness but there were none to be found. He didn't drink alcohol. He didn't smoke cigarettes. He didn't use drugs. In fact He despised all of those things. In thinking about it I wished He were a drug addict or alcohol abuser because then maybe His madness could have been attached to these and my prayers to God for a remedy to my situation could have been more precise. His insanity would have made more sense to me if I could have blamed it on something like that. But since He was drug and alcohol free, His insanity always left me flabbergasted! I just wanted Christmas to hurry up and pass so that I could play with my new truck and get back to school where I felt safer. Over my brother Lijah's crying I could hear Him trying to tip toe and sneak down the hallway stairs, to no avail. By this time my body and mind were physically trained in the excellence of knowing and being able to identify every movement in our home without being able to even see who was creating the stir. It was my way of staying alive in my house and I had developed it no differently than animals develop their own sensitivities to the environments they grow up in. I knew the difference between His walk, my mother's walk, Halia's walk and Lijah's crawl and this was definitely one of His sneaky ass tip toeing around techniques that I was so familiar with. I quickly and quietly gestured to Halia to sit down but she was either too busy making noise and being a typical three year old to notice me, or she just couldn't hear me over Lijah's whaling, so this time she'd just be ass out. I thought to myself, *she's going to have to learn the hard way,* as it was too late to give her any more warning. I straightened my back out and sat upright on the couch to be in perfect sitting position. I placed my hands in my lap and starting staring at a dusty, weak legged coffee table positioned in front of me across the room. An old black and white television struggled to sit atop the table but somehow managed to do so, both of them probably afraid to fall or collapse in fear of what He'd do to them if they did, so that table just held the TV up for dear life. Mr. Rogers' Neighborhood was playing on the TV set as he sat there on screen wearing the same damn sweater he wore every day.

Though the television was loud enough I couldn't hear Mr. Roger's rambling dialogue on how to be a good neighbor and kid, over the pounding sounds of my heart beating through my chest mixed in with Lijah's crying, Halia's dancing and His creepy failed attempt at tip toeing down our loud metal covered stairs. I just stared blankly through Mr. Roger's sweater to a place of concentration and preparation for what I already knew was coming next. He peeked His head around the corner of the stairway wall to see if anyone was paying attention. I knew better than to look at Him so I continued to stare at the television screen as if I hadn't noticed His obvious cat like prowling. It was too late for Halia as she was still happily spinning in a continuous circle round and round the living room. He leaped around the corner with a tomahawk battle cry springing from His lungs snatching her up by her tiny arms with little effort immediately causing her to scream. Her screaming made Lijah cry even more as if he was trying to best her in competition. The sounds of both their terror seemed to fuel His ambition to hurt someone even more than His normal craving. "What's all of this damn noise you makin' down here, huh Halia?" He seriously asked her as if she really could understand Him at her age. "All yous tryins' ta do is wake up the neighborhood so that I can step out there and kills one of these jokers right?" He was looking her right in the eye as He gripped her by the arms like a rag doll. She was so afraid that now no sound was coming from her lips. She just blankly stared at Him frozen by fear soundlessly screaming at what would have been the top of her voice, but was now pure and terrifying silence. I believe her silence even scared Him a little so He put her on the floor and smacked her backside with His bare hand. "Get your stupid ass over there and sit down already!" The smack put sound back into her lungs as she cried out painfully and ran over to the couch and jumped next to me. I just continued to stare like a statue at the television. I was a pro by this time and knew that the odds of Him bothering me would highly decrease if I didn't make a move or sound. I found out this was the best technique to use against Him as it worked 50% of the time, which was the highest ratio that I had seen since we met. I also knew this was just the first part of His tirade and the second part was quickly approaching. "All ya'll do is fuck up everything around here don't ya?" His question was rhetorical at best. "But the moment ya' think ya' free and one of those cotton pickin' niggas tries to help ya' I'm going to take this knife and cut his throat from ear to got damn ear! Then his bitch gone' be cyrin' and beggin' me to stop and that's when I's go cut that bitch too! And she just gone' be screamin' and screamin' and theys 'both gone' be screamin' and dyin' like two dogs, together! And then ya' knows what Imma' dos' next?" He slid His hand to His back pocket and pulled an old yellow handled screwdriver out from the glove and sock holder He had invented. Halia was gripping my arm hugging and holding onto it for dear life. He then leaped toward me and pressed the screwdriver to my throat. He had His forehead nudged against the side of my head and whispered into my ear "I's gonna' kill you but not until ya' fully see them die in a pool of their own blood first!" The screwdriver's tip had a cold steel feel on my neck. It was lodged so close to my Adam's apple that if I had swallowed or gulped it would have pierced my skin. Halia jumped away from holding onto my arm at that point in fear for her own safety. *Smart girl,* I thought as I just stayed motionless, face as blank as the first sheet of paper in a freshly opened notebook. I was staring well past Mr. Roger's sweater now. I was looking all the way past the dark buttons on his lightly colored plaid shirt, past the tiny grey hairs that lay on his flat bairn chest and through his saintly pulsing heart to a tundra floored place inside my brain. There I stood alone in the middle of a frozen treeless forest of snow and ice as far as the eyes could see. I kneeled down to touch the tiny blades of frozen grass on battered knees and put my hands together one gripping the other, thumbs in chest and looked up at the sky past the vultures circling over head to a crimson bathed sun and cried out "God give me the strength of Sampson so that I can rise up against my oppressor and strike Him dead before your eyes and in the glory of your holy name. Give me this oh Lord and I will serve you undeniably indefinitely for the rest of my days. If not, then let Him kill me now for this cross, unlike your son, I can no longer bear!" Whatever else He was whispering in my ear I had not heard as I was waiting for God to empower my body with the strength I had asked him for. My eyes began to water, not from fear but from going minutes upon minutes of not once blinking in anticipation of God's spirit entering my body so that I could rise up from the couch and rip His cowardly head from His rock solid body. But no strength came, only the sound of my mom beckoning Him to join her for breakfast before His food gets cold. I could smell the frustration of me being un-rattled by His antics lingering from the sweat of His brow. He reluctantly removed the screwdriver from my throat, placed it back inside the glove of His back pocket and be-bopped off to the kitchen to enjoy His meal. The living room was silent now as it always was anytime He came down to eat and would stay this way until He decided to go back upstairs to His den. Halia was mimicking my every breath trying to learn how to survive. Lijah was lying quietly between two pillows strategically placed to keep him from rolling off the armchair hitting the cold tiled floor. Coincidently even Mr. Roger's television show was having technical difficulties, so the TV was at a hush and the screen was full of static and snow. There we all were statues in time waiting for Him to go away so that the world could exhale. A world I truly didn't know how long I could be a part of.

I patiently sat in my bed staring at the ceiling counting the swirls and popcorn hanging from it. There was no way for me to trick my mind into going back to sleep and counting sheep just never seemed to work for me. However, counting cracks and pops in the ceiling and walls of my room usually did the trick, but not today. Christmas mornings always made me feel a little better than most mornings because even He wouldn't be a complete asshole on Christmas. In fact, He would act as if we had the best life ever and He was pleased with all that we were as a family. I didn't mind that at all because a win was a win and I needed to take as many wins as I could get. No matter what day it was, Christmas or no Christmas the same rules applied. So I had to wait in the bed until I heard my mom walk downstairs as the cue that it was ok to get up and start the day. Finally I heard her house shoes sliding across the floor and before she could complete her one step at a time trot down our steps I leaped out of bed and ran to the bathroom to snatch up the trash. Once I finished taking out the garbage I ran to my mom and gave her a big hug. "Whoa there boy, what's all this about?" She asked inquisitively as if she didn't already know it was Christmas day. "Merry Christmas mama!" I squeezed her harder to show my enthusiasm for the day. "I'm ready to open up some gifts if you are!" I screeched! To look around our house you wouldn't see the typical Christmas scene. We didn't have a Christmas tree with presents spread out underneath. There were no mistletoes hanging overhead or pretty wreaths swinging from entrance doors. Christmas colors were absent from our scheme, no red, gold or green to be found. But what we would have was one or two gifts to open and a great Christmas dinner to eat. In fact, my mom could only cook holiday food well, which was odd. Typical breakfast and dinner was not her forte, but holiday meals were right up her alley. The usual routine would be to skip breakfast and just eat holiday food instead. I loved that about the few holidays we did celebrate. If there was anything I could depend on it was holiday meals. As far as Christmases went, this would be my third Christmas with Him. The first one was very hard because it was the first one I had to spend alone without my true family. Leslie and Manny had a great Christmas that year, full of gifts and new clothes. I know because they rubbed it in my face all winter. The second one was better because I was used to all the solidarity by then and my expectations were so low that it wasn't possible for any disappointment to occur. However, this Christmas would be the best of all because it would be filled with the presence of the new toy truck I'd been waiting to get all year! "So...where is it mama? Where do you have it hidden???!!!" I said politely trying to mask an impossible enthusiasm. "Where's what boy?" Her tone was one that told me she truly had no idea what I was referring to. I stepped back and looked at her crossly with an expression that said *this is not the time to being making jokes!* I looked around the living room and noticed that there weren't any gift looking boxes anywhere to be found. "Where's my truck mama?" I worriedly asked. That's when she gave me one of those looks that sales people give you after the sale has been complete and you're upset with the results but you already signed the contract. "I told you that if I gave you money for school that you wasn't gettin' no truck, didn't I? And you took the money...so no truck." The words were like little daggers rapidly sticking me in my ears by the breath. I started feeling dazed as if this was a boxing match and round one had not gone that well for me. The question would be did I have enough courage to continue round two? Of course I did! What she didn't know is that I already knew she bought the truck because I saw it weeks ago hiding under clothes in her closet. I heard Him leave earlier that morning so this would be the perfect time for me to run upstairs and just take the truck. Certainly mama was just trying to stall. I ran upstairs and rummaged through her closet with haste. I had to hurry because if He ever caught me up in their closet with or without permission it would end up bad for me. I tossed clothes everywhere but to no avail. The truck was nowhere to be found. The bag wasn't even there that it was hiding in! And then it all hit me like a flurry of uppercuts, left and right hooks and stiff armed jabs. I suddenly realized that not only was I going to lose round two, but also I was on the verge of truly being knocked out for the count! *I had to do something, but what?* I ran back downstairs and did the only thing left in the deck for me to pull. *I had to tell her that I knew she bought the truck and demand its whereabouts.* "Mama, I know you bought that truck. I seen it in the plastic store bag when I was getting your purse, so I know you bought it already. So where is it? I'd like to play with my truck now." I had prepared myself for the lashing that I would receive once she found out that I was snooping through her closet, as that lashing would be worth it to corner her against the ropes as a last ditch effort to get my truck. It was round three now and I just couldn't take another loss like the previous rounds. But she just stood there, cool, calm and collected. She never even looked up from the food she was preparing for today's feast. "I told you that if I gave you the money for school that you wasn't getting' no truck. So I gave you the money and took the truck back. You certainly don't think I's would says somethin' and not keep my word, does ya? I said if you takes the money, no truck so you took the money and I took the truck back, like I said...no truck!" Oh, she parried and covered up so well that the few blows I gave her either missed or just barely bounced off of her body. But I wasn't giving up so easy. The last power punch I had would have to come from a place that we were almost equal in strength in, math! "That doesn't make any sense!" I screamed. "You gave me $5.00 for school. That truck had to cost at least

$30.00 or more. So since you bought the truck either that truck's still here or based off of my calculations you owe me at least $25.00! So which one is it?" There it was, a power punch of all power punches. I gave her the ol' hook line and sinker. Once I added factual simple math to the conversation the fight would have to swing my way. Who could argue with numbers since numbers don't lie? Mama could, that's who! She took that punch like a man, like an adult and responded like I already knew she would! "I told you if I's gave you the money for school, you wasn't getting' no truck! I gave you's the money so you's don't gets no truck, period! Now get outta' my face before you be the reason why dinner's not done before your father gets home and I tell Him it's all your fault!" I blankly looked at her but she couldn't look me in the eye. She just kept her head fixed on her dinner task and I knew that was her way of being beaten but using her authority to win regardless. "Down goes Frazier! Down goes Frazier!" I could hear the words ringing in my head, as I knew I wouldn't be able to recover from her last blow. I could always try to keep the discussion going but at what cost? Once she threw Him into the mix my corner threw in the towel anyway, so lying on the floor in the middle of the ring was the appropriate thing to do. And that's exactly what I did. I went to my room and just stared up at the ceiling to reflect what had just taken place. *Could I truly be mad at my own mother for being consistent and doing exactly what she said she would do, even if technically she screwed me out of at least $25.00? Or should I be mad at Grandma for not being here because if she were she would never allow me to have a shitty Christmas? Maybe I should be angry with Leslie and Manny since I'm sure their Christmas was a splendid adventure full of new toys and clothes! Then again, a lot of Manny's hand me downs Auntie Lorene would give to me, so more power to him for having a great Christmas. But if there was anyone that I could blame all of this on, it would be Him. He was the true reason why everything was so fucked up all of the time. Even when He wasn't, He was!* That's when I decided that every, and all holidays were just regular days that people often overreact about. And that's when I made my mind up that I couldn't be one of those people anymore. I couldn't allow myself to be disappointed and my faith in people being broken any longer. My expectations of them would have to be lower for their sake and my survival regardless of our relation. I stayed in my room the entire day lying in the bed, staring at the ceiling and praying for God to honor my request to save me from this path God had given me. I had to turn my head to the side to stop my tears from going in my ears. I wanted to hear God's voice when God told me everything would be alright, like how old people in church used to say they heard. How could they hear God's voice so easily when they always complained telling me to speak up because they could barely hear mine. God never answered any of my questions. All I could hear was the pounding of my own voice inside my head telling me to survive at all costs, to never give in and to never allow Him or anyone else to see you cry. The voice sounded familiar and not because it was my own. It sounded like Grandma's!

The school year had went by pretty quickly after Christmas. Before I knew it we were finally getting our final report card and mine had all "A's" as promised. I figured Grandma in her deep sleep was extremely proud and that's what kept me going. It was the last day of school and everyone was talking about what their families would be doing for the summer. Most of the conversations revolved around going on trips to amusement parks or out of state. Since most of us lived in the same neighborhood I knew that these were all lies, but it was fun for us to dream big and stretch those imaginations. I was once again dreading the summer. Every time it came around the days seemed to get longer and longer before school, my safe haven was back in play. We were all sitting in the auditorium listening to different teachers go on stage and give out awards to the students in their classes who had done extremely well that school year. My teacher hated me so much that she barely wanted to call my name out when giving the award for straight A' students. But I could hear Leslie from the audience scream out "You go boy! That's how it's done!" when my teacher reluctantly called out my name. This would go on for over an hour as each class had their own specific awards to present. For most children it was just a delay in getting dismissed from school to enjoy summer vacation. Finally Mrs. Sanders took the stage to do a final announcement. Because she was the principal and was known to demand respect, the entire auditorium went silent when she began to speak. She started off talking about how great of a year we had and what negative things not to get caught up in during the summer. She had a wide range of topics from safety to heroism and as tedious as it seemed no one's attention was lost. Then Mrs. Sanders starting talking about the importance of a good education in our society. In her hand she had two large plaques to present to two special students for their accomplishments throughout the year. As she kept deliberating on education and brilliance it began to be obvious that these awards were going to be given out to two students who were highly intelligent. She rambled on about the scholastic state test taken throughout the year and how these two individuals had the highest test results in the school and because of this they would be going to a new school next year for advanced learners. She said it was an honor our school had never seen the likes of previously and that we all should be very proud to have these two students among us. Once she said that I had a pretty good idea who one of these two students were. The 1st would be Jin Choi. He was the only Asian in our school and he was smart as hell. He was a 5th grader and since he was the only Asian in our school he was popular by default. I just assumed he was smart because at recess while all of us were running around playing hopscotch and dodge ball he would sit on the school bench and read. He was the only student who would wear his book bag while on the playground, which of course he got teased for unimaginably. And his entire disposition reeked of nerdism. I remember walking up to him on the playground one day asking him why he read so much? He told me that he was reading to understand all things. At the time that made some sense to me, since I had been reading about aerospace engineering to understand that. But to take it as far as reading on the playground during recess was just not an option for me as that would be social suicide at its finest! When I told Jin that he started laughing, shook my hand and said "You're pretty smart for a 3rd grader." I was pretty positive that Jin would be getting one of the plagues Mrs. Sanders was holding. The second student to get the other plaque I was positive wouldn't be anyone else I knew, and that was a good enough guess for me as any. The rest of us were too worried about what day we'd be getting pizza for school lunch and how many peanut butter cookies we could collect and sneak into our pants pockets to take back to eat during class. The auditorium was packed with friends and family of us students and just when it seemed like maybe some of the parents were getting a little impatient with Mrs. Sanders' speech, she revealed the names of the students to receive the awards. "Please give a huge round of applause for Jin Choi and…" her voice paused the same way it would when she'd be talking to a teacher in the hallway and see someone doing something wrong out the corner of her hawk eye. I eagerly looked around the auditorium to see what idiot had Mrs. Sanders' attention as this would be the dumbest time to get into trouble, being that we were only minutes from being dismissed for the year. Jin Choi was already walking toward the stage but stopped, as he too was confused as to why Mrs. Sanders had paused so suddenly. It was as if the entire room was filled with toxic gas and all of us were holding our breath for dear life. Mrs. Sanders began to walk across the stage and proceeded on… "This next student has certainly come a very long way in their development of becoming a great student and example to us all of how to take adversity and turn it into a golden opportunity…" She was walking towards our side of the room and was suddenly very close to where our class of 3rd graders were sitting. I was super excited now and was sitting on my knees in my seat trying to find out which child or adult Mrs. Sanders had caught disobediently chewing bubble gum or foolishly sleeping during her presentation. As I feverishly looked to and fro completely pivoted around in my seat trying to find the culprit, I suddenly felt the chill of all the eyes in the auditorium fixed on me, which could only mean that Mrs. Sanders was standing directly behind me. I sadly lowered my head as I already knew that she must had mistaken my looking all around as a sign of disrespect but had no idea that I was only trying to find the disruptive party that had caused her to walk off the stage in the first place! In knowing that there would be no way for me to explain it I just lowered my head in defeat and waited for the tap on my shoulder that I'd surely receive. "Everyone please stand up and give a huge round of applause for Jesse Benson!" Mrs. Sanders grabbed my arm, twisted me around and gave me the biggest hug I had ever received from anyone. She held my hand and led me up the stage stairs with Jin Choi. She was smiling and saying something to me I couldn't hear over the roar and applause of the crowd. She handed us the plaques while flashes from the cameras partially blinded my view. What little I could see was Mrs. Wiggins jumping up and down in some weird proud way. She was more excited than my current teacher who was just standing there in some awkward negative awe that my name was part of something other than mischief. I looked over to where Leslie's and Emanuel's classes were and both of them were clapping and pointing at me in acknowledgment to their friends. Auntie Lorene and my mom were cheering along with all the other adults as well. It was one of the finest moments of recognition I had in my entire life and the only thing I could think of was *I'm so glad He's not here to embarrass me this time! Even He can't take this one away from me!*

It had been three long years since Grandma's passing. I finally understood that she wasn't sleeping but instead was just dead, no differently than knowing that the Easter Bunny and Santa Claus were also two made up stories given to naive little children. And that was something I was not. Children were sweet and innocent, playful and curious. I wasn't any of those things. In fact I was just there. I felt like a blade of blue grass in a beautiful green field, but still too small to even stick out and be noticed. Days and nights would pass but time for me was as still as death. The only way I knew I was alive was from the definition given to us in school…if it breathes and grows then it's alive. I only could tell I was growing because all of my clothes were too small for my body. Emanuel did his usual good Samaritan act and gave me all the clothes he no longer wanted, with the price of harassing and wrestling with me from time to time. Manny was my strength in the summer and my best friend. I wasn't allowed to visit with my cousins too often even though they lived less than half a block away. I could see their apartment from our living room window and often wondered how much better life would be if I just lived with them again. My mom would visit her sister at least once a week to borrow sugar or butter and those visits would often be for hours. The longer the visit the better, anything to keep out of the house and out of His way. That's how I found out Manny was starting to play pop warner football. He stood there in his living room with his pads and uniform on holding a football helmet that looked far too big for his tiny head. I immediately started making fun of him because I knew that my chances of doing so were always few and far between. But truly I was amazed at how much bigger his entire outfit made him look. He looked like a little grown man! He was getting ready to walk out the door to go to football practice and while my mother and auntie were deeply engrossed into some I'm sure meaningless conversation, he gave me a look that I was all too familiar with. It was a quick but highly registered look of "let's go, you can go with me if you hurry up and sneak out right now!" "Aye, Aye captain!" Manny didn't have to give me the signal twice as I slipped out the door with him while no one was paying us any attention. I knew that I'd be in some type of trouble for going with Manny without permission but since this would be trouble with my mom I didn't truly mind. Any chance that I could get to hang out with Manny was a chance that I just couldn't pass up. Manny was the only person that knew me and what my life was about before He came in and took it over. It was as if Manny was one of the few witnesses on the planet that could vouch that I was truly normal and anything else was being forced upon me. I only felt alive when I was around him and Leslie. In my mind they were my true family and everything else was a contradiction, a facade, a fake or phony rendition of the truth. Every so often I let out a snicker because Manny was walking funny in his football cleats. It was like he was wearing women's shoes with too tall of a heel for him to manage. He knew I was making fun of him in my mind and gave me a look that told me I could have stayed back instead of coming along. That look was enough to pipe my snickers down to a minimum. "Don't embarrass me out here!" Manny jarred at me his expectations for allowing me to come to his football practice. "All you're allowed to do is quietly sit there and watch. If you can't do that you might as well just turn around and go home." Well there was no way I was going back home so I gave Manny the nod of understanding as we walked up onto the practice field. Today was elimination day and coaches had to pick a small number of children to make the team, the North Side Knights! There were so many children there that I was blown away by the amount of children I didn't know that probably went to other elementary schools across the North side of town. To say the least it was a little intimidating. These kids had been coming to the practice field for a few weeks now trying to learn and be impressive to the coaches that had to make a decision on what kids would make the team and what kids would have to go home and try again next year. It was like a poor sports like version of a reality TV singing competition, except the grand prize for these kids would only be bruises and bragging rights instead of a million dollar recording contract. Right in the middle of my awe suddenly the coaches starting yelling at everyone to line up in their appropriate age groups for practice. "Now sit here and watch how it's done little cat!" Manny patted me on the head and ran off to get in line. The whole thing was weird to me because some kids had their equipment and uniforms on and some didn't. I was confused and couldn't tell the wanna' be players from the spectators. But after a while I realized that I was the only spectator there. All the children had lined up accordingly and awaited the coaches' next instructions. Then a loud whistle blew and kids started jogging around the field. Running was something that I loved to do and I was so excited to see the kids trying to do it. Some were good at it but most of them were struggling before they could complete one lap. The coaches were hollering and blowing their whistles in an attempt to encourage the kids to run faster and to not give up. The entire scene gave me chills of enthusiasm, as I had never seen anything like it before. Suddenly in the mist of my amazement a coach ran up to me and starting yelling "what do you think this is boy...a view master party? Let's go! Get moving!" He was so aggressive that out of fear I didn't even attempt to argue with him. I immediately started jogging around the field in congruence with the other children. "Watch that one G, he's a slick one, a slacker, keep an eye out for that one!" I heard the coach that yelled at me tell the main coach on the field. So to show that I wasn't a slacker I decided to pick up the pace. I started passing up children one kid at a time. Then the main coach blew his whistle very loudly instructing us to gather round back into the lines we were in earlier. He wanted us to run some routes and do some catching exercises. Since I hadn't started off in any of the lines I was confused as to which line to get in, so I just looked around to find Manny because I didn't know what to do. What I did know was that I didn't want the coach that yelled at me for not running to yell at me again and call me a slacker for not getting in line in a timely fashion. I saw Manny off in a line with some of the bigger kids so I just jumped into the back of that one. One at a time the coach would whisper something into one of our ears, blow his whistle and we would take off running, do some type of twist, jerk or move and then turn around to catch the football being hurled at us pretty hard. If one of us caught the ball everyone would cheer and clap. But if one of us dropped the ball then we would get yelled at, called some type of stupid name and then have to do 5 push ups. I couldn't hear what the coach was whispering into each child's ear and since I had never been to any practices before, I was really nervous. What the hell had I gotten myself into??!! Since I was at the back of the line I figured I had some time to figure out what was going on so I started watching all the lines and what the kids were doing when it was their turn to go. But each kid would do something different each time, so I couldn't figure out what I was supposed to do when it was my turn. The coaches kept yelling and antagonizing the kids because most of them were doing things incorrectly and dropping the ball. Many of them were either turning the wrong way or not even turning around at all and missing the ball completely. I watched as ball after ball bounced off of the kids' chests, hands and sometimes heads. Every dropped ball or botched up play resulted in humiliation and pushups, neither of which were unfamiliar to me. Manny's turn was next and I was secretly rooting for him deep inside my gut. I thought to myself *I hope you haven't treated this like your schoolwork. I hope you studied...you big dummy! You better catch this ball Manny or it's push ups for you!* The coach whispered something into Manny's ear, blew his whistle and off Manny went. Manny wasn't the fastest when it came to foot speed but he was a muscular kid. He planted his foot into the dirt and twisted. Some dust flew up from his cleats but his movements were right in sync with whatever the coach had told him to do. And just when I thought he was in the clear, he turned around to catch the already thrown football and boink! The football hit him in his clumpy shoulder pads, bounced off his hands and hit the ground. Manny had barely dropped the ball, but dropped it he had. At first I was disappointed but when Manny had to drop down and do push ups I couldn't help but to laugh aloud. The coach that originally caught me not running earlier happened to be watching me while I was laughing at Manny. "Oh, that's funny huh?" he looked at me with a cynical grimace and motioned me to come over. "This one's up next coach!" He pulled me to the front of the line and handed me over to the head coach. Manny stood up from the ground to see who was causing all the commotion and when he realized it was me he just shook his head and stood off to the side to watch the show. I was so nervous because no more lines were going through the exercise. They were all looking at me now as I awaited my instructions. I was certain that I wouldn't understand the play call since this was the first practice I had attended, but I was also sure that embarrassment wasn't an option. The coach whispered into my ear "run out 5 steps, sharp shoot to the right and take 3 more steps and turn around to catch the ball." I thought to myself *is that it? I know my right from left and I know how to count so...* Before I could finish my thought the whistle sounded off awfully loud in my ear and away I went. I was a very fast kid for my age so my five steps were over and done with before I could even count. I sharply turned to the right took exactly three steps as instructed and turned around. To my surprise the football was already whirling through the air at my head. I put my hands up to stop the ball from hitting me in the face but remembered that if I didn't catch it I would be called some silly name and have to do push ups, both of which in my opinion were highly unacceptable. So I clenched my hands together and caught the ball. With that some applause came and some people started to cheer. I smugly gave the ball back to the coach that yelled at me and started to make my way back to the end of the line when I heard the coach yell out "naw...that was too easy. Get your ass back up here!" I acted like I didn't hear him in a futile attempt to quit while I was ahead, but he just wouldn't let it go. He grabbed me from the back of the line and put me right back in front and said to the head coach "give em' another one G. But make this play harder." The head coached whispered in my ear "run out 10 steps this time, make a slant to the left 5 steps and turn around to catch the ball." He blew the whistle and off I went. I ran faster this time as I wanted to get the entire situation over with, but I did exactly what the coach asked. This time I anticipated that the ball was going to be in flight before I turned around, so my hands were already up ready to catch the ball prematurely. And catch it I did! People began to clap and cheer again and it made me feel good to have someone on my side, as it was so clear to me that the other coach was not. I trotted back and gave the football back to him but this time I did it politely, as I didn't want to encourage him to put me up for a third time. At this point I really just wanted to go back to watching everyone else try to make the grade. "G, you're being to soft on this little cat. Let me show you how it's done!" The coach grabbed me before I could even attempt to get to the back of the line. "Go 15 steps out, turn around and the ball's coming." The head coached stepped out of the way to let him take over the quarterback job for the last catching expedition. I truly wanted the head coach to throw me the football because this other guy obviously didn't have my best interest at heart. 15 steps was a good distance out there and no one had caught a ball thrown that far out thus far. The whistle blew and I was off to the races. I took 15 steps and turned around. To my surprise the ball was thrown extremely hard and entirely too fast for me to catch it with my hands. So I jumped in the air to make the ball hit me in my stomach and then wrapped my hands around the ball. It was thrown so hard that it slightly knocked the wind out of me causing my legs to fly up in the air and my back to hit the ground with a heavy thud. I lay there for a moment looking over at the sun as it was starting to set. The orange clouds were thinly stretched over a purple and blue hazed sky that seemed to nod its head at me with approval to rise. I knew the stars I saw were not real, but only stars from being dazed by the impact of my body slamming into the dirt. But for some reason I liked those stars too. I sat up and looked down at my lap and sure enough there was the ball cradled between my arms and my upset stomach. I stood up, shook myself off and jogged back over to the team. At first there was no cheering, no clapping, just eyes wide and jaws dropped. "Now that's how you catch a damn football!" the head coach yelled out and broke the silence of all the lambs. "Everybody gather round. It's time to find out who made the team and what ya'll gone' need to do next." I dropped the football on the ground and started to walk away from all the rustle and bustle of the crowd of kids anxious to know if they had made the cut. That's when the coach that tried to kill me with the bullet pass ran up to me and said "hey little man...you got exactly what we're looking for to win some games this year! I want you to take this form home to your folks. If you get it back to us signed by tomorrow, you're on the team. Congratulations!" Manny walked over with his paper in his hand as well as he too had made the squad. All the way home I teased Manny about how I had made the team without having to wear funny football shoes! Then we reminisced on the passes I caught, in particular the last pass that put me on my ass. We laughed and laughed as I showed him my bruised stomach with pride and that's when I recognized how much I missed Manny, barely any differently than missing Grandma. The only difference was I could actually see Manny every now and then. Now I'd be able to spend more time with him because we would be on the same football team, going to practice and playing in games together. I couldn't wait to tell my mom the good news! And just when I think things are starting to look up, down they go again. In the midst of all the excitement of maybe becoming a young football star I forgot how much time had passed. I thought Manny and I would be at football practice maybe 30 minutes at best, but we had been gone for a couple of hours. By the time we got back to his house it was dark. All I was praying was that my mom still be there when we walked in, but she was gone! *Why? God why would she leave knowing that I wasn't with her?* "Boy ya' knows you needs to get home, now ya' hear?! Yo, mama done' been left." Auntie Lorene was pointing her finger at me the way she used to when we all lived together. "And ya' knows ya' shouldn't have taken him out theres witcha' Manuel...anyways did ya' makes the team?" Manny handed his mom his paperwork with his chest all pumped out, to answer her question. "Of course I made the team. And this dummy made the team too!" I held my hand up high and planted my football form midair as if it was a revolutionary flag and I had just conquered the beautiful lands of some neighboring enemy! Auntie Lorene looked at me with so much pride you'd thought I'd been a child of hers. But I was not. So she quickly wiped her smile from her face and focused back on the task at hand. "Good job. Now get ya' behind home before ya' mama bes' worried sick not knowing where you at!" But she did know where I was. Even though I had snuck out with Manny there's no way that she didn't know I'd taken off with him. I used to always take off with him or Leslie our entire childhood. When we all lived together they would always try to leave me behind and I'd always find a way to catch up with them and tag along. Grandma used to get on their cases all the time about trying to leave me behind. She would make Leslie take Emanuel and make Emanuel drag me along. It was family law. It was tradition. And in my mind it was just yesterday. But in all actuality it wasn't just yesterday. That was all in my head. It had nearly been almost four years since Grandma's death and in that time everything and everyone was indeed different. *Why in the hell did my mom leave? Why couldn't she just had waited for me to get back before walking home? Because she didn't wait I'd have to enter my house without her by my side. I'd have to confront Him alone for being late. Without her support I could literally end up dead tonight. Did my auntie know that? Of course not or she wouldn't even let me leave. Should I tell her? No, because then their lives would be in danger just as much as mine, and this cross was to be carried by me and me alone.* Leslie looked at me with encouraging eyes telling me to hurry home. Manny just turned around and stormed upstairs to his room. I could tell he was angry at the idea that I'd be in trouble for accompanying him to a football practice. So I sadly turned around, pushed out of the door to begin the forever walk home that was only half a block away.

Chapter 7
Be the Ant

Tiny pieces of paper delicately floated towards the ground in sprinkles no differently than how confetti falls on television game shows once a winner has been announced, except this show was minus the balloons and applause. But it did have all the makings of what great television shows have, conflict and suspense. I was literally waiting for His hands to wrap around my throat after they had torn up the football permission slip but instead they were reaching for something else. At the same time I could barely hear my mom scolding me for running off with Manny without telling her because my mind was in such a blank daze. Disappearing was the only way I could cope with any of this so it was prime time to get back to finding something to fix my attention on. This time it wouldn't be a roach on a wall or a crack in the ceiling as those were already previously used. Instead it would be an old acorn tree outside our living room window. I often wondered in amazement over that tree in how big and strong it was. It certainly had to be here way before any of us were considering its size. It had deep dark brown grooves all around its trunk and its branches reached far out over the roofs of many of the adjoining apartments tickling the toes of the reclined clouds above. It had many residents on its shoulders from ants and butterflies to birds and squirrels all living in harmony together, no two days symphonically playing the same tune twice. The beauty of such was hard to be distracted from, but was certainly being challenged by my mom's antagonizing ridicule and His hands which had begun to cut the cord from an old iron that no longer worked properly. Cutting the cord was not that easy to do as the outer layer was wrapped in tightly woven cloth, revealing the iron's old age. My ears matched the sawing sound of His knife's ridiculously dull blade with the scratching rhythm of a stray cat trying to sharpen its claws at the root of the tree. The knife aggressively plowed through the cord, as the cat shot up the tree in a futile attempt to catch a squirrel. I was sitting there nearly naked in front of Halia and Lijah, stripped of not only clothing…but also of pride and dignity. The lesson that was about to be given was obviously not intended for me alone. Now thoroughly cut to His satisfaction, He looped both ends of the cord together around the grip of His hands and swung down with brute force against my thighs. I had been whipped many times with a belt previously and my tolerance was strong in that regard. And though there would be some pain in addition to this humiliation, I was accustomed to both and could weather this storm no differently than the others before it. However, I had no idea how different this one would actually be. The belt was short and flat so when lashed across your skin the pain resembled just that, short and flat…painful but quick. However, the ironing cord was long and thick, and the first strike was very unfamiliar to me. The moment it touched my skin for the first time the pain rippled through my legs with the wave of a cement block being hurled into a small pond. The cord stretched across the top of my legs angrily and wrapped around the sides furiously. The pain was so intense that before He could strike again I placed my arms over my legs to block the blow. Big mistake! The second lash came slicing down against my arms, whistling through the air an off tune sound that haunts me even now. The cord ruptured my skin forcefully and pulsated all the way through my arms' bones. The pain riddled up my arms, past my shoulders, through my neck and down my spine until I could feel it evilly tickling the soles of my feet. The pain was so intense that I nearly puked but swallowed my vomit to avoid making Him even angrier for creating more of a mess. He hit me repeatedly over and over as I rotated back and forth covering and uncovering my legs with my arms accordingly as best as possible, trying to compensate one pain for another. The tree was long gone now as my attention was fixated on the growls coming from His mouth and the snarls grinding from His teeth. I looked over to Halia to see if she was ok. A look of pure terror hovered over her as she silently screamed inside her head. I knew she wanted to run, look away even… but at this point she was completely too afraid to move. So instead she just rocked back and forth with her hands over her ears. Every time the cord whistled down, right before it struck me she shuddered and flinched in frightful anticipation of the pain I was enduring. It hurt me that she had to see this, more than the beating did. I looked over to Lijah who thankfully somehow in the midst of what was taking place, had fallen peacefully asleep. There was one thing that was consistent in all of the beatings I had received, and once again rang true here. The beatings would commence in 3 stages. Stage 1 would be the initial introduction of the punishment, warm up strikes into Stage 2. Stage 2, which would be the most intense of all 3 stages would be based off of His ability to maintain the stamina needed to make the beatings worthwhile. And then the final stage would be the wind down, cool down stage. I usually could last all 3 stages without shedding any tears because I had built up a pretty good tolerance over the years. But I guess this is why He decided to move on to greater forms of punishment with me in the first place. He was obviously intimidated by my tolerance and had decided today to make an adjustment. Mission accomplished! His adjustment buckled me like the knees of a black stallion finally submitting to the whip and will of its owner. I tumbled over to the floor balled up like a fetus. In submission I cried because my will to stay strong and endure had been broken before the end of stage 2. Now stage 3 would end with me whaling with my face in my hands and His rage against my back. And just when I thought I couldn't take another strike, it all ended. He dropped the cord and commenced to trod back upstairs to His lair. All was quiet now. Halia was curled up on the couch with her knees in her chest. What she had just witnessed would be burned into her brain forever. My mom had left for the kitchen during stage 1 of my punishment. All she had on her mind was finishing up dinner and going to bed. The cord lay there in front of me, copper wire dangling from one end where it had been cut reminding me of the mouth of a fire breathing snake I had once seen on a cartoon. What had just so vividly tortured me was now lying lifelessly in front of me, mocking me after the fact. I reached out, grabbed it by the neck and weakly through it against the wall. I was physically and mentally too exhausted to throw it as hard as I wished to. I began to gather my scattered clothes from off the floor and embarrassingly held them against the front and back of my exposed self. My gaze made its way back outside the living room window to the scene outside and to my surprise it had slightly changed. The tree was still colorfully old and bright. The life it housed still rested on its leaves and branches. Everything was the same except it didn't feel the same to me as before. I didn't want to look at it anymore. My appreciation of it was dwindling and my hatred of it was beginning to grow. But then I immediately realized how jealous, yet amazed I was of that old tree. Through the rain, and snowstorms, sleet and the hail…year after year it stood strong. It would bend with the wind but never break. It would smoke from the sun but never burn. In that moment I realized that the same reason I hated that old tree, was also the same reason why I loved it so much. And I thought to myself *if an old tree can survive, so can I!*

I couldn't wait for the new school year to start again. Being at home for extended periods of time was truly a drag and waiting for the start of a new school year for me was like everyone else waiting for Christmas to come. I tried to act like I didn't hear her calling me but I could only play that card so long. "Jesse Wayne, now yous' comes here boy! Don't have me keeps callin' ya!" My mom was yelling at the top of her lungs now so I had to comply before He heard her. I certainly didn't want her loud yappin' to wake up the beast. "Yes mama?" I reluctantly asked, "What can I do for you?" The question was rhetorical as I already knew that all she wanted was to send me over to the Mission to get her a newspaper. The Mission was this huge homeless shelter that fortunately and unfortunately sat right in front of our apartment. It was fortunate because they had rooms for homeless people to live, which in turn helped to keep them off the street and they'd also feed them dinner every day like clockwork at 6:00pm. There'd be a long line of people standing outside waiting for their turn to go in and get a hot plate every evening. There were many nights that we too had to stand in that line. Unfortunately, the Mission also attracted a lot of individuals to itself that young kids in our neighborhood should've never had to interact with, like convicted murderers and rapists, drug addicts that would *shoot up* right in front of our faces and con artists waiting for the next victim to come along their scamming path. Every afternoon mama would send me to the Mission to buy a newspaper and I hated it. I would procrastinate as much as possible each day hoping that she'd forget, but she rarely did. In my mind a 9-yearold kid shouldn't have to walk the long, grey mile through drug addicts and prostitutes for a lousy newspaper. Obviously mama didn't feel the same. However, it wasn't just the smelly old men, winos and prostitutes that intimidated me each day…they were harmless. It was punk ass Tori Tucker that trumped that cake! Tori was a neighborhood bully that used to sit and wait for me outside my door every afternoon. He promised me on many occasions by gesturing with his fist pounding into his hand that when he finally got them on me he was going to whoop my ass. From time to time he'd yell profanities towards my bedroom window and I'd reply by sticking my middle finger up at him before shutting my blinds. Even though Tori was two years older than me I never worried about him catching me because he was just too slow. Every day he'd be waiting outside my door knowing I had to make that trip to the Mission. And every day I'd just run right by him, safely in and safely out. The scene barely any different than the Looney Tune cartoons where The Wiley Coyote could never catch The Road Runner no matter how hard he tried. Obviously Tori was the slow, dumb Coyote! But for some strange reason Tori was nowhere to be seen today, so I assumed my trip to the Mission would be a peaceful one. Every so often looking around for Tori I made my way over to the Mission, opened the big steel door and went inside. The place reeked of sweaty old men's testicles and onion ripe armpits! I had to pull my t-shirt over my nose to immediately slow myself from vomiting from their stench while sidestepping and hurdling over sleeping bodies as I made my way to the front counter. The place was dimly lit so I could barely see where I was going but since I had done it so many times before I could literally make it there with my eyes closed. The security guard sat behind the counter waiving his hand to maneuver me through the sleeping herd as if this was my first rodeo. The top part of the counter had bars on it with just one small slot used to pass items back and forth. It humored me to see a guard behind bars because in my neighborhood it was usually the other way around, but I knew he was behind them only for his protection.

"What's up little man? Whatcha' gots for me today?"

I answered him by reaching up with one hand and sliding a quarter through the counter slot ensuring there was no break in holding my shirt over my nose.

"I'm sorry little man but today's paper cost four quarters, not one!"

I knew the guard was joking with me. He'd say the same joke every single time waiting for me to react. I was holding my breath so I didn't have time to play with him but I knew if I didn't react our transaction would take even longer than preferred. So I bowed my head in sadness and turned around as if to walk away. "Ahhh…I'm just joking little man. Your money is good to go here. One newspaper coming right up."

Smiling, he handed me the paper through the counter slot and ended our transaction with his famous "Be safe out there little man and stay out of trouble. Don't end up like these goons!"

I politely nodded in agreement and quickly ran to the exit. As soon as I got outside I placed my hands on my knees gasping for air. It felt good to be able to breathe freely again until I felt my shoulders being forcibly whipped around.

"Finally got that bitch ass! Haha…yeahhhhhh mutha fucka!"

As soon as I heard his annoying voice it sent chills down my spine and I knew I had been caught slipping. In all the trauma of trying not to breathe in the Mission's stench, I totally forgot about Tori Tucker!

"Get your sorry bitch ass over here boy!"

I could hear the victory in his bolstering tone as he dragged me in a headlock around to the side of the building and threw my back up against the wall.

"What's up now punk ass nigga?!! I got yo' dumbass now boy!"

I could tell Tori was overly excited. After all this time of chasing me to no avail he had now finally caught me! He was so excited he didn't know what to do with himself and because I was no stranger to intimidation I decide to stick up for myself.

"Ok, you finally caught me. I get it. Big dealllllll. You got me so now what?" I smugly replied.

I could tell the question stumped him for a second no differently than correctly buttoning up his shirt had. The look of stupidity on his face made me sarcastically chuckle and Tori didn't like that at all. "Here's what's now bitch!"

He lifted up his shirt and pulled a small black handgun from his waist.

He cocked it sideways and pointed it directly in my face. "I should shoot your shiny, bitch ass nose right off!"

All of a sudden I was terrified. Though seen many times in the movies I had never seen a real gun before. Mov ies bring a psychologically harmless look to guns, but in actual real life they're mentally crippling. I completely zoned out. I could see Tori's lips moving but couldn't hear a single word that was coming out of his mouth because I was no longer there. I was mentally back inside my house watching Him antagonize me for only taking out the garbage 4 times a day instead of 5, or because I didn't say "yes sir" loud enough for Him to hear me. I could feel His dark breath fluttering across my face as He held one of His rusty screwdrivers to my throat promising to thrust it through my windpipe if I ever disobeyed any of His directives at any time. And suddenly I realized how important it was for me to get home before He came downstairs to find me not there. I'd rather be shot by Tori than to be mutilated by Him any day of the week!

"What the fuck's wrong with you nigga? Can you not hear me? Do you not understand I'm about to fuck you up right now?" Tori screamed as he waived the gun back and forth in front of my face scrapping my nose with the barrel.

I felt an extreme amount of heat flourish up over my face as I was no longer just terrified, but furiously annoyed as well. I put my foot up against the wall and pushed off to have the gun pressed against my forehead and looked Tori directly in his eyes.

"Get the fuck off of me." I gritted. "If you're going to kill me, get on with it. If not, then let me go because I'm already going to be in trouble with Him because I'm late."

I slowly turned my back to Tori and started to walk away. My knees were shaking because I was afraid he was going to shoot me right in the back of my head. But I knew I couldn't turn around to see if he would because that cowardly action might just set him off to do so. Slowly I placed one foot in front of the other like a baby learning how to walk for the first time. I hadn't made it too far before I could hear Tori running up on me from behind. Just when I thought he was going to pull the trigger he jumped in front of me and said,

"Yo man look...you got some huge balls on you my nigga! That shit was crazy man! You just turned yo' back to a nigga, like WHAT! I should've shot yo' dumbass though. But that shit took some gorilla, elephant type balls to do my nigga. You lucky I ain't shoot yo' crazy dumbass though. You was ramblin' off some crazy shit back there too. I don't know what you was saying but yo' crazy ass is crazy. Here, you dropped this weak ass shit too by the way."

Tori shoved the newspaper into my chest. In all of the excitement I hadn't even noticed I had dropped it. I folded the newspaper under my arm and turned to walk off. Tori grabbed my arm and said,

"Wait nigga! You ain't no punk. Yo ass is crazy. But yo punk ass ain't no bitch like I thought you was. You ain't gotta' worry about me chasing yo ass anymore. In fact, you and me is straight. You my nigga now. If anybody bother you or anything like that just holla at a nigga and I got you. Feel me?"

Wow, it was like music to my ears. Tori was a very popular kid in my neighborhood. Not only was he older than me, but he was way more notorious and that kind of notoriety is priceless where I'm from. He stuck his fist out and I pounded it in agreement.

"Later my nigga." Tori tucked the gun back into his waist and whistled at some guy he obviously knew up the road and took off.

What the hell just happened? Did I just turn one of my formidable enemies into a friend? Had I just figured out some ancient unknown puzzle to making my life better

moving forward? In any case I was completely stoked about the entire occurrence to the point I was no longer concerned if punishment awaited me at home. I proudly shuffled along as if I had just won the lottery. *Today was a good day!*

The sun was beating down on us something extreme. The only way to endure the beating was to find some type of tree to linger under and hope the occasional breeze would brush up against our skin for a moment of much needed relief. No one in the Projects had air conditioners or central air so everyone had their windows and doors wide open. We had to pick and choose what days to have our portable fans on because on days like today having them run would be pointless and just hike up our electric bills for no reason. The last thing any of us could afford would be an increase in a bill we already couldn't pay as is. So instead we all had to find inexpensive alternatives to the typical means of staying cool. And one of those means would be to trip the neighborhood fire hydrant and let all the kids run through the exploding water to stay cool. It was like a poor kid's waterpark with free entry, no slides to slip down and no concession stands to fill the belly up when the adventures brought hunger on. All we had was us and during extreme temperatures that seemed to be enough. I loved when summer time turned into unbearably hot temperatures because it was the only time He would allow us to be outside freely. All other times we were kept hostage in our own home, but during extreme temperatures like today He'd force us to be outside. I guess He wanted to be miserable inside all by himself. So mom would sit on the porch with Lijah and Halia while I got to sparingly play with the other children in the neighborhood, at least within reason. I always had to act like I wasn't enjoying myself when playing with other children because over time I realized that if I ever showed any signs of excitement or happiness, for whatever reason these were triggers that would make Him come out and embarrass me in front of the entire world. He seemed to find enjoyment in doing so and I really didn't want Him to enjoy anything at all. "Hey ya'll, here's some watermelon for you guys. Stay cool out here today!" Some guy a couple of apartments down said pointing to me and a few other kids running around the fire hydrant. *Oh man... how that watermelon would hit the spot right about now,* I thought. All us kids liked watermelon and any other melon that was cool and sweet, and right about now it would be exactly what the good Lord ordered. There were about eight of us different kids out there playing today and the nice man gave all of us a huge, juicy, red slice of watermelon to cool us down and to fill our stomachs all at the same time. Because I rarely got to interact with anyone I didn't know the guy's name. But I did know he peacefully lived a few doors down with his lady friend. Other adults sitting on their porches said "Thanks Greg, that's so nice of you to do!" Greg was a pretty tall guy, slim but muscular built and couldn't have been no more than 30 years old. Greg and his lady friend were just sitting on their porch trying to stay cool like everyone else. It was 102 degrees outside that day and with humidity it seemed like 115, so all of us kids were happy to get some watermelon relief. Some of us started clinking our watermelons together like adults would do when toasting champagne on New Year's Eve. Then we'd laugh and take big bites of our watermelon, juices splashing everywhere and stickiness sliding down our shirtless bodies. One kid was covered in sloppy red juices, his face looking like a dirty smudged up clown whose make up was starting to run from the watermelon drool slushing all over him. He looked at me grinning and I couldn't help myself from busting out laughing. I was having a great time now, making new friends, beating the heat and not concerned with the darkness that surrounded my true existence. It was like I was on a mini vacation to some great get away with boats and beaches, all the cares of my world being washed upon shore never to reach me again as I swam further and further away from reality. "Where in the hell did you get that fucking messy ass bullshit from boy?" His piercing words popped the make believe balloon that I (for a short time) thought was actually real. No, it wasn't real at all, not even close. Here comes the real. Here comes the reality that I knew all too well, the crippling darkness that wouldn't let me stand up for myself or run to safety that I was oh so familiar with. He slapped the watermelon out of my hands so hard that it split in half and splashed all over my shoes when falling to the ground, ruined. "Did I say you could have this shit?" He yelled louder in an attempt to get the entire neighborhood to hear Him. "Who the fuck gave it to you nigga?" I helplessly looked around because I didn't want anyone to have to go through what I already knew was going to occur. I didn't want to rat Greg out and get him involved because this was truly my fault. I wasn't on top of my game like I'd normally be because if I were I would have never even accepted the watermelon from Greg in the first place. But I was hot, hungry and wanted to fit in with all the other normal kids on our block. However, I wasn't normal and my life was far from that, so this was my fault entirely. That's when He slapped me in the face and said "I'm not going to ask you again boy, who the fuck gave you that nasty ass shit?"

"Hey yo! Chill out man. There's no need to get on him for this. I'm the one that gave him the watermelon. I gave all the kids watermelon because it's burning up out here today. He didn't ask for anything. I just offered it to him no differently than I offered it to all of them. If I thought it was going to be all like this I wouldn't have passed it out to anyone. Honestly, it isn't his fault at all. I should have asked before offering, so the faults all mine. Be cool man." Greg said emphatically while coming off the porch to my rescue as if I were his own child. It was an admirable thing to do but also a foolish one. I looked over to Greg with my eyes wide trying to gesture to him with my face not to come off that porch.

"Nooooo!" I unintentionally screamed to warn him as he walked down the steps. Each step he took forward was placing him in intimate danger with a monster he'd never understand or be able to effectively communicate with. Little did Greg know that his efforts at this time would be pointless and his best interest would be to just be quiet and let it go.

"Don't!" I stiffly pushed my arm out like a crossing guard but it was too late. Greg had already made it off his porch and was calm as if this was a normal situation. I knew his innocence would be the death of him.

"What the fuck you say to me nigga? Are you telling me how to raise my fucking son, bitch?" The monster was loose and His tongue had no respect of persons. He didn't care if Greg was someone He didn't know. All He saw Greg as was an opportunity to prove He was the alpha and that Greg was just another weak bitch. He took His hand and reached for His back pocket full of knives and screwdrivers and rested it there as if it were a holster holding a pistol. A lesser or smarter man would have just let it go at that point, but Greg seemed to be neither. In fact, immediately Greg showed his true colors. The guy I thought was just another nice guy in the neighborhood turned out to be just another guy easily swayed to kick someone's ass if necessary.

"Oh, you got me fucked up baby. I know you don't think I'm scared of yo' crazy ass like the rest of these clowns around here? I'll fuck yo' old ass up nigga, for real!" Greg was walking right up towards the devil without any fear at all, and that impressed the hell out of me whether I thought it was stupid or not. Greg was brave. Stupid, but brave nonetheless.

"I ain't gone talk. I'm done talking bitch!" He pulled some knives from his back pocket and started some type of warrior like trot towards Greg that I had never seen Him do before. He had something hovering around Him more than pure bravery, more than the ill advised confidence that Greg had. It was of a psychotic, unnatural origin…something animalistic. "Hold up bitch ass nigga!" Greg growled as he backed up, not from fear but from the adrenaline of the moment like he enjoyed what was about to unfold.

"I got something specifically for bitch ass niggas like you. Let me get this heater for yo' bitch ass!" Greg ran inside to get his gun. I could hear his lady friend begging and pleading with him to stay inside. He too ran inside as well but He wasn't going to get a gun. He didn't believe in those. Just as expected He came back out holding a long handled steel bladed ax. The handle was a smooth, blood red color with a deep black blade that sharply shined as its tip glistened underneath the sun's blare. He was swinging it back and forth in a rhythm that suggested a sure death throw was to follow. Neighbors went inside their homes but stood watching from their doorways to be witnesses to the free fight that was about to go down. I could hear Greg screaming at his lady friend to move. She was standing between him and the doorway pleading and stopping him from leaving. She was a big lady and probably in most settings could hold Greg back, but this time was different and she was clearly struggling.

"Get out his way fat ass mama! As soon as he comes out here Imma' cut his fucking ass up and then your fat ass is next!" He was taunting them both trying to instigate the situation even more. I was so nervous for Greg's life. A part of me was hoping that his lady friend could hold him inside because even though he was coming out with a gun, I wasn't completely sure that would be enough to stop Him. But I was also intrigued to see someone stand up to Him. Finally I'd get to see if He was as bullet proof as He always claimed. *Was He faster than a bullet? Was He as gruesome as His stories of death and carnage that He forced us to listen to repeatedly over and over again like a broken record? Was He as great of a monster that I had made Him out to be? In the movies they eventually kill the monster and the good citizens lived happily ever after. Was this our opportunity to live on as normal human beings? Yes, this had to be that moment!* I prayed inside of my mind, *God please let this be the moment to the start of my freedom. Please give Greg the strength to pull the trigger faster than it has ever been pulled, and allow Him to come to a slow but agonizing sure death. Please God? Please hear me this time.* I was rooting for Greg to come back outside and to shoot His head clean off His shoulders. I had to be careful not to show Him my enthusiasm for the opposition, but somehow deep down inside I knew He already knew where I stood. But Greg never came back out. After while neighbors started to close their doors for lack of entertainment. Greg's lady slammed their door but not before screaming some last ditch profanities out at us. In the distance I could hear the sirens of fire trucks coming to shut off the fire hydrant that was still pumping gallons upon gallons of free water to the street. That's when He looked back at me and said,

"I told you all these mother fuckers out here are the same, didn't I? They all weak and pathetic and they all bitches. If his bitch ass would have came out that house, there would have been three deaths today. I would have killed him first. I would have split him with this ax from the soles of his feet to the crown of his head and left it there to rest. Then his fat whore would have been crying and that's when I would have taken this knife and cut her eyes out and stuffed them so far up her fat ass that she'd be able to see how full of shit she is. Then I would have slit her throat and watched her bleed all over her dead nigga. And last but not least I would have ended it all by pulling the ax from his head and swinging it right through your raggedy ass neck and watched your head roll right over there with both their dead asses. Fuck all three of ya'll! They could of buried all three of ya'll bitch asses together in the same hole for all I care."

He stared at me for a few minutes and then turned and walked in the house. There was nobody left outside except me. I just stood there still, cold and afraid to move. As hot as it was out there I was shaking and heartbroken. *Why hadn't God heard my cries? Why had he abandoned me at a time I know he could have orchestrated and delivered? If there was any moment that he could have saved me, this was that moment.* Yet, God had turned his back on me no differently than my mom had when she went inside as soon as the ruckus began. I looked down at my shoes and dried up watermelon wasn't the only thing on them. I had been standing still there for so long that ants had also begun to crawl up and down my shoes and legs reaping the benefits of sweet melon, taking all that they could back to their homes in the dirt. I just stood there, motionless watching them carry what they could back and forth, to and fro. There was a whole other world going on beneath my feet. A world so small, but because I felt so small it all felt familiar. And I thought to myself, *if these ants can make it out here in this world as small as they are…then so can I!* I took my shoes off and shook the dried up watermelon off from on top of them, took a deep breath, opened the rusty screen door to my house and cautiously walked inside.

Chapter 8
the Gifted One

My life seemed to be standing still near the edge of a great cliff, small rocks sliding under feet as they take the plunge first with no sound or sight of them hitting bottom. But there were small gestures of safety that I believed God was giving me as signs of liberation. I would now be venturing to my new school all the way across town. I had taken the city bus plenty of times, but never had I taken   a bus to school before. It would be full of other children all across the city who also had scored high on their state school tests. We were all going to be in class together in a new city school project called *"The Gifted Program"* and we were all excited to be a part of it. The best part about the project was that it had children in it with different nationalities from all different walks of life. For me it was the experience of a lifetime because it allowed me to quickly understand the truth about the world that was previously hidden from me. The truth that all people though they may look different ultimately want the same things. They want to be liked by many and loved by all. They want to be treated fairly and given a chance to prove their worth. And when they do well they want to be rewarded for their hard work. It didn't matter what size they were, big or small. It didn't matter what color their skin was, their gender or their financial status. The undeniable truth ended up being that all in all they were all the same. Of course, this is not the assumption I first had, but after time this was my conclusion. It didn't take us long to come together as a unit because no matter where you go, human nature has the tendency to find a way to divide and separate itself. We were just a few hundred smart kids outnumbered in a school by 500 typical students. I personally wished they hadn't given us the title of *"Gifted Children"* because of that and the fact that our classrooms were bigger and nicer. Our schoolbooks were newer. And instead of having one teacher like every other normal elementary school student, we had multiple teachers that specialized in their own particular subjects, no differently than if we were in high school and these things immediately made the *"normal"* students hate us *"gifted"* ones. Normal kids had to sit in limited desks in small rooms with old textbooks and dusty chalk boards. We got to sit in large rooms with bean bag chairs and computers. We were definitely getting an advanced education that many took offense too, including parents and teachers of the regular students, and this quickly began to drive an inevitable wedge between us and them. But with segregation comes unity, a priceless lesson we were taught first hand. Because the regular students ousted and hated us so much, we had no choice but to band together in spite of our differences. And it was this banding together that taught me some of the most valuable lessons life had to offer in regards to love, ethnicity and humanity. For me it would become three years of priceless learning that I wouldn't trade in for any schooling from all the Ivy League colleges combined in the world today.

West Elementary was certainly different than the "hood" school I used to attend. Everything about it was cleaner, bigger and had way more resources. There were multiple libraries, gymnasiums and play areas for us to indulge in. And because of my crew, there were also no dull moments any days of the week. I never knew 4th grade could be so fun! I had friends from every walk of life imaginable. Kim Kim was an Asian girl that had a talent for artwork. She would draw and paint amazing pictures that often won citywide competitions. I always measured my paintings against hers to know if I was waiving my artistic hand in the right direction. Maisa was an Arabic girl that I ended up having a crush on. She taught me how to play Chess over Checkers, which helps me successfully maneuver through life even today. I never told her I had a crush on her because that would have just been plain weird, but nonetheless she was my friend and still is my friend even now. Dione was probably the hottest girl in the school and didn't even know it. I had a crush on her too. In fact, everyone liked her because she was a jewel inside and out. Jason and Ambrose were my boys, my heavy hitters. We had an unbreakable bond because we sat next to each other on the bus. It was an hour ride home daily and we entertained each other without fail every minute of that exhausting ride. Because of them I never wanted that bus ride to end. They kept my spirit high in spite of the constant low that awaited me after school each day. All in all I had white friends. I had black friends. I had guy friends. I had gal friends. And to my surprise I even had teacher friends. In fact, they started off as my friends and ended up becoming my family. My life had two portions to it now, the one He dominated in the palm of His hand where He squeezed and squeezed the life out of me, and the other one they had in the palm of theirs that they pumped life back into. Death was knocking at my door a solemn pound while life itself would somehow find a way to open it and let death know that I wasn't home. Elementary school was not only now quickly becoming some of the best years of my life, but was saving my life as well!

Although I loved going to school I hated waiting for the bus to pick me up in the morning because most days He'd be waiting outside at the bus stop with me. A normal parent would wait at the bus stop with their child because they wanted to make sure he or she was safe, but He certainly could care less about my safety so this was all for show. He only wanted to ensure that His audience didn't forget that He was the toughest guy in existence. But all I think they really understood was that He was mentally impaired and dangerous. All I knew was that every morning I was being embarrassed, so the bus wait was an agonizing one. It was the same routine each and every morning. First He'd start be-bopping up and down the street swinging His head left and right as if He was anticipating a sneak attack from some unknown enemy. Then He'd turn around and make a mad dash for the street pole that I considered the official bus stop. He'd grab a few knives out of His back pocket and start stabbing and slicing at the pole screaming at the top of His lungs as if He was killing a wild beast. Then He'd jump back and throw some knives into the pole and run back up onto it and start shadowboxing all around it. Even though I was kind of impressed with His ability to actually accurately throw knives into the pole, I know His entire show was to tell me and anybody dumb enough to watch that He'd have no problem killing any of us at any time. I was already a believer so He had no reason to continue trying to convince me. The routine would always get to its most extreme when He'd finally see my bus coming down the road. Whatever level He was previously on, He'd up it times twenty when big number 44 was dustily speeding to our stop. His screams would get louder. His hands would move faster. And His knives would pierce harder into the wood causing pieces of splint shards to fly all over my clothes. I'm surprised my bus driver Bud was brave enough to stop and pick me up every day.

"Uh huh. Woooohoooo!" He chummed as the bus door opened.

I walked up the steps and down the isle with my head down because I already knew that if I made eye contact with anyone the questions their eyes had, my eyes would not be able to answer. Bud wouldn't even respond to Him. Bud would just close the door as if no one was waiting at the bus stop with me. I guess it only took a week of His shenanigans for Bud to no longer be amused, and he pulled off before I could even get to my seat, which made me fall into it.

"Man, your father is a crazy mofo!" Ambrose singingly

chimed as I slid my backpack off. "He's not my father!" I yelled loud enough for the entire bus to hear just in case anyone once again was confused on that fact.

"Well yo' real daddy need to come out and kick yo' wanna' be daddy's ass because that mofo crazy' than a bitch!" Jason squawked and started laughing.

"Yeah, I'll get right on that as soon as we get to school I'll give my real daddy a call." I sarcastically answered. Everyone on the bus was laughing now and instead of being embarrassed I began to feel loved. This is how it would be every morning for the next 3 years and somehow I hated and loved every morning just the same. I hated Him for what He'd put me through and loved them for getting me through it. And this in my life would become a common theme.

Waiting for the bus everyday with an animal was the least of my school concerns. There were other things happening that would have greater impacts on the shaping of my character than that. I was growing up in a time and city where fashion could make or break your entire being. Michael Jackson owned the music scene so you were really a badass if you could afford one of his expensive jackets. There were starting to be cases in the neighborhood where people were getting robbed for them, that's how special they were to us. I never had to worry about being robbed for a black many zippered jacket or a red space looking one because I couldn't afford either. In fact, I didn't have a jacket at all. It was either not cold enough for a coat or it was. A jacket was for in-between weather and my family never had in-between money. It was also the era of the tennis shoe craze. There were so many name brand tennis shoes on the scene that it made it difficult for anyone to know what was in and what was out. Adidas was taking over the neighborhood because the famous rap group Run DMC wore them in their music videos. British Knights were also a hot commodity because of their diamond stud emblem. Nike was competing with Reebok for the title of the greatest sports shoe. At the time in our eyes Reebok was winning that battle because they had invented a basketball shoe with a pump on the tongue that made us believe by pumping it we'd be able to unimaginably jump higher. We had Troop, Pony, Puma, L.A. Gear, Fila, and Kangaroos. All of these were of course shoes I couldn't afford, but longed to have. But my popularity allowed me to get away with wearing shoes like Hoops and Jordache for a short period of time. Anything less than those, like the famous ProWings tennis shoes I often had would have been social status suicide! One day a boy in my class named Shane decided to give me a hard time about the new Jordache tennis shoes I had on. This was early in the Gifted Program days and I was still fresh out of the Project public school I had just come from. In my opinion Shane was just another typical white kid, but I had no true idea what white children were about because we didn't have any in the school or neighborhood I was from. *Were white children different from black children? Did they like to have fun? Did they have the same problems in life that I had?* These were questions that wouldn't take long to be answered. The small family and friends I had at home told me that white people were the devil and that they bleed blue so always beware. But Sesame Street and Mr. Rogers on television were telling me something different and I liked those programs more than my family, so I was leaning towards their beliefs more. Shane was about to help me understand what I truly needed to know because he was sort of a bully. I had peeped him out bullying some other white children in our class on a few different occasions and they were surely afraid of him because they never stood up for themselves. All I ever did in the projects was stand up for myself because anything less could literally get you killed. I had already made up in my mind that if Shane brought any of that bullying action my way I'd not hesitate to kick his ass. I had noticed that he hadn't tested anyone of color with his attitude yet, but for some reason out of all the people in the class he could have decided to break that ice with today, he chose me. "What in the heck are those?" Shane insultingly pointed down at my shoes. "They're Jordache" I confidently said knowing that the confidence in my tone may be the only thing keeping me from being exposed and embarrassed that my shoes weren't as expensive as some of my peers' in the class. "Jordache? Boy those are some cheap, weak, never should be on your feet shoes…that's what those are!" The entire class started laughing so my confident tone had failed. "Where'd you get those shoes from huh, a gas station?" Shane went on and on. I truly didn't want to get suspended from school for fighting especially since He would beat me for doing so, but this current humiliation was far more detrimental to my well being than the assumed aftermath. I was desperately trying to keep it together but I could feel a streak of heat consuming my face and my disposition. So I abruptly stood up, the force of which flipped my desk over and it slammed against the floor. I crouched down to pick Shane up by his lower torso so that I could slam him to the floor so that his body could resemble my now bent up desk. There was an overwhelming look of fear and surprise flourishing over Shane's face, as he was still shocked that a desk had toppled over with ease and a fight was about to break loose. For him this was new territory since no one ever stood up to him before. For me it was just another typical day that I was going to kick somebody's ass over something they said or did, business as usual. I was certain that I'd whoop Shane's ass so bad that they'd probably kick me out of the Gifted Program, but I didn't care. No one gets to embarrass me other than Him. NO ONE! But then out of nowhere a white kid with a smaller frame and gel spiked hair jumped in front of me and said to Shane "I like his Jordache, they're gnarly dude. At least his shoes are new. Those Nikes you got on are old and played out…like totally scuffed up and everything dude!" *Dude? What was going on?* All of a sudden I felt like I was in an episode of the Twilight Zone. *Who says dude anyway? And who was this little white kid, sticking up for me that I didn't even know?* Shane used to talk shit to him all the time and I never got involved because I thought it was typical white boy banter and also none of my business. And by the one sided banter it was clear that Shane could easily whoop his ass, but nonetheless he jumped in the middle of what was about to be an ass whooping lesson that Shane and the class would never forget. "You got saved by the bell this time playa' pimp, instead of me ringing the bells in that big dome ass head of yours." I nodded and pointed at Shane with a sinister grin. "But you can bet your punk ass mama there won't be another save, I promise you that. Now try me again, bitch!" My verbiage and tone alone almost made Shane piss his pants. I could hear his heart racing, pounding inside of his throat along with the pin drop hitting the floor if anyone had one to drop. I picked up my desk and books and sat back down as if nothing odd had occurred. Shane wobbly walked back to his corner of the room and the gawky little white kid sat right back down next to me. "Man, you shouldn't have done that, but it was pretty cool that you did. You could have gotten punched in the face over my Jordache and I probably wouldn't have saved you…but then again who knows? I'm Jess, by the way. And you are?" He looked at me all excited to finally have a conversation. "I'm Ray, and dude it's radically cool man! Keep your head up bro. You'd obviously cream that dude, but for what? And…I like your shoes man. Do you like mine?" He stuck his foot out all weird showing off some orange and lime Nikes that I would have died to have. "Yeah dude" I started laughing. "I love your shoes, the same ones that you could have gotten all scuffed up trying to defend mine." And that's how Ray and I became good friends. In fact, besides my second grade teacher Miss Wiggins (which didn't count because she was my teacher and an adult) he was the first white friend I ever had. And he had just taught me a very valuable and unforgettable lesson. It didn't matter what color of skin their bones possessed, there were black bullies and there were white bullies. There were black assholes and there were white assholes. And last but certainly not least there were genuinely good people of all different shapes, sizes and colors including white people all across the world that I just hadn't met yet. The world was bigger than the projects that I was subjected to and certainly bigger than the treacherous madhouse I was growing up in. My family had either lied to me or was simply misinformed about the possible beauties of diversity and racial differences. And it was that day I promised myself to be open minded to all things and to come to my own decisions about people and life, based off of my own experiences and not the experiences of others. Shane and I became good friends as well. I found out later on that his family too wasn't financially or emotionally as stable as most. And as long as Ray and I stayed friends it seemed like kids of color took less opportunities to tease Ray, and white kids were more open to building a relationship and getting to know me for who I truly was. School had become a place of enlightenment and adventure and I began to wish it were my home. In many instances, it felt like a home and life I once knew before He entered and ruined them both.

Chapter 9
a Train WreckⒸWrasahtching a Plane

School wasn't the only thing that was changing my perception of the world. Church was beginning to wrap its impressionable soaked hands around that clay to try and shape me into being a worthy soldier in God's army too. But I wasn't going to church every Sunday for the mission. I was only going once again to get away from Him and also for the donuts! Mama decided to join a new church right across the street from the neighborhood park that He used to slap and embarrass me in. Out of nowhere we became one of those real spiritual fanatical families that would have their entire world revolve around the belief that God was the only thing in our existence of importance and that our lives were meant to super serve his will. I didn't mind this concept because He would never go to church with us and every Sunday the church would pass out massive bags of donuts (bigger than the size of my body) to the needy families in the neighborhood. And to our luck there were no families in more need than ours. To my surprise in spite of Him rarely ever going to church with us, He highly believed in God. But His belief was a weird one. He believed that God was inspiring Him to be the crazy man that He was. He believed that God wanted Him to kill anyone that looked at Him wrong. And though no one would ever look at Him cross, He always thought that they were so He wanted to kill everyone. I quickly got into the habit of not looking at Him at all just to be safe, but I think that just irritated Him more than my face did. So now our new church would be my second safe haven other than school. Mama was obsessed with our new church. Before we used to go to church every other Sunday or so. But this new place had an immediate grip on my mom that I had never seen before. At first I thought it was the fact that they had a church van that would come and pick up members that didn't have vehicles to get to church on their own. I thought that was special since our old church didn't have that. Or maybe it was the members who seemed to care about the whereabout destinations of everyone's souls in the afterlife. Until the new church I had never heard so much talk of people going to hell when they die and maybe that scared her into wanting us to be permanent members. Whatever it was that convinced her that we should be there, I agreed with. Anything was better than being prisoners in our own home. We were going to church four days a week during the school year and seven days a week during the summer. So needless to say we quickly began to have a church family outside of our prison one. And I believe that's the true reason mama loved the church so much. Maybe she too needed an extended family, a way to survive the madness?

"It's holiness or hell. You can't get to heaven being holy on Sunday and ungodly on Monday!" Pastor's voice cut through the air carving its way to the ears of all the sinners sitting in the audience. "Amen" the crowd roared, "preach!" The entire church seemed to be in some type of well-practiced, melodic unison that would easily scare any newcomer that's not used to such congruence. "God is a seven day a week God when it comes to what you need, but when it comes to serving God you only show up on Sunday." Pastor continued in a tone that demanded attention and participation from the listeners. "Turn to your neighbor and say, neighbor I ain't gone' be no only on Sunday saint…I'm gone' be an all day every day saint, praise God!" Once again the crowd chimed in unison. Even the musicians had a significant way they played their instruments in harmony in-between each phrase Pastor would belt. You couldn't find a more in sync group in Olympic synchronized swimming than you could find in this temple. It was amusingly impressive to say the least and I was certainly entertained. Our last church was a complete snooze fest compared to this one. This was almost as good as Saturday morning cartoons (He-Man or Transformers) or Nintendo! After the lengthy message the church decided to raise yet another offering to coincide with the previous two it had already raised. And once again in unison the crowd rose to its feet, one isle at a time and walked to the front of the church to pay for the message from God they had received. Coming off of a recent history lesson on finances in school earlier that week I thought to myself, *man God's charging three times a day, multiple days a week for the same one message...that's more than George Washington's taxes and this economy's inflation. Maybe Grandma was wrong about me becoming an engineer and I should just become a preacher instead. I wouldn't even need to keep getting good grades to excel at that. I'd just need to brush up on my speech game!*

The feeling of being lost is something I'd not wish on my worst enemy. And this was a feeling that homelessly took up refuge in my heart, worthlessly sleeping on my soul, staying over without invitation. I was mentally being pulled in three different directions living three distinctly different lives all at the same time. In school I was sharpening my mind with unimaginable creativity continuing to follow through on the promise I gave Grandma to take my education seriously so that I could financially become who I thought I should be in life. There was no school subject that I didn't highly understand or excel in and they were all beginning to seem pretty primitive to me. In church I was quickly becoming a contradiction to what the normality was. The Bible for most people was hard to understand because of its weirdly written content in a foreign dialect, but for me the understanding was no different than that of a Math or English book. As long as you followed the rules when reading, understanding was inevitable. And though school was beginning to bore me, the Bible was highly entertaining. It had everything in it your typical blockbuster movie hit had…murder, deception, betrayal, irrational behavior, tyrants, life, death and the most infamous of them all, love! What was even more entertaining than the Bible was the so called experts trying to interpret its meaning. Being in daily human analysis with Him my entire life quickly forced me to become an expert in people relations and human characteristics. I literally had become an expert in human behavior, as the study of such was my only chance at staying alive. And the most comical thing happening at our church was the constant misinterpretation of the Bible's meaning and the reaction of the congregation to the misinformed deliveries they regularly received. It was the equivalent of a train wreck watching a plane crash. All views and perception of any recollection of events were undoubtedly compromised to say the least! Knowing most were confused, my intelligence and ability to not be easily swayed in perception of the Bible quickly allowed my actions in church to be considered devilish and me to be easily labeled as a "needing Jesus" or a "nothing but the devil in him" church member. At home I continued to be harassed and ridiculed at every turn. No matter how hard I tried to stay to myself to keep out of harms way He always found a way to pull me back into His vindictive life. When at home I just wanted to be alone. I would spend countless hours in my room staring and thinking, thinking and staring blankly out the window or at the ceiling. If I wasn't staring there, then I'd be staring at my own lap just hoping and praying that He wouldn't come around to bother me. Hope eluded me and those prayers never worked. He had it set in His blackened heart to make me a priority of His ruin. Between all three lives I could barely remember who to be and when to be that person, and if it was confusing for me it had to be confusing for all those who had to interact with me on a regular basis. But out of all three lives, my home life was sure to rise above the others and kill us all if I let it. I felt the golden pendulum that hung from the neck of life's grandfather clock swinging slower for me than everyone else, allowing my chaos to be in slow motion for every eye to see and my agony of torment to be easily heard by every ear. But this was not true. No one seemed to notice my sloth of a death in regards to my life. My mother was too occupied testifying of her glorious Christ oriented redemption and praying for magnificent financial breakthroughs, while giving all of her non earned government assisted money to the church's building fund to even notice that I was barely holding on to life by a spider's thread. *How long would she live unsuccessfully on her knees was the only question I wanted to ask her.* But our communication with each other had flew the coup not long after Grandma's death so I'd never get a chance to spring that on her. My teachers were blinded by the light of my high test scores and stellar grades that they too got lost in their glare while I continued to die in the shadows of my own success. In fact this would be my 3rd and final year in the Gifted Program as my middle school and high school years were scheduled to be completed back in my neighborhood school district. The transition back to the typical public school routine from my Gifted one would later prove to be most catastrophic to say the least. But for now I had a chance to just simply enjoy my 6th grade graduation ceremony. All of the students, teachers, principles and parents huddled together in the auditorium in anticipation for all of the passing students to walk across the stage and accept their graduation certificates and pardons to move on to the next phase of their academic life, Jr. High School. Each time a student's name was called there was cheering and applauding from everyone, however the parents' cheers of that particular student could always be clearly heard over the others as their proud "yays" and "wooohooos" were goose bump worthy and emotionally inspiring. And this was what frightened me, as for each cheer that rumbled the air kept me on edge about what noise would occur when my name was called, since neither of my parents were in attendance. I began to severely panic. *How embarrassing it would be for the sound of a pen drop to be heard after the spewing of my name.* Beads of sweat that occupied my brows began to creep over the sides as I tried to raise them to keep the little sweat droplets from seeping into my eyes, but to no avail. My mom said there'd be a chance of her attending if she could find a ride but I knew she'd be a no show. She made it her business on all occasions that if she couldn't find a ride to church she'd simply walk for Jesus. But walking for Jesse would be out of the question and that just made me angry and jealous, two sins I didn't mind committing. "Jesse Benson" the school principal belted my name out of his mouth as if there was some type of mistake on his graduation list. I had been in his office plenty of times for bad behavior so who could blame him. Thank God behavior wasn't a school subject because I certainly wouldn't have passed that class at all. I awkwardly started my shuffle across the stage anticipating the sound of a loose board embarrassingly loudly squeaking as I stepped on it to get from one side to the next. *Was the sound of my heartbeat as loud to them as it was to me, pounding in my ears as it dropped a mile into my stomach? Was this sweat or tears in my eyes making it blurry and hard for me to see where I was going? I should have stayed home today. Nope, scratch that. Anything was better and safer than being around Him for any amount of time.* I fiercely argued back and forth with myself inside of my head, while my legs began to forget what their purpose was. I could feel myself about to collapse. Then I heard one of my favorite teachers yell out with his hands cupped around his mouth, "If anyone deserves a round of applause, it's that young man right there!" He stood up, whistled and clapped intensely enough for the entire room to dare not to follow his lead. Then others stood up and cheered. Before I knew it the entire room was encouraging me as I walked what I previously viewed as the plank, but was now an inspirational majestic platform. My legs not only found themselves again, but also found wings along the way as I timidly hovered over to the principal and accepted my reward. And just like that I felt the warmth of Grandma's spirit floating over me whispering in my ear, *"You're almost there son, you're almost right where you promised me you'd be. So pick your head up and be proud of a job well done !"*

Chapter 10
Praying in Piss

How interesting of a summer was it going to be this time? Well, if history repeats itself the way it often did there was no reason for me to entertain that thought. It wouldn't be interesting at all for us but it would certainly be entertaining for any spectators. But we were the only spectators and we weren't entertained. We had a new addition to our family, Paul. He was two years old and for the most part a quiet fellow. However, He wasn't a fan of Paul's so between Him and mother they kept him literally tied up in the corner of the living room all day. I felt sorry for Paul because he was just a curious baby that liked to explore. He certainly was a lot easier to babysit than Lijah and Halia were when they were his age. But He and mama had Paul tied up with ropes, in the corner in his playpen all day, every day as if he was an animal. The playpen was tied up between the living room closet and kitchen doors creating a strong web like structure to hold Paul in. Before they created that web Paul had been flipping out of the playpen constantly just trying to get free and have fun like two year olds normally do. But He and mama hated having to manage Paul so they just tied him up, regularly. So while Lijah and Halia roamed free and I sat statue still in the same spot on that dirty couch aimlessly staring at PBS educational television programs, there was Paul just tied up in the corner of the room sadly watching everything like a thief recently caught stealing by an aggressive owner of some poor convenience store. The entire thing was inhuman to say the least. *But what wasn't inhuman here?* Lijah was already a running rebel as he seemed to not be afraid to get beatings. There were times He or mama would beat the breaks off of Lijah and Lijah would remember the beating for a few hours and then instantly forget and be right back to doing whatever thing that had got him beat in the first place. I liked that about Lijah. He had a certain type of recklessness that you couldn't learn, you just had to be born with and he would do things at five years old that I didn't have the balls to do until I was well into double digit age. Halia got beat way less because she was a girl and everything she did was softer and quieter. She mostly got beat by mama, which mama focused on beating the boys for disciplinary measure way more than she did Halia. And I because of my tenure got beat the least. I had learned all of the little quirks not to do to stir up trouble, so whenever I got a beating it wasn't because of behavior, but more from being under the overall beating quota. You just had to get beat sometime just to be reminded that you were a child. At least that was the excuse mama often gave me. She would say things like "You's a just gettin' too big for ya britches boy!" or "Ya smellin' yas' selves today ain'tcha?" Both of which I never understood or cared to understand what she meant. All in all though I still loved her because I knew her before Him and I knew she was just putting on a show for Him from time to time. In fact, I believe mama would beat us just to stop Him from doing so. It was like some weird protective motherly instinct she had. She just knew when He was ready to unjustly do so and would beat Him to the punch because her punches were much lighter. Today however she wasn't being her usual destructive/ counterproductive self. She was intensely reading a letter that had come in the mail. *What was so important about this letter that made mama not throw it in the pile of forsaken bills, useless magazines and PCH dreams of being rich ads like all the other mail we got?* She was so engrossed in the letter that she wasn't paying attention to Lijah trying to do backflips off the couch and Paul trying to emulate and do the same ridiculous backflips in his spiderweb of a pen, both of which were creating a loud, extremely loud by His standard type racket. This letter had her undivided attention and because it had hers, she now had mine. That's why I missed Him creeping down the stairs like a black panther ready to pounce on all of us! "What the fuck is goin' on down here?" He was angrier than His normal disposition. "Ya'll think everythang' just sweet around this bitch huh?" Oh how I hated these rhetorical questions because in a normal world they'd be just that, rhetorical. But in the world of a penniless soul these were actual questions that He anticipated getting a response from. "No sir!" Lijah said emphatically half twisted up on the floor from the last unsuccessful backflip he just maneuvered. "No sir." Halia quietly mumbled with her head down and legs submissively crossed in a futile attempt to make up for Paul, who was still doing backflips or whatever they were considered to be. They were more like pathetic back flops than backflips, and they just happened to be the most entertainment I had seen in the house in awhile, which made me laugh inside. Paul was too inexperienced to know how much trouble we all were in so his continued flips were warranted. That didn't stop Him from slapping Paul in the ass making him immediately sit down in his web and cry. Then He looked at me as if I were breaking some unforgivable law of His. I knew what He wanted and He wasn't getting that shit from me today. I wasn't a kid anymore, I was twelve years old and from the Projects. And twelve year olds from the Projects don't scare easy. I just stared at Him like the asshole He was and started silently screaming at God in my head.

THIS IS YOUR FAULT GOD! I HAVE BEEN KNEELING IN THAT PISSY GOT' DAMN CLOSET FOR YEARS BEGGING YOU TO GET RID OF THIS LUNATIC AND IT HAS FALLEN UPON DEAF EARS! WHY GOD? I DIDN'T EVEN ASK YOU TO ALLOW THUGS TO BEAT HIM MERCILESSLY AND THEN ROB HIM OF EVERYTHING HE HAD, AND THEN FOR HIM TO LIE THERE BLOODY

AND BUTT ASS NAKED, AND FOR STRAY ALLEY CATS TO THEN SWARM AROUND HIS LEAKING BODY LIKE BEES AND SCRATCH HIS HONEY SUCKING SKIN FROM HIS BONES ALLOWING WHAT REMAINED TO BE RUN OVER BY A MILLION SEMI TRUCKS UNTIL HALF HIS BONE DUST TRICKLED AWAY IN THE WIND AND UP HIS OWN NOSE WHILE HE

BREATHED HIS LAST BREATH. I just asked you to let Him slightly bump His head on a falling rock and from amnesia for you to let Him get lost on His way home never to return to this place again and you couldn't even do that?

Just when He was ready to take out one of His knives from His pocket to intimidate me to say yes sir like the others had, mama grabbed His arm and said "Look at this! Look at this!" She was waiving around the letter she had been drooling over all afternoon. She took Him away into the kitchen and that's when they started arguing.

Fear is an interesting beast. Sometimes you can find yourself feeding on it and other times you can find it feeding on you. Fear can be so small today that yesterday's scare went unnoticed, yet somehow tomorrow's shiver can grow so large that when it merely breathes next to you it can render you frozen, immobile and helpless. It is nearly untamable, even for Him who made it a religious practice to prove to us daily that He had no fear. There were instances that I got to see it clearly that fear had no respect of persons and even He had to shake beneath its massive roar. There was one thing I realized that He was afraid of, government authority. Anything that could land Him back in prison He was surely not a fan. What got Him thrown there in the first place was jealousy and anger, two other beast He failed to be able to control. Thirty years before meeting my mom He was married to another. He came home early from work one day and caught His wife in the bed having sex with another man. The man barely got away from Him jumping out the bedroom window to safety, but His wife was not as fortunate. She found His hands maliciously wrapped around her neck squeezing and squeezing until all life had slipped out from her small limp body. But not before stabbing her repeatedly and beating her senselessly unconscious. He spent thirty long years in prison for the act and was unfortunately released early to ruin my life not long after. You would think that most men would be ashamed of such gruesome circumstances, but not Him. In fact He relished in telling us all about it in punishing detail often. Why? Because He wanted to feed the beast! He wanted to feed our fear of Him but often in doing so He couldn't help to feed His own fear of going back to prison, something He regularly reminded us He'd never do. Even if He did kill someone again (which He always promised would be me) He'd never allow them to put Him back in prison for it. So He promised that after He killed me He would off Himself just to keep His commitment of never going back. So in part fear was actually a friend of mine because I believed fear was the only thing keeping me alive. Well it also just so happened to be that fear was the only thing about to give me the chance to go to college as well. The letter that mama had received in the mail was one rendering good news. All the other mail we received was stacked in a mountainous heap of never to be read bills and disconnect notices, only to be used as half torn notebook paper to house unaffordable corner store grocery lists. But this letter had made it to expressive hands along with a heated argument in the kitchen! And oh what a special letter it was. It was a letter of congratulations from The Ohio State University stating that because of my impressive scoring in state regulated testing and continued academic success, along with being highly below the country's average income level...I had been selected to participate in a program that would allow me to receive a forty thousand dollar college scholarship, fully paid to attend the university. I basically at the age of twelve had pretty much locked up my college tuition and wouldn't need to worry about grants or loans after graduating high school! All I had to do was continue to do well in regards to my grades between middle and high school and also participate in on campus youth summer classes at the university throughout those adolescent years consecutively. The youth classes in the summer would even count towards my college graduation credits. And the entire program would be 100% free! Of course at this time I had no idea what the contents of the letter were. All I could hear was mama passionately saying "I'm not going to allow you to get in front of this one, this time. This is a blessing from God!" I slapped my hand against my forehead and shook it miserably in disbelief. *Oh no, not more blessings from God.* I thought. *I can't take anymore of these God blessings. God's the one that blessed us with this fool to begin with! Who gets blessed with a lunatic/convict of a felon like this anyway? If these are God blessings, I'd hate to know what being cursed by the Almighty feels like!* My thoughts were interrupted by the kitchen door slamming up against the wall from Him storming through it. He was obviously highly irritated about this letter that I assumed was just another utility bill that we couldn't pay. He grabbed His coat and made a mad rush for the front door, but not before glaring at me and saying "You think ya' smart but ya' not. Don't let ya' bright ideas write a check that ya' punk ass heart can't cash. When ya' think ya' a man, just let me know so I can drive one of these knives right through ya' weak ass skull!" Then He finished His dramatic exit with the slamming of the front door. Mama came over next to me and gave me a big hug. I still had no idea what was going on but between her hug and His rant I knew something was going down. "What's going on mama?" She grabbed my face with both her hands and with a crackly voice said "Ya's done did   it son. This is tha' letta' that's going to change ya's life!" She was so excited that she started rocking back and forth laughing and crying at the same time, in unison with Paul's exact rocking back and forth in his rope webbed corner. "This letta' says that ya's getting a scholarship son. Ya' won't have ta' spend tha' rest of ya' life living like this. You can gets ta' that goods living!" She screeched in joy holding the letter up with two hands for me to read as if   it were a sacred scroll. And in spite of all the wonderful news all I could think of was *when would He be returning home to make my life a living hell again?*

Chapter 11
a College Vacation

"Too legit to quit…" the entire bus rang out in a chorus of children conducted by a boom box blaring M.C. Hammer's latest musical hit. One of the children had brought their stereo system to play music on this 3 hour bus ride to the University. There were about twenty five of us on that bus from different parts of the city and I was astonished how quickly in spite of being complete strangers, everyone was becoming friends. Since we couldn't afford to have cable television at home I didn't know any of the lyrics to MC Hammer's jam except for that popular chorus that everyone knew. So I just smiled and waited patiently watching everyone belt out line after line until my part came around and then I'd jump up out my seat and join in with the others… "Too legit, too legit to quit…!" It was a three hour ride to the city of Columbus and I was glad that we had some entertainment along the way. A lot of the children seemed on edge and nervous probably because this was going to be their first time away from home, away from their parents, and away from the life they knew. For me it was the exact opposite. I was overly anxious to get to my destination. *How many chances would I get to be away from Him for three whole weeks? How many times had I gotten to wake up or go to bed in peace, without the fear of being stabbed by a rusty screwdriver or axed to death by a Tomahawk flathead?* The answer is never and I had never felt so free in my entire life. A few hours in and I had to pinch myself just to see if the entire experience was real. Yep, it was real alright! I was happy when the bus was driving on the freeway, but when it finally pulled into The Ohio State University campus I was blown away. We had entered an entourage of artistically architectural buildings and structures of all sorts. The people occupying the steps of them were just as interesting. They were of all different kinds of race, color and age…wearing clothing of all different kinds of cloth, shapes, and shades. Some were dressed up in expensive suits while others flaunting next to them were comfortably relaxed in their pajamas. I felt like I was in literally in a colorful scene from the movie Alice in Wonderland, and I loved it. The bus finally stopped at the dormitories that we would be residing in for the next three weeks. When I stepped off the bus I felt something that I hadn't felt since Grandma's passing…hope!

"Hey…wake yo dumb ass up boy!" Cleo screamed in my ear.

The peaceful sleep I was in was new to me. At home I usually had to sleep with one eye open because I was always anticipating Him coming into my room and offing me in my sleep. But today I was just snoring away, something I never got to do so I was completely startled when Cleo yelled at me. So startled that I jumped up and hit my eye on the corner of the bunk bed. It split the skin right open above my eye lid and blood started gushing down my face.

"Damn son, what'd you jump up like a maniac for? I wasn't trying to kill you. I was just trying to say good morning." Cleo was just weirdly staring at me with a little uncertainty in his tone while I held my hand over where I had just hit my head.

This was obviously his way of apologizing. I didn't mind because not only was he my roommate, but he was also one of the few friends I had on this trip. I surely wasn't about to ruin our friendship over a bloody eye. I'd already experienced so much worse than a bloody eye growing up in the Projects. But this was not some regular cut that you could just throw a bandaid on, kiss the boo

boo and go about your merry old way. The blood would not stop pouring out from my eye so Cleo rushed down the hall   to get help from our student monitor who was responsible for all of us visiting his dorm floor for the next three weeks. The cut was so deep he ultimately had to take me to the hospital to get stitches. As I sat with the nurse in the operating room I blamed myself, not Cleo for the accident. I mean…if I was a normal person I would have easily been able to get screamed at in the ear and not jump up and bang my eye against a steel railing. But I wasn't normal. My life wasn't normal. Life and I both at this point were far removed from being anything close to the norm. I knew what a normal life in a normal family resembled. I had watched plenty of episodes on TV of what the word family meant and how families were supposed to interact with each other. Hit television shows like "Family Ties" and "The Cosby Show" never left me confused in what love and understanding truly meant when properly delivered from parents to their children. But the difference with these was that I never saw "The Keatons" or "The Huxtables" go through any type of adverse moments in life that I was going through with my family. I mean I could relate to "Alex P Keaton" an adventurous young teen with a passion for finances and wealth because I was nearly a young teen myself and had those same passions. I could also relate to "Theo Huxtable" a clever but troubled teen with learning opportunities, as Theo definitely reminded me of Manny. But what was completely out in left field for me was the love and compassion that those families had for each other. They took time throughout their day to teach, care and understand one another and that was aggressively missing from my family. But it wasn't missing from the old one. When Grandma was alive my family had all of that and then some. Every day we laughed together. We loved together. And we lived together. We may have been poor, but we never felt poor. But with Grandma gone and Him running the show I knew our lives would never reflect that of "The Huxtables" or "The Keatons." I mean "Cliff

Huxtable" was a doctor and his wife "Clair" was a lawyer. At that time I didn't even know black people could become either of those. All the Cliffs and Clairs I knew were doctors of the wine bottle and lawyers of the crack pipe. But a boy can dream even if that dream in about two and a half more weeks would easily be going back to a nightmare when this scholastic summer camp was over! "Well, that a do it. You're all patched up and ready to go!" The nurse chimed in interrupting my reflective thoughts with her high pitched puppy voice while patting my head in the same way. I couldn't wait to get back on campus so I could show Cleo the stitches in my eye that he so heavily contributed to. "Thank you Clair…I mean ma'am." I shook the nurse's hand and eagerly headed towards the exit.

The next few weeks went by in a blur. We were literally one minute taking college courses, the next having adventurous fun with all of our comrades old and new from across the state and then finally we were standing outside of our dorm buildings on the last night of our trip hugging and crying because we would all be going back to our home towns and back to our regular lives the next morning. One would be surprised how close people can become in such short periods of time when the experiences are new and togetherness is the tightening bond. As many people that were homesick on the way there, were just as many that now didn't want to leave. Kids were crying. Professors were crying. Men, women, boys and girls alike all crying and hugging as if the world was coming to a close. With as many cute girls there were on site I didn't mind all of the hugging. I was hugging girls I didn't even know just because it was so easy to show compassion in a crowd where everyone's looking to be consoled. It was about that time for us anyway. The age where boys and girls try to find themselves by expressive ways that flirt with their own identity in sexuality. So there I was like a lot of the boys in my crew counting how many female hugs we could get that included us gently placing our hands near or on their asses. What jerks we were, but happy jerks indeed! Even though I wasn't tear shedding like many of my peers, I was pretty sad that our time together for this summer was coming to an end. Most of these people I wouldn't get to see again until next summer because they either lived in other cities or would be going to a different school than me when we returned back to our hometown. Some of them I'd never see again because if we didn't keep our grades at an acceptable school average we'd lose our scholarships and not be allowed to attend next summer's event. We only had to make it through six more years of Jr High/High School to officially accept our scholarships, but many of us wouldn't even make it through our first year of Jr High School to return back to The Ohio State University next summer. I guess for some of us it was already too hard to maintain excellence in school considering the shitty home and school environments we had. Some of us would become drug dealers and gangsters that year. Others of us were already that! Many girls would become pregnant that following year or the next so that would be their demise in keeping their grades above the scholarship guideline minimum. As I looked at all the rats in the race I tried to predict which of us would fall victim first to the poisonous traps that life had so distinctly set in our paths. *Who would be kicked out of the scholarship program? Oh you're well on your way,* I thought aloud at some kid with his pants sagged so low that you could see his bright red boxers sticking out so fashionably under his not long enough, newly purchased white T-shirt. *You and the chick giggling next to you as if every word you speak is the funniest of all men. She and ye are destined to the dungeon of mediocracy, forthright!* And that was why I was sad. Coupled with the fact that I was only hours away from having to return back to my own dungeon. I *wonder what evil and diabolical plans He had conjured and prepared with the Devil himself for my immediate arrival?* My body shuddered at the thought and I had my cup's full of tonight's festivities and could swallow no more. So I left Cleo and my other friends down in the courtyard to continue the party without me. Tomorrow's bus ride home would be a long and disappointing one for me and I knew tonight's anxiety would not allow peaceful slumber as the few weeks before it.

"Good night Ohio State University. Hello hell, I know you missed me!" I whispered to myself before falsely shutting my eyes.

I knew there'd be no sleep tonight but played along no differently than I had done my entire life. What I did not know was what the universe had in store for the second half of my penniless soul.

Chapter 12
the Day She Lost Me

The wind was biting extremely hard today. I could feel the chill of its teeth sinking into the depths of my bones making my body shiver uncontrollably. I could barely see the traces of life escaping from the frozen passages of my nose through blurred vision, eyes watering from the sharpness of the cold. Thin white puffs of my breath seemed to dangle from my mouth like small stiff clouds frozen in the winter sky. To make matters even more unbearable it began to rain. *How could it be this cold and the rain not turn to snow? I would gladly except snow over this! At least with snow our gear wouldn't be soaked.* Rain always made the cold much worse than the snow did. It had my uniform sticking to me like a cheap suit. Out of the corner of my eye I could see my drill sergeant's piercing gaze blanketing all of us, just begging to notice one of us flinching or fidgeting during our instructor's lesson. Today we were being lectured on all the rules and regulations of how to properly handle and dislodge a grenade. But it was so cold it seemed as if all of her words were freezing right outside my ear canals, no way to paddle in. I was a little embarrassed because there she was some small woman in just her military shirt and pants easily withstanding the cold, while I stood knees shaking in full military thermals beneath my shirt, pants and winter battle dress coat ready to collapse at any moment. But I dare not do so in front of Drill Sergeant Moreland. Though I liked him very much because he always made me laugh, he was still a force to be reckoned with. If he even noticed you for a moment out of focus or screwing around he would be all over you like white on rice! Moreland was physically huge. He was one of the biggest and strongest of all the drills. We also had Drill Sergeant White and Drill Sergeant Williams. But today, to his enjoyment Moreland had us all to himself. He was already looking at me in anticipation to chastise. But today I refused to give him that pleasure. The instructor motioned us to sit down on the bleachers we were standing in front of. When my ass hit the cold steel of the seat I almost jumped back up, but I knew I had to keep my composure. *What the hell was I thinking in joining this cause? I don't believe I truly belong here.* The thoughts of questioning my decision to join the Army just burrowed through my skull like a groundhog of regret. Sure I had to do something once I graduated high school to get out of the gloom type situation of a life that I had. *But did it have to be running off to the armed forces as a way out? I couldn't of figured out another way to get back to college?* I needed a piece of paper with the name Jesse Benson written across it to hang in my office one day exploiting that I had paid my dues and was an expert at whatever craft. *But did I need to get it this way? Yes, you do dummy! If you hadn't lost that scholarship to The Ohio State University, then we wouldn't be in the mess in the first place. We would have never needed to leave our unfortunate, but indeed warmer than this home only to venture out here in the middle of who knows where, butt fucking Fort Knox, Kentucky! You have fucked us to our doom unfuckingly!* The words of my alter ego were banging inside my head drowning out the words of the instructor with ease. At this point it was easy for me to agree with him. Sometimes it would get cold at home, but nothing like this. We would be all cozy in a familiar place right now had I not just up and joined the Army. I had only told two people I was joining the military, my girlfriend who was devastated that I was leaving her on her birthday of all days and one of my best friends Mooka. I hadn't even told my mom I was leaving. I had grown to hate her almost as much as I hated Him. *But at least if I was back home I wouldn't be soaking wet freezing my balls off in this miserable weather. I'd be miserable, but a dry and warm miserable I'd be, not this unbearable shit!*

"Attention!" Moreland's voice snapped through the air like a herd master's whip. We all immediately stood up in unison ready for the next command.

"Right face!" Like synchronized watches we all turned right not one of our boots hitting the ground later than another's.

"March...yo left!" Moreland was leading us to the area where we'd be practicing throwing dummy grenades following what we had learned the past hour from the instructor.

I had only learned that a man could literally freeze to death before going to practice dying by grenade.

"Man on the code it's cold as fuck out here today, gotttttt damnnnnnn!" Ahmad whispered through slightly opened lips knowing that if we got caught talking in formation we'd pay a hefty penalty.

But at this point we both were experts at being able to converse without being discovered by the mighty Moreland.

"Man, it's colder than a penguin's dick out here!" I chuckled back. Ahmad was my battle buddy and one of the guys I trusted in our platoon.

In a few long months we had become great friends. We would always jive back and forth on our military journeys. Like today there were many days I didn't know how I'd emotionally survive boot camp without him. It could have been me getting into all types of trouble all by myself, but with Ahmad by my side I had the pleasure of knowing I'd never be alone in my quest for being reprimanded. We had just made it to the practice grounds when Drill Sergeant Moreland prompted us to jump down into some mud holes to get ready to throw the dummy grenades.

"This ain't a game numb nuts! I'm tellin' ya' right now that one of you gone' make the mistake of fucking up today. But today gone' be different. Because of the *seriousnicity* of the amount of danger we could all be in when one of you ass monkeys fucks up and does somethin' I already know your weak ass mamas and daddies taught ya, which is gone' be the exact opposite of what the fuck the instructor just taught ya. For the safety of all mankind this is one of the few times that instead of yelling at you I am allowed to hog tackle your McMuffin asses, dick first right into the got damn dirt! And ohhhhhhhh I can't mutha fucking wait for it to be you!" Moreland rattled on and on and though he was talking to all of us, he was certain to keep his gaze fixed on Ahmad and I while he spoke.

"Drill Sergeant gone' bust yo' ass today Benson." Ahmad snickered next to me as we stood beneath some low hanging trees.

Drill Sergeant Moreland was right. Normally drills couldn't put their hands on you physically, but because we could take some slight injury from a dummy grenade's explosion, for safety reasons a drill could tackle you to save us few from being harmed. Moreland had been talking about it for weeks saying it was his favorite day of the entire basic training because he'd get to hurt one of us legally!

"Man I'd crack Moreland in his big ass head if I even had a thought he was about put a pinky finger on me, let alone a damn football smash." I looked at Ahmad and we both laughed knowing I was talking shit way above my feeble capabilities.

"Get down!" Moreland piped.

Ahmad and I jumped face first into the freezing mud. Slushy rain water splash through my uniform soaking my body even more making my clothes cling to my shivering bones. My hands were extremely cold to the point where they were swelling up. I could barely hold the dummy grenade. We had to wait for Moreland to give us each command on queue to complete his directive, the first being to get down.

"Prepare to throw!" At this point we had to hold the grenade with two hands propped against our chest, pull the pin and wait for Moreland to give the command to throw it across the field well out of harms way.

We were specifically trained on how to hold the grenade with the clip pinned against the thumb of our throwing hand so that in a real situation if we decided not to throw the grenade, we could easily reinsert the pin back in place without issue. As long as the clip stays in place the pin can be removed back and forth at will. But if the clip ever pops the pin cannot be reinserted and the grenade must be thrown within four to five seconds before it explodes. We knew the drill well since we had been training on it for days. Ahmad and I simultaneously pulled the pins from the grenades, except there was one problem. My hands were so swollen from the cold that I couldn't grip it close enough against my thumb to keep the clip down. My grenade immediately started to fizz up while we were just sitting there waiting for Moreland to give us the "throw" command. I was so cold and distracted that I couldn't hear the grenade fizzling, but Ahmad heard it loud and clear. He freaked out, looked at me and yelled "throw it, throw it, throw it" well before Moreland could give the command to do so. We both jumped up and threw our grenades at the same time. Ahmad's landed and exploded on time across the field where it was meant to. But my grenade exploded prematurely right above our heads in the trees. Bits of broken branches and debris fell down on our heads and a hint of smoke was in the air just enough to cause us to wheeze when we breathed. I began to cough and wipe the dust from my face when I noticed out the corner of my eye Ahmad jumping off to the side as if he were trying to avoid some type of collision. I hit the ground so hard that I'm sure my back left an imprint in the wet soil. The air had been knocked completely out of me and I was dazed. I had felt something like this before but I couldn't quite put my finger on it. *Where was I? This felt familiar.* I could hardly catch my breath as I lay in the cold mud. Again I thought to myself, *when couldn't I breathe like this before? Oh yeah, I remember now. It was that time Manny was finally coming home from juvenile jail.* He had been locked up all of spring and most of the summer. I hadn't seen him for nearly an entire year and today was the day of his release. I saw him coming down the road in the distance and ran up to greet him. But instead of giving him a hug how most people do after missing someone, I lovingly pushed him with two hands in the chest,

"What's up boooooooy!" I yelled out through a mouthful of happy teeth.

Manny gave me the look he always gave me right before we'd get into a heated tussle.

"Don't push me like that again nigga."

There were two reasons why I wasn't afraid of Manny. Number one, he was my cousin/brother (whichever you prefer) so I knew he'd never truly purposely ever try to harm me in any way. And number two, all the physical fights we had always proved to end in my favor because though I was the younger of us two, I was also the brightest, the feistiest and the more courageous of us as well. So when Manny said not to push him again I believed that to be an invitation to do the exact opposite. So I pushed him again, but this time I pushed him even harder than the first. In doing so I noticed his chest felt thicker than usual and the harder push barely budged him.

"Nigga, didn't I say not to push me again!" Manny grabbed me by the shoulders, picked me up off the ground and slammed me back first onto the hood of an old, rusty Cadillac de Ville. Air gusted from my lungs leaving me breathless. Once it returned my spine screamed out along with me,

"Ok, ok, okaaaaaaaay! Get yo' big gorilla manila hands up off of me!"

But to prove how strong he was, Manny just held me down on that car relentlessly. And that was my first lesson in understanding how strong some men become after spending significant time behind bars.

I shook the daze from around my head and noticed the shadow of a giant looming over me. The blinding sun behind him was hiding his face but not warming my cold body on this mushy ground. But at least the rain had stopped.

"Ahhhhhh yeahhhhhhh! I told ya'll monkey asses that one of you numb nuts would do me the pleasure of being able to knock your dumbass dick in the dirt. Congratulations Bennet. You've made the money cut once again!"

Oh no. I hated when he called me Bennet and now it was all coming back to me clearly. Drill Sergeant Moreland had taken the luxury of tackling me straight to the ground for botching up the grenade toss. And he was enjoying every bit of my humiliation. That bastard! I gave Ahmad a look that stated, *if it was a little warmer out here I'd kick his big gorilla looking ass.* Ahmad returned my gaze with his own, *yeah ok, if you say so* look while reaching out his hand to help me up off the ground. I brushed my shoulders off as if I had completed a job well done and we both busted out laughing knowing that I had not.

On the march back to our barracks my head pounded around *how I slid into the Army in the first place?* We had about a five mile hike so I had plenty of time to think. *What prompted me to believe this was truly where I wanted to be? No one back home even knew where I was except for my best friend Mook and my girlfriend Christie.* And those two only knew that I was in the military but didn't know physically where I was or what branch I had joined. I just jumped up one day, tiptoed out the door, climbed into the Army recruiter's car and never looked back. With Manny gone, Leslie having her own life crisis being a young single mother, and Him literally trying to kill me…I could take no more. I knew that if I hadn't left it would be the death of me and I wanted to live. Thirteen long years I had been beaten, tortured and humiliated. For once I wanted to breathe in the earth's air under the influence of my own decisions and choices, not someone else's. It started right after high school Graduation. Mama wasn't there when I walked the stage. In fact, I barely remember getting my diploma. I would have had it mailed to me to avoid the shame of walking the stage alone that night if I thought He could have been civilized and not burnt it up before I could receive it. But He ached at every turn to get an opportunity to crush my spirit, so I only went to graduation to stay one step ahead of Him. I also was preoccupied with someone I believed was way more interesting than His hate for me and her name was Christie. She was the most beautiful thing the world had offered me so far and in that I saw a glimmer of hope that there was a chance for me to have a normal life. Her hair was brown and curly, the locks dancing off her shoulders when she walked. Her face was heavenly and her skin looked like she was only born a day before. She had a timid yet seductive way about her. She would pull you in with her eyes but turn away before yours could ever meet. She had a way of not speaking but still being heard, and when she did speak her voice strummed my ears until my heartbeat fluttered the moon. At the time I was positive that Aphrodite could have placed no better in front of me. We were juniors in high school when we first met. She lived outside the city so we attended different schools, but we stayed in constant communication daily through phone calls and letters. It was truly an intoxicating relationship. We both enjoyed being a part of something that wasn't typical. In fact, we thrived on how close we were in spite of the physical distance between us. She lived in a more suburban, upper class type neighborhood while I still struggled to survive in the darkest parts of the city. By far this was the truest definition of opposites attracting to each other. But every time the roots of goodness would sprout its head above ground, life itself would find a way to strangle it limp dead, usually in the form of whatever punishment He desired. He lacked nothing in terms of vile creativity. But in my eyes Christie was worth all the risk as spending time with her made me forget how bad things actually were at home. She crowded my mind and left little room for any other thoughts to muster. So when I made the decision to just up and leave, it was one made under the umbrella of life and death circumstances. One very late evening I had decided to call Christie on the phone. Because Christie's father worked early in the mornings her and I were already under the understanding that the perfect but latest time for me to call her home would be right before 10:00pm. I would let the phone only ring twice. If she didn't answer then I would hang up and simply try again the next evening. So like clockwork at 9:59pm every day I would call her and right on queue she would pick up the phone. We'd talk for at least an hour (maybe two if we were lucky) about all kinds of things. Sometimes we'd just read letters that we wrote each other during school that day, that we couldn't patiently wait to give to each other the next time we were scheduled to meet in person. We were just in young love heaven. The only problem that I had was that I wasn't allowed to talk on the phone at all without permission. Here I was seventeen years old and I was only allowed to answer the phone, but not make personal phone calls. People rarely called our home because if He answered He'd give them hell. The only one that was allowed to talk on the phone regularly was Mama. The good news for me was that everyone had early bed times as another stupid house rule. So by 8:00pm everyone would be upstairs in bed fast asleep. Everyone except me. There was an unspoken 8:00pm curfew rule as well that I never followed. By this time I hated my life and the world containing it, so much that all rules He made for me I declared unconstitutional. As a child He could manipulate me with fear. But now as a young adult I was less afraid and more immune to His tactics. I was younger, stronger, smarter and faster than Him and we both knew those truths. The only thing that He still had over me was His cynicism and that was simply because that trait did not abide within me. One evening I came home right about the time I was scheduled to call Christie. Everyone as usual was already in bed so it seemed that tonight would be no less intertwined with ambiance than any other night when speaking with her. And as expected she picked up the phone after the first ring.

"Hello Baby!" Christie whispered as excitingly as a whisper could be. "How's tonight my handsome prince?"

It was typical for us to speak to each other in the form of a Shakespeare sonnet since we both were huge fans of poetic dialogue.

"The evening is drearily long and less the moon's light to guide it without the sound of your voice to gather us all my love." Since I was used to reading the bible in church daily it was always easy for me to impress Christie with renaissance speech.

I could hear her blushing through her giggle. "Bravo my dear! Bravo!" She cheered. "Let me read you this letter I wrote you earlier today during study hall."

Oh how I couldn't wait for her to read. It was like listening to the sounds of tranquillity from a meditational tape recorded by a humming bird raised by Mother Teresa. Within moments I'd be lost, deep in thought. But I've unfortunately learned that the same things that can bring you peace in this life can also bring you pain. And it was her voice that had summoned me until I did not hear Him sneaking down the stairs like a hungry beast hunting a quickened prey. Her love had distracted me. So while one was serenading me, the other was stalking me. One slow footstep at a time He made His way down the steps, making it impossible for me to hear any of them. Suddenly He jumped around the corner on top of me and slammed something quickly into my chest and then pulled back. It had hit hard and it had hit bone. A heavy weight pressed the wind up out of my lungs as I lifted my head up to see what was going on. There He stood in a defensive position peering at me with an eerie glee waiting for a reaction. But I gave Him none. I just stood there blankly staring back at Him as if nothing had occurred as the tune of her voice began to be slightly muffled by a pounding clang of rage heightening in between my ears. I could feel a surge of heat steaming up inside of my eyes as my glare pushed His back into His head. An un-calm shade of uneasiness lowered over His face that I had never seen before as He was obviously looking for a different reaction from me. Fear for a quick moment reeked from His pores sending goosebumps down the back of my neck. No matter how anxious I was, I was intent on never letting Christie know how nasty a life I had. That burden was for me to carry and for me to carry alone. So in a attempt to continue discretion I calmly cut in on her reading and said,

"Honey, let me give you a call back in a few minutes because I have a small matter currently that I must attend to."

She stopped reading and said "Is everything alright?" "Of course." I robotically replied. "Things could not be

better. If you fall asleep before I can call back I'll just come see you tomorrow evening at the restaurant. You can finish reading your letter to me in person and I'll give you mine. Love you. Good bye for now."

I hung the phone up not waiting or allowing her to respond. The pounding against the walls in my head were getting louder. They were at least loud enough for Him to see. He was unfamiliar with this type of energy expelling from me and so was I. It was the calm before the storm, but the storm was unnatural. I just stood there still... breathing...an invisible dragon's fire ripping through my flared nostrils. He turned around and ran back up the stairs. But I knew He wasn't running because He was afraid. I knew He was just going to retrieve His bigger weapon from

His bedroom drawer, the axe. Stabbing me in the chest with one of His knives obviously wasn't good enough because it hadn't broken me as intended. Instead it had only vexed me causing some unknown rage to be awakened inside of my soul that I never knew existed. While He ran up the stairs to retrieved His axe to help His cause, I ran out the back door, up the street to use a payphone to call my friends to help me achieve mine. One of us had to die tonight and I didn't want it to be me because as of late I was just starting to feel alive. But as far as I was concerned He had terrorized me for the last time. And if I had to die to ensure that His terror ended, then so be it!

Ten minutes is all it took? Really? Just ten minutes? My friends are no joke! By this time they all knew He was crazy. I mean, they had been watching His shenanigans since we were young kids. But even this was just too far out of control for their comfort level. Something had to be done about Him, and not the done that monsters can come back from. Once they heard that He had stabbed me in the chest they jumped in their cars and drove across town to my rescue and that made me feel loved. But at the time I couldn't feel anything but hate. I hated Him and I wanted to kill Him. And instantly that want turned into a need. By the time my friends got to me I was mentally vacant. But when they did get to me they got to me bearing gifts, two guns to be exact. The first was a black and brown colored 22 caliber pistol. It was pretty small and I wasn't in a small mood. The second was a shinier black gun that was much bigger, heavier and fit the mood that I was in. I had absolutely zero experience with guns but I was pretty sure bigger was better. The least that He was going to get tonight was the pistol whipping of a lifetime! As we drove down the road towards my house my friends were talking to me trying to calm me down. They were also trying to tell me about the guns but I couldn't hear any of them. I was mentally so far away from them that their voices sounded like mumbled thoughts muffled out by the roar of a great storm. Such a storm was slamming against the walls inside my head. All I could hear was how much I hated Him. I got out the car and stashed the smaller gun in a bush across the street in the neighbor's yard. I figured the fight that was about to take place had potential to end up all over the street, so one gun stashed in a bush is better than two guns dropped on the ground. My plan was to walk right into the house, dodge His first swing at me with the axe, tackle His ass to the floor and beat the dog shit out of Him until I could see pieces of His skull slightly exposed through His face. But when I tried to get back into the house all the doors were locked, even the basement door I often used to get in. That door had never been locked the entire time we lived there until tonight. *If He was so big and mighty like He had been claiming my entire life, why would He lock all the doors to the house? Because He was a fucking coward and His cowardice was now being exposed!* The words coward continuously rang inside my head banging against the insides of my ears like a metallic ball inside a busted pinball machine. But this machine was making an insufferable noise that I couldn't control. All the lights were out in the house as if no one was home, but I knew everyone was there. I ran to the front of the house and started screaming at the top bedroom window where He, my mom and Paul slept. Those two probably were sleep at this hour but I new He'd be wide awake. He was probably just standing in the room listening to me scream and just waiting for me to go away. But I wasn't going away.

"Coward! Unlock the door and come face me like a man! Bring your cowardly bitch ass out here and come do to me what you've been telling me you'd do all these years! I'm right here and I'm ready bitch! I'm ohhhhhhh soooooo fucking ready to to do this shit right now you weak ass bitch! Let's go! Let's go coward! You fucking coward...!" I gnawingly screamed over and over at the top of my lungs.

I had never been this angry before in my entire life. I could hear the red inside my head. It was so loud that it was beginning to bleed into my eyes. I picked up a nice size rock and hurled it up through their bedroom window. Since their bed was directly under that window I knew that would get their attention. I was hoping that all the shards of glass would crash into His eyes and blind Him forever. The bedroom light immediately came on and with the window now shattered I knew He'd be able to easily hear my cries.

"Yeah bitch! Wake your weak ass up! What? You thought you'd just stab me and go back to sleep like all's well in fuckland? Well I got news for your bitch ass! It ain't going down like that this time! Your cowardly ass needs to get out here and face this mother fucking death music, you bitch ass, coward ass nigga!" I was screaming so loud that everyone in the neighborhood could probably hear me.

And had we been in the Projects no one would have cared. But this was a pretty decent neighborhood that we had just moved to that Section 8 had given us. The neighbors across the street were white and we had never lived by white people before. My friends were yelling something to me while they crossed the street to get away from the drama but I couldn't hear them. Between the noise in my head and the noise from my mouth I couldn't hear anything, not even the sirens from police who were speeding down the street, most likely called by the neighbors. I was a madman jumping up and down in the front yard screaming obscenities at the top of my lungs every few seconds while the pounding rage in my head just kept getting louder and louder. Not only couldn't I hear anything, but I also couldn't see anything. Everything I looked at had a crimson red splash to it nearly blinding me. And then all of a sudden everything went completely mute. It was as if all space and time had frozen. I couldn't hear my movements. I couldn't hear my feet shuffling over the grass. I couldn't hear my friends pleading from across the street. I couldn't hear anything. I couldn't see anything. And I couldn't feel anything. It was as if my body was suspended separately in outer space and my mind was detached even further away. Until suddenly I was being tackled to the ground. My chest and shoulders slammed into the grass. My arms were being restrained by bigger ones that surrounded my upper body. I could feel the weight of a large person holding me down and putting pressure on top of me so that I couldn't move. With my head turned to the side I was staring into the steel toes of a pair of black uniformed boots. I could hear radio communications in the background and flashing lights flickering back and forth across the ground that began to give me a headache adding to the slight pain I was already beginning to feel from the officer laying on top of my body.

"What in the tarnation is wrong with you boy? You can't hear somebody when they're speaking to you? You really just wanted me to get all muddied up with you, huh?" The officer said while frisking around my body.

"Oh, we got one Sarge…this one has a gun on em'!" The officer had felt the gun in my waistband while searching me.

I could tell by his tone and sudden increased pressure against my back that he was infuriated by his find. He handed the gun over to the sergeant and continued his frisk.

"And what was you planning to do with this, huh?" The sergeant yelled as he shoved the barrel of the gun up against my temple. "You was gonna try to kill somebody tonight, huh? Maybe kill me? Maybe kill my partner and these nice people in this here house? I otta' kill you with this gun right here that you was gone' do all the damage with! How'd you like it if I did that boy?"

He was digging the gun into my head so hard that I could feel the other side of my face making an imprint in the grass. That's when it dawned on me that I could now possibly be in a lot of trouble. Carrying a gun as a minor could land me in jail. But then I thought a*ny place would be better than where I currently was. At least in juvenile jail I wouldn't have to worry about being stabbed for talking on the phone…or would I?* My anxious thoughts were interrupted by the officer holding me down. His cautionary voice leaped out in a plea to his sergeant. "Sarge, it's ok!

It's ok Sarge! It's a B.B. gun! It's just a god damn B.B. gun!"

B.B. gun? B.B. gun? You mean to tell me that I had picked the heaviest, darkest of the two guns presented to me and the one I picked was a B.B. gun? So if I real ly got into a situation where I needed to shoot His evil ass I would have been pumping out B.Bees???!!!! I would have been trying to slay a demon with a bunch of light ass B.Bees???!!!!

"Boy, you are so lucky that this is just a B.B gun. You better thank God because your little ass was about to be grass young buck!" The sergeant snarled and glanced across the street where my friends cautiously stood.

"Get his dumbass up and into the back of the car please. We've got better things to do than to be coming out here all late at night for some young wannabe thug punks! Ain't ya'll got somewhere to be?"

Jason yelled back, "Nope…we good right here!"

As the officer shuffled me over to the police car I thought to myself how thankful I was that it was just a B.B. gun, and how lucky I was to have hid the other "real" gun in the bushes across the street that the officers had no idea about.

"Just sit back here and keep your mouth shut." The officer directed and slammed the door.

I never knew how uncomfortable sitting in the back of a police car while handcuffed could be until then. I had to sit propped up to avoid the cuffs from cutting into my wrist. The front seat window was slightly down so I could hear some of the rumblings of conversation going on outside between Him and the officers, but not much. Maybe I couldn't hear as much because I was sitting in awe of what seemed to be an impossible metamorphosis of the human body happening right in front of my very eyes that I had never seen before. There He stood all slumped over with His knees bent with one arm holding onto the fence as if He needed it for support. He had on pajamas that I had never seen Him in instead of His usual dingy kakis. The pajamas made Him look homely, less threatening. His other hand was shaking while He was pointing to my friends across the street as if He could barely hold His arm up from lack of strength. His voice sounded like it was struggling to climb out of His mouth as it rattled on to describe the events of the evening.

"Sir could you explain to us what's going on here tonight?" The Sergeant was gesturing over towards me and then over to my friends.

"Yes sir." He rattled. "The boy has basically lost his mind sir. His mother and I are at our wits end about what to do with him. We can't control him when he's like this. They can't control him at school either. He's drunk off the alcohol all the time and doing all kinds of different types of drugs and thangs. He's in a gang causing all kinds of trouble for his mother and I. Those are his gang buddies over there across the street. I told them to stay away from here. We just moved here from those Westlake Apartments over there on the North side of town trying to better ourselves and improve our lives. We told him and his gang friends that if they wanted to keep up with all the foolishness they could stay over there on the North side. We know these good people over here don't want all that ruckus and gang nonsense going on in these parts. He's embarrassing us! We're good Christian folks, you know? We go to church every Sunday and pay our dues. We got three more beautiful young kids inside that are doing good in school and trying to better themselves. Everybody is this home is trying to love one another and care for one another. The only problem that we have in this house and this entire neighborhood is that unruly young man you got sitting in the back of that car over there. At this point we're all afraid of him because we just can't handle him anymore. His mama is afraid of him. The kids are afraid of him. And I'm afraid that I may not be strong enough to handle him while he's intoxicated on them drugs. Can you just take him away officer? Can you get him out of here and into one of those homes where they keep all the bad children who don't listen to their parents? You see his gang buddies over there? I know they're selling them drugs. They're selling them drugs all over the city and we're forced to just sit back and take it. Well I don't wanna take it anymore! Can you take him and his god damn buddies away from here???!!! Lock em' all up so the world can be a better place! Can you do that for all of our sakes sir?"

The words were pouring out of His mouth as steady as a freshly opened bottle of new wine. It was as if He were on a broadway stage performing a play He had written Himself and rehearsed since birth. He was using the word sir which I had only heard Him use once before when He was washing some rich white folks' cars for cash. He was being overly polite and articulating His words with much more grace than His usual slander of unnecessary profanities. But out of all of these, nothing flabbergasted me more than how elderly He had just became. He had literally just become the oldest human being on the planet earth. The way He made His body hunch over and His head shake while His voice squawked out words from His scrawny neck like an injured bird was Oscar award worthy to say the least. I was appalled, impressed and enraged all at the same time.

I started banging my head up against the back of the passenger seat and screaming out "Are you fucking kidding me right now! He's a fucking pussy! He's a fucking coward ass, pussy ass faker! And He's not old! I mean... He is old, but not the old that He's showing ya'll asses right now! He's a con artist! A trickster! He's a fucking trickster and He's tricking the hell out of everyone! Drugs? I don't do drugs! And I don't drink alcohol! And I'm not in a gang! And, and...and He's a got' damn liar and a fucking trickster!"

The officer made his way back to me, opened up the backdoor and told me to cool it.

"What the fuck is wrong with you?" he asked. "Are you trying to go to jail tonight?"

I looked up at him sarcastically and said, "Would you be able to cool it if your father, I mean step father had just stabbed you for no reason?!!!"

The officer looked at me in disbelief, "yeah, yeah, yeah ok. The world is all bad and everyone's against you and you're the only one that's doing things right. I know. I know. I've heard it all before kid."

He turned back to ensure his partner was still ok, which he was, as he was still being entertained by Shakespeare in the flesh.

"I want my mom. I'm telling you this guy is doing a number on you cops that is making you both look like amateurs. Where is my mom? She'll tell you who this fool truly is once she finds out that I've been stabbed by His crazy ass!" I looked at him with pleading eyes so he decided to oblige.

"Sarge, he's asking for his mom. He said she'll be able to sort everything out for us. Sir, where's your wife? We're going to need her to come out here."

So He reluctantly turned and wobbly walked up the stairs and into the house. After about the longest 10 minutes I have ever encountered and just when the sergeant was growing impatient He came back outside.

"She said she doesn't want to have anything to do with him. She's tired of his foolishness. She's tired of the drugs and drinking. And she's tired of him terrorizing us."

He motioned the officers to take me away as He already previously suggested.

I screamed at the officer next to me and said "He's a fucking liar and a trickster! She said nothing of the sorts. I'm telling you that He's the terrorist and I'm the vic tim here. How many times do I have to tell you that HE STABBED ME?!!!"

The officer looked at me in disbelief again but because I was freaking out hysterically he decided to entertain what

I had said.

"Ok, your father stabbed you, right? Where in the hell did the old man stab you? I don't see any stabs."

I looked down at my chest and the officer was right. From first glance it looked as if I only had on a couple of dirty black t-shirts with small holes in them. And in the mist of everything going on I never truly checked to see how I was stabbed or if I was even ok.

"He stabbed me dead in the middle of my chest." I said emphatically with my head turned up in a manner of disrespect.

The officer had just about enough of the entire situation so he grabbed me and lifted my shirt up. I looked down to evaluate myself along with him and what I saw threw me into a panic. What could have easily been mistaken for body sweat with my shirt down had now been revealed as blood gushing from the stab wound. It was flowing down my chest and stomach into my pants that were also black which is probably why it had went unnoticed originally. Once I had saw my own blood I started my hysterical rants once more.

"I fucking told you! I told you guys He's a fucking trickster and a liar! He's a fucking coward! And now I'm going to die in the backseat of some punk ass police car with some gullible police officers who don't know when they're being bamboozled! He's probably holding my mom hostage inside the house as we speak. There is no way in hell that she knows He stabbed me. If she new that she'd be telling you guys how much of a terrorist He is and that I'm the good one, not Him!"

The officer spun away from the vehicle making his way back to his partner.

"He's stabbed Sarge. He's been stabbed right in the chest just like he stated." The officer turned to Him sternly, "Sir I'm going to ask you to have your wife come out here one more time and if she doesn't come out, based off of the situation we're going to need to come in. So either you're going to get her out here or I am. What's it gong to be?"

I could tell He was cracking. His frustration was starting to show as His attempt to pull the wool over their eyes had been undermined by me. He gave me an evil look of disgust as He made his way back into the house. I began to feel a surge of relief swimming through my veins. It calmed me down as it was a feeling of hope. I hadn't felt hope in a long time and it felt good. I knew if there was any chance for us to finally be rid of this monster, that chance was now. Certainly the police would have to arrest Him for attempted murder, endangering a child and trying to obstruct justice or something like that for all of His crimes. At least that's how it always happened on television. That's when hope arrived walking down the stairs towards the sergeant and she looked as if she had no idea of what was going on. She looked over at me sitting there held hostage and I could tell the visual had broken something within her soul. *This was it! Mama was going to tell them everything. She would tell them of all the indecencies He had inflicted on us all these years. She would tell them because she was tired, I was tired and the world was tired of Him. She would tell them because He had crossed a line that could not be uncrossed in stabbing me and literally trying to kill me which He had been close, but had never crossed that line before with any of us. She would tell them because she wanted our lives to go back however close possible to what they were before He entered them. She would tell them because she loved us. She would tell them because this would be our only chance within the past twelve years to rectify the insanity once and for all. She would tell them because she loved me!* Because of how low and soft my mother's voice was I couldn't make out what she was saying. I did hear the officer tell her that I was injured and was claiming to have been stabbed by Him. The sergeant wanted an explanation of what was going on and trying to get a third opinion on the matter sine he had mine and His already, which were two totally completely different interpretations of what had taken place. But I sat back in confidence knowing that Mama had heard my rendition of events and that I was bleeding in the backseat of a cruiser at the hands of Him. *It wouldn't be long now before Him and I were trading places in that police car and I'd be back in the house tending to my wound. All would be good now and we could finally live how God intended us to live in the first place, in peace.*

I finally heard the Sarge say to my mom, "Ma'am, they both cannot stay here after what has happened tonight, so somebody has to go to jail. Who's it going to be?"

Exactly I thought. *These cuffs are pretty tight. Let's get them off of me and onto Him so that I can get tidied up and He can get tidied off back to prison where He belonged. I'm sure we can get into more details during the trial and I'll be gladly testifying to all the treacherous acts that He has committed in full detail with audio and visual effects just to ensure He gets a life sentencing.* It wasn't long before the two officers were making their way towards me. The sergeant jumped into the driver seat and I assumed the other officer that I had already become familiar with would be opening my door to un-cuff me and set me free. I looked at him in anticipation like how a dog looks at his owner when the front door is about to be opened for the dog to be taken on a much needed walk. But the officer's hand passed my door and proceeded to open his own. He looked at me in pity. His face showing huge disappointment knowing that a major injustice was occurring that he couldn't do anything about.

He sat down in the passenger seat and said "Well kid, it looks like we're off to the hospital to get you all cleaned up and then it's off to the jail house because I have no idea what just happened there. But you can't stay here and your mom just took sides with your dad. So there's nothing more we can do from here except get you medical attention and get you to safety."

His words cut through me and severed the hope that had

just made its presence known only minutes before. I looked out the window at my mom as the police car pulled away. I couldn't look at Him because He had won. But I could look at her. She just stood there staring and when our eyes met she lowered her head and shrugged her shoulders the way she would when she felt that anything bad happening to me was because I hadn't "given my life over to the Lord enough" and this in her mind was the repercussions of me being a full blown sinner. She had finally done what I had always imagined she could never do and that was abandon me for Him. I always thought her love for me was stronger, deeper than anything they had. But I was wrong. She had chosen to serve me up to death and I could never forgive her for that choice. And in that moment I felt all my love for her fizzle out of my heart like air from a balloon with a pinhole in it.

Chapter 13

What Goes Around

"Platoon halt!" Drill Sergeant Moreland's voice rang out as loud as ever but not loud enough to interrupt my thoughts, so I just kept on marching while everyone else stopped.

"Bennet, if your brain was any smaller it'd be pecked by birds boy! When in the hell did halt mean not halt?!!!"

I hated when Moreland called me Bennet. In fact, it was because of him that Drill Sergeant Williams and Drill Sergeant Wright was also calling me Bennet. All of them knew my last name was Benson, but Bennet was their way of reminding me that I was a peon and they were superior.

"Sorry Drill Sergeant!" I replied quickly and ran back to my place in formation.

Ahmad was laughing so hard that I started laughing too. "Bennet, Bennet, Bennet…man you are outta' there. Where in the hell did you just go?"

"I was at home reminiscing for a quick minute, but now I'm back in this hellhole. What? Did you get lonely out here without me?" I replied with a chuckle.

"Hell no!" Ahmad laughed. "Yo' ass is bad news upon bad news boy. If you was back home you could've stayed back there and marched all the way back to yo' got damn house for all I care. Every time I'm next to yo' Bennet lookin' ass trouble is standing next to mine!"

Moreland dismissed us for the rest of the day which

made everyone happy. It was well overdue that we got a break to have some free time to ourselves without one of the Drills breathing down our necks and making us do pushups or jumping jacks every time we turned the wrong way or did the wrong thing. But just because Moreland was done with us didn't mean that Williams or Wright was. I was certain that they would pick up where Moreland left off. Drill Sergeant Williams was a tall, skinny African American from Oklahoma. His accent was so southern heavy that half the time he spoke I could barely understand anything he was saying. Drill Sergeant Wright a Caucasian male, much shorter and smaller than both Williams and Moreland. They were all so different, but still a great team. The one thing that all three of them had in common was giving me a hell of a hard time the entire stint of my basic training. Williams and Wright both walked into our bay not even 20 minutes after our dismissal which let me know that it would be both of them to continue tormenting us in Moreland's absence. Williams immediately started talking to us about an important inspection that we had coming up that could help or hinder some of us in whether or not we would be graduating basic training. Right when Williams started talking about how some of us may not make the cut, Wright started peering right at Ahmad and I. Wright was looking at me the same way He used to, but not as evil. It still irritated me. So I jumped up and said,

"You know, Drill Sergeant Wright you're the littlest of all the Drills but you talk just as much shit as they do as if you're just as strong. But if it wasn't for the United States government backing you up I'd show you just how weak you actually are…with your cotton candy ass!"

The entire platoon went dead silent. Everyone knew that speaking to a Drill that way would instantly result in some extreme repercussions. The only question would be if those repercussions were to be shared by all or solemnly dispersed to me alone? I'm sure that everyone was hoping that whatever the punishment was to be rendered that I'd be receiving it all by myself. But there was no rhyme or reasoning to how they'd dish it out, it could go either way. Drill Sergeant Williams gave us a look that pointed more toward everyone getting smoked. But Drill Sergeant Wright's eyes just lit up with excitement and stayed fixed on me while he shuffled past through the door. He quickly returned carrying two buckets filled to the brim with water. He set one carefully down in front of me and kept the other in his hand. There he stood facing me as if we were about to engage in a standoff battle for our manhood. It was quite intimidating but I stared back at him with courage leaping from my eyes.

"Pick up the bucket, Bucky!" Wright said. "Hold the bucket with one arm straight out like this." Wright was holding the bucket of water straight out with his fist clenched like he was ready to give me a fist bump. "We'll both hold the buckets out like this in front of each other like a standoff. Whichever of us drops the bucket or spills water out of their bucket first is a fucking pussy!"

I was immediately offended. *Did this scrawny little white guy think that he was going to beat me at a test of strength and will? I had been through so many things that were much worse than holding a bucket of water. I never let Him break me. So why would I start now in letting some tiny Drill Sergeant who probably had his entire life handed to him on a silver platter break me? Naw...it ain't going down like that,* I thought.

"Ok, I'm in." I picked up the bucket of water and mirrored Wright.

There we stood almost fist to fist and at first neither of us flinched or blinked. The entire platoon circled around us for the showdown. Even Drill Sergeant Williams was interested in this challenge as he pulled up right to the front row behind Wright to support his battle buddy. That didn't bother me one bit because behind me I had Ahmad and all the other Privates that wanted to finally see one of us challenge a Drill and win that fight, as it had never happened before. *How hard could it be to outlast some skinny white dude from the suburbs anyway?* I'd find out very hard soon enough. At first I was very confident that I was going to beat Wright. If the eyes are the windows to someone's soul, then I was peering into the depths of his with determination steaming from mine like how Superman burns through the enemy with his heat seeking vision. But what I soon found out is that I was lacking in the area of super human strength. But Wright seemed to be fairing just fine. He just stood there steel faced and calm with his arm stretched out unwavering. In what seemed to be several minutes but was only a few my arm started to tense up. The muscles in my shoulder began to tighten like a slow turning screw. Before I knew it I was severely struggling to keep my arm from shaking. It was taking all of my strength and concentration to keep the water in my bucket from swashing around and splashing over the sides. I could feel beads of sweat popping up on my forehead like a hot skillet holding kernels of corn shaking over a blazing fire pit. All the while Wright stood there as if it was just another day at the beach. At one point he even yawned as if he were growing tired of our spectacle and that made matters worse for me. I was buckling. The water in my bucket began to splash back and forth against the sides like tides against the shore. I could hear my comrades passionately yelling over my shoulder trying to motivate me to victory but their words were falling on deaf ears. Sweat was now flowing over my brows into my eyes causing them to sting. So much for not blinking! I squinted through irritated eyes just in time to see a small curve make way to one corner of Wright's lips. It was so obvious he was enjoying my struggle to stay in the game. Well he wouldn't get to enjoy it for long. My arm could take no more punishment and neither could my ego. I exhaustingly dropped the bucket to the floor causing water to splash everywhere. Ahmad let out a big sigh right before he busted out with an even bigger laugh encored by the rest of my peers. Yet Wright still stood there calm, relaxed and in the same position he held from the beginning of the challenge…unmoving, unwieldy and unrelenting. To add insult to injury he hadn't even broke a sweat.

"Let him live Drill Sergeant Wright," Drill Sergeant Williams joked. "Let his dumbass live, please?"

Wright gently set his bucket down on the floor next to mine. It didn't look like he spilled a bit of water from it at all. I stood there with my head hung lower than the shallow end thinking to myself what a fool I was. Wright came over, put his hand on my shoulder and whispered in my ear.

"And that's why you don't judge a book by its cover. You gave it all you had, so never hang your head in defeat. Besides, nothing's down there that you haven't already seen."

Then he walked away. Then everyone else walked away. And just like that it was over. Drill Sergeant Williams of course made me get down and do a bunch of pushups on the wet floor before commanding me to clean up the entire barracks. But other than that it had ended just as quickly as it had begun. And that's when I realized all things come and go except for the story that you leave behind.

All in all my basic training experience in the Army was not as difficult for me as it was for everyone else. My life before joining the military was pretty poor so basic training was actually a breath of fresh air for me. I figured nothing could compare to what I had already been through in my life and if anything could compare, it would need to be more than some excessive yelling and pathetic insults from a few Drill Sergeants. My life before basic training was based off those things and then some. My thoughts just wouldn't stop as we patiently waited for Moreland to meet us outside for our marching orders for the day. While we waited I reminisced on times past. After graduating from The Gifted Program my life was in a tug of war between a horrific Project terrace lifestyle and a religious Jesus take the wheel one. I was torn between trying to become a child of God bathed in the holiness of the Almighty and washed in the blood of his lamb, the ever perfect Jesus of Nazareth or becoming a hard as nails soldier in the Army of the most definitely damned poverty stricken hood where drug dealing, prostitution and homelessness was a common meal destined to be eagerly eaten by all who lived there. The war was at a dead even kill with the hood holding onto my body and the church having a grip on my mind. But that surely was a recipe that couldn't stay in my life cookbook for long. I was being stretched too far between the two. Every morning I'd walk the green mile to Hayes Jr High along with all the other neighborhood kids. And at night I'd walk an even greener mile to church. In fact my family and I used to walk everywhere. Walking for us was as common as driving was for everyone else. *I mean I walked so much that if my feet earned frequent flyer miles I could have taken a free flight to Neptune at least twice.* But all of the walking truly was making me physically and mentally stronger at an early age than most by default, which was one of the reasons why all the shenanigans of basic training never really bothered me. That school year was destined to be an interesting one. On the first day of school Manny and I would get to walk to school together because Manny was in and out of juvenile jail so often the past two years that he assumed he had flunked the 8th grade and would have to repeat it. Leslie was already a sophomore in High school so I was pretty stoked that Manny had flunked because then I'd at least have somebody in school with me that truly had my back. Manny didn't care that he had flunked because he wasn't going to school for the same reasons I was. Manny was going to school to have fun with his friends and I was going to school to do what Grandma had said, which was to get good grades to become an engineer. Manny and I certainly had different priorities but I knew that in the end we both wanted the same thing, freedom from the lives we had. It was the first day of school and everyone knew the first day of school rule. The rule was you had to be "fresh to death" meaning all your clothes had to be new if you wanted to start off the school year in the right direction and end up with the "cool kids." In elementary school I was the cool kid. But Jr High would be different because it would be bigger than Elementary school and there'd be students there coming from schools I had never attended. I'd also be like the new kid because for the past three years I'd been going to school in another district and most of the kids I went to school with in Elementary would not be going to school with me ever again. I knew I would have to rebuild my reputation as a badass and those aren't the easiest reputations to come by. I left my house early in the morning to pick Manny up for school. Leslie had already left and Manny was taking his good old time getting ready. When he came downstairs to leave I checked out his outfit and he checked out mine.

"Lookin' like the starting point guard for an after school special! Lookin' like the 1st baseman for Pee Wee's Playhouse! Lookin' like the anchorman for nerd news at 6pm! HAHAHAHAHA!" Manny just laughed and laugh as he slanged joke after joke about my gear. "And look at those shoes! I thought I told you to get the Adidas and not those whatchamacallits transformer shoes. Man transform your ass into a big bird and fly your sesame street lookin' ass up out of my face! Hahahahaah!"

Manny could crack jokes really well. In fact we both could but I could never win against Manny because his jokes would always make me laugh but he'd rarely laugh at mine. I often found myself using Manny's jokes about me on other people later, that's how funny he was.

I tried to make a comeback. "Shut up lookin' all neighborly with that Mr. Rogers sweater. Lookin' like the Cosby kid that didn't make the cut. Your jeans so starched that when you sit down at your desk today they're going to snap in half like a number 2 pencil."

The first few jokes Manny just looked at me with the face he made when expressing that what I said wasn't funny. He'd just twist his lips up to one side of his mouth and roll his eyes. But the starched jeans joke he couldn't resist and he busted out laughing.

"Let's go dumbass," Manny giggled! "You're stupid as hell for that one!"

We walked outside and began our early morning trot to school. First it was just Manny and me on a peaceful journey which made me think that this would be a regular occurrence, but it wasn't long before others joined us on our route. Everyone from the Projects walked the same way to school so before I knew it we had a crowd of about twenty kids making our way up the street. There were so many of us that we'd walk in the middle of the street because there wasn't enough room for all of us on the sidewalk. Most of the kids I knew but some I didn't. Manny knew everyone because he was very popular in our neighborhood. He would hang out at all the neighborhood corner stores and hot spots. The people that did know me most likely knew me because of Manny, so they knew me as little Manny, or they knew me because of my stepfather who they made fun of every chance they got because of how crazy He was. The walk to school was going just fine until one of the kids turned to me and started cracking jokes. Normally I'd just crack back but I didn't know this kid so I was reluctant to stand up for myself. I didn't want to get into a fight on the first day of school. Manny on the other hand didn't care about the first day from the last day. If he wanted to fight, he'd just fight.

"Hey, your shoes are fly man. What kind are those?" the kid sarcastically asked. I knew he was just trying to start trouble so I ignored him. I looked over to Manny who gave me an *I told you so* type of look. That's when I knew he wasn't going to step in and assist me. This one I would have to handle on my own. The boy bent down to get a closer look at my wears.

"Jordache? What the fuck? Oh damn...this nigga' got on some Jordache! Oh, damn damn damn damn damn! What the fuck is a Jordache? Hey them shoes look like you painted them yourself. Your shoes look like them joints are some paint by number type shits. Ha! Your shoes look like they made out of a plastic milk carton. Nigga' be eatin' cereal out his shoes!"

The kid was on a roll about my shoes and the entire group was laughing hysterically at me. I was so embarrassed that I just put my head down and stopped walking. Damn it! Why didn't I listen to Manny and get the Adidas. There were plenty of kids in the group that had on the same Adidas that Manny had told me to get one day when our parents were out shopping for our new school clothes. I had got the Jordache because I liked them and they were cheaper. I knew we didn't have much money so I wanted to make things easier on Mama, but now I was regretting that decision. The kids just continued walking and laughing. I let them get way far ahead of me before I started walking again. I could still hear them laughing about what the kid had said 10 minutes after the fact. This was not a good start to the school year and we hadn't even got to school yet. If this was what Jr. High was going to be about I knew I was in for a rough season. Manny ended upcoming back to walk to school with me. At this pace we're going to be late on the first day. When we finally reached the school standing in front of the cafeteria door entrance was someone I certainly didn't want to see on the first day.

"Wait a got damn minute. Is that Tito or is that Tony?" Manny was squinting at the door to get clarity on what he was looking at.

"I think that's Tito so I'm sure Tony is somewhere close. Shit, let's just go around to the other side Manny." I said worriedly. If there was anything that I didn't want it was an early school year confrontation with Johnny and them. I had my fair share of that in the 3rd grade and I was completely full. It was just our luck to run into one of the clan members and I knew we couldn't afford to run into the other two.

"Bullshit! I've been waiting to catch his punk ass

outside for a minute now. I'm about to jack his ass up with the quickness!" Manny triumphantly said while looking around the ground as if he had lost something.

What in the world was he looking for? And what did he mean "jack his ass up...?" We hated Johnny and Them. But we at least respected them enough not to be the ones to start anything up with that group. If anything went down between us it was them who would always initiate the fights, not us. Our rule was to stay out the way and to only fight if necessary. What was Manny about to get us into? I can't be be tearing up my new clothes fighting with these knuckle heads, not on the first day of school. I'm sure we'd have plenty of time to fuck around with them all throughout the school year. No need to start today!

Manny found what he was looking for, a huge rock. He picked it up and chucked it right at Tito. The rock bare ly missed Tito's head and slammed loudly up against the door. Waaaccckkk! Tito jumped as he was startled by the noise. Once he realized someone had thrown a rock at him he was highly annoyed. I couldn't believe what Manny had done.

"Are you fucking crazy? Are you trying to get our asses beat on the first day of school? What the hell is wrong with you??!!!" I whispered crossly to Manny as I didn't want to draw Tito's attention our way. He had yet to realize that the rock was thrown from our direction.

"Nigga' please! You got me fucked up. Ain't nobody scared of no punk as Tito, Tony, Tata, Tiny, TooToo or any fucking body else with a T in their got damn name for no reason. Let his ass say something to me and I bet I beat his ass, for real for real!" Manny was purposely talking loud so that Tito could hear him, which he did. He was peering right in our direction and I knew it was too late to try and act like someone else had said those ridiculous comments. I could tell Tito knew that the insults and the stone had been thrown from our direction. Manny picked up another relatively large rock while Tito was glaring at us and hurled it towards him. This time the rock didn't miss. It hit Tito right in the knee.

"Ouch, son of a bitch!" Tito screamed out hopping up and down on one leg.

Manny started running towards Tito while I just stood there in awe. I dropped my book bag from off my shoulder and bent down to make sure my shoes were all laced up as I anticipated that this entire situation was about to turn into an ugly brawl. *Why would Manny start something with these clowns? He knows better than to start shit with them. What was he doing? And why was he running toward the danger instead of staying clear? This was clearly a new, different type of Manny. This was the Manny that nearly broke my back on the hood of that Cadillac when he first got out of jail. This new Manny was definitely not like the old one I knew. This new one was fearless and reckless. I may not like this new Manny.*

"Oh, you calling me a bitch now?" Manny was all up in Tito's face. He grabbed Tito with both hands by his shirt and slammed Tito up against the wall. Next thing I saw was Tito's feet levitating off the ground as Manny was lifting him up by his neck.

"Come on Manuel, we cool homie! I wasn't calling you a bitch at all! We good man, we good!" The words struggled to make it out of Tito's choked out throat. "It ain't even gotta' be like this Manuel! Please let me alone man. Please!" Tito begged and begged but Manny was hearing none of it. He threw Tito face first to the ground and then put his foot on his back.

"And when I see Tony and Johnny Imma' beat they ass too. You let em' know what they can look forward to getting, ok little Tito?" Manny had his foot on Tito's back as if his back was a piece of land he had just discovered and was naming it Mannytown!

"Ok Manuel. Ok man. Just let me go. Please!" Tito cried. "Manny stop!" I accidentally yelled out. I didn't care for Tito much at all but even this was more than I could stomach. Manny was like an untamed beast just released from his cage. I was actually scared for Tito's well being. It was as if Manny wanted to seriously hurt Tito and that I didn't appreciate.

"You lucky my weak ass little brother likes your sorry ass for some reason. If it wasn't for him I'd break your damn back to the point you wouldn't be able to walk again, bitch! And you done' pissed your pants. Get your sorry ass up outta' here!" Manny laughed. He took his foot off of Tito's back and Tito jumped up and ran off. Then he walked over towards me very cross.

"Don't be feeling sorry for these weak ass niggas around here because they ain't gone' feel sorry for your soft ass no time soon." Manny growled at me before kicking my book bag. "I'm going inside to the principal's office to get my class schedule. Wait here. I'll be back." I just stood there amazed. I watched Manny as he walked into the school. He was pretty big and a strong looking dude now. I hadn't noticed how much so until he picked Tito up by the neck and tossed him to the ground like an unwanted peanut butter sandwich. *Manny was a monster!* The thought raised the hairs on my arms. *It was exciting and frightening at the same time as I was relieved and afraid. I wasn't afraid for myself because I knew Manny would never hurt me, ever. But someone else…he'd certainly hurt. And I didn't want to see him get hurt in the process of hurting someone else. But at least I'd have him with me this year so I'd have nothing to worry about trying to adjust to this new school.* At least that's what I thought until Manny came back out of the school with this evil looking grin on his face.

"Man, I'm at the wrong school little ass nigga. They don't have a schedule for me because I graduated Jr. High. I can't believe they passed me with all the school I missed last year. But whatever. I'm off to High school my nigga. I'm about to go up here and run the shit out of High school! Be cool boy. I'll see you back at the bricks."

Manny gave me a hug and walked off to get to the High school which was only another 15 minute walk from my school. I just stood there staring as he walked away until his body got smaller and smaller, until I could see him no longer. A sadness came over me because all I ever wanted was to be back in school with my brother. And just when I thought that wish had come true, it quickly disappeared as fast as it had came. *I wish Manny had flunked Jr. High.* And that thought also made me sad because I knew it was a selfish one. I picked my book bag up and started my walk towards the main entrance of the school. The second bell was ringing to alarm all students to get to class or they'd be considered late. I didn't care about being late. All I could think about was *how bad Manny had messed up Tito and what they were going to do to me once they found out Manny wasn't with me anymore. Fuck me!*

Chapter 14
a Bird...a Plane...a Buffer?

Fuck me! What the hell was that? Something had plummeted from the sky and hit the ground in front of us with a loud thud. I couldn't tell what had fallen because when in military formation it's against the rules for anyone to move in any shape, form or fashion, period. In vain I tried to shift my eyes to the left to get a better look. *What the fuck could it have been?* Moreland was furious. I could tell by the way he was shuffling his feet back and forth breathing heavily and making grunting sounds without saying a word, as if he were turning from man to beast right in front of our eyes. He'd always do that before lashing out at us with a series of demeaning insults and ravishing physical exercises to torture us when we made a mistake. The bigger the mistakes, the more creative the insults and punishments would become. Most of the time Moreland enjoyed the theatrics that came along with punishing us and this time was no different. It halfway reminded me of someone else in another life now far away from this one. But the difference was Moreland legitimately was trying to help me, not kill me. But the pressure of it all had finally gotten to one of us and none of us had seen this coming, not even Moreland. From the sound it made when it struck the ground in front of us, whatever had fallen from the sky was pretty heavy. Moreland still hadn't said any words. He was paused and then not paused, grunting and then not grunting as if he were trying to figure out which one of us was responsible for the obnoxious occurrence by twisting and turning noisily back and forth in hopes of catching the guilty party moving. But none of us moved. An entire platoon made up of more than fifty men and not a one of them moving as if we all were standing upright in coffins. So Moreland gave up the grunting approach and went with his typical *oh you muthafuckers done did it now* anthem.

"Oh you mutherfuckers done did it now, ain't ya?" Moreland started his tirade angrily pacing back and forth in front of our formation.

"You'd think after all this time of endless support and direction you numb nuts would have your fucking shit together like one ply toilet paper between a grizzly bear's ass cheeks! But nooooooooooo...you measly mind fuckery ass maggot dickwads couldn't pee straight if your tiny penises were lined up between two mosquito wood splints being held by tweezers as a kickstand!"

Moreland was on a roll and when he got this way it was known to end with me getting into a lot of trouble from laughing. Moreland always knew how to make me laugh. He would purposely mix his anger with good old fashion humor just to get a smirk or snicker out of us, mainly me. No matter how hard I tried I would always crack under pressure and at minimum, giggle. However, what none of us was brave enough to do was to flat out bust into a full blown circus clown of laughter. That would be a death sentence. But it was like Moreland was on stage at the Apollo for the last time in his comedic career and was knocking it out of the park. My eyes were already tearing up after the first few phrases. Ahmad was standing right next to me and his little snickers weren't making it any easier to keep my composure. Moreland's voice started to sound more muffled and further away which meant he was turned the other direction facing the latter end of the platoon. I knew I only had moments to quickly turn my head to see what had fallen. If Moreland caught anyone moving they'd be as good as minced meat. I turned my head and was baffled by the sight of one of our floor buffers with its long, bright yellow cord all mangled up hanging from the sky. *A buffer? A buffer? How in the world did a buffer come flying from up above? Certainly Jesus had not been cleaning heaven's golden floors with it and lost control of it and just dropped it over the edge. So what the fuck?* The yellow cord was still dangling in the air but there just wasn't enough time for me to follow where it was coming from as Moreland had already spun back around to address our end of the frightened group.

"Ain't every mutherfucker posed to be where they posed to be, all day every day? Then why in the flying forest monkeys' fuck are mutherfuckers not where they posed to be, when they're supposed to be there? You needle dick, dirty damn dummies think this shit is a game don't ya? Ya'll think that shit out here is sweet as fuck huh? I'm bout ready to can somebody's knuckle headed ass right now…" Moreland just rambled on and on with a fiery focus I hadn't been privy to seeing before. Ahmad and I were hanging on by a thread in keeping it cool. I was on the verge of losing it and Ahmad was snickering all over the place. My body was starting to shake from trying not to laugh. Moreland's voice once again drifted away so I took another shot at turning my head to finish my investigation of what the fuck was happening with the falling buffer from outer space. I followed the hanging yellow cord to where its trail led like Hansel and Gretel following breadcrumbs to find their way out of the woods. The cord led my eyes all the way from the ground where we stood up to the top window of the fourth floor of our Barracks, and I saw something that in my wildest dreams I could have never imagined. There in the window with a yellow buffer cord tied around his neck was one of our comrades standing with his eyes squeezed tightly shut, shaking with his face scrunched all up as if he had just sucked on the most sour grape known to man. There he stood bare chested with his small pointy shoulders hunched up like a small helpless bat with a yellow cord as a necktie loosely dangling from his wormlike throat. And that's when the clarity of the entire situation unfolded for me and I realized what had taken place.

No wonder Moreland was howling about people not being where they're supposed to be and how dangerous that was. This poor kid (who by the way was already very depressed about going through basic training) had basically tried to commit suicide by tying a buffer around his neck and throwing it out the window. Now on paper this would seem like a good plan knowing how heavy our buffers are and figuring that if tied around someone's neck and thrown from a four story window, the weight of the buffer would probably break their neck, especially someone with the neck of a chicken. But again, on paper it looks good. In theory it sounds good. But the kid didn't equate for one essential detail when conforming his plan. Military buffers are industrial for commercial use, not residential. That means they usually come with extremely long cords considering that those buffers will be used to clean long hallways and large facilities with the expectation of not having to be unplugged to cover long distances. So where the buffer was probably heavy enough to break this kid's neck, the cord however was not short enough. There it lay in slack all over the ground causing absolutely no pressure to come to the kid's neck at all. Smart move Sherlock!

And that's when I couldn't hold it together any further. The shock and reality of what had occurred had flowed over my composure like hurricane waves over the banks of a shoreline. The rush was unbearable and I just busted out laughing. *What a moron! Grandma taught me long ago that if you're going to do something, commit and do it right, know the details and execute on them precisely. What in the hell was this kid thinking?* I couldn't stop my stomach from crunching up from the laughter that was swelling up inside of it. Even when Moreland turned back towards our side of the formation, I couldn't stop laughing. I was in full blown hysteric jester and there was nothing I (or anyone else for that matter) could do to stop it. "Some of ya'll think this shit is really funny don't ya?" Drill Sergeant

Moreland ask. "Ya'll think everything sweet huh? Ain't that right Bennet?"

I tried to stop laughing but between Ahmad's snickering, my chuckling and the image Mr Non Suicide had burned into my frontal lobe I just couldn't do it. But what we all knew was that anytime a drill sergeant asked you a question we were all programed by law to respond with a "yes drill sergeant" or "no drill sergeant" accordingly. If we did not respond that way, trouble and punishment would inevitably follow. I hadn't heard Bennet respond yet (whoever Bennet was I hadn't remembered a private named Bennet but with more than 50 recruits I may have missed knowing someone) but maybe I couldn't hear him over my own laughter or loudness inside my head. All I could do was focus all of my energy on trying not to laugh, which wasn't working so far. I think what really had me going was how Moreland was speaking to us as if we were the priority, not the ridiculous looking kid still standing there in the window. Moreland was basically ignoring that he was even there! *How? The buffer had barely missed Moreland when it came crashing down from the sky behind him. How could he just act as if the kid didn't just try to seriously hurt himself? Wasn't he afraid the kid might figure out just to jump from the window to complete his original mission? Obviously not. Moreland was more concerned with lashing out at us for not noticing that one of our battle buddies was missing from their post!*

"When your partners are not where they're posed to be, people die. And when one person dies, we all can die. But you donkey brained imbeciles think that shit's funny as hell don't you Bennet?" Moreland's voice rose as he was getting closer and closer to our side of the group. I was beginning to get irritated because this Bennet character was about to have all of our asses in trouble from not answering Moreland's questions. This would be considered a blatant show of disrespect and we'd all have to pay the price for it soon. And that to me was not funny at all. Even

Ahmad had managed to straighten up as he too could feel Moreland getting closer and closer to us. I was trying my best to get it together but the image of that kid's fuck up just wouldn't fully let me. But the other foul up of Bennet ignoring Moreland's questions was quickly helping me get back into control of myself. I was no longer quivering with laughter. All that remained was a small smirk on my face and justifiably so considering all that had occurred. That's when I heard Moreland's boots make a sudden stop right behind my back and the brim of his large, round Drill hat slammed onto my head right above my ear.

"I said ya'll think everything out here is funny as hell and a big fat joke. And I clearly said AIN'T THAT MUTHAFUCKIN' RIGHT BENNET???!!!" Moreland

screamed into my ear at the top of his lungs. And that's when I realized the entire time he was speaking he was referring to me. I was Bennet! *But my name isn't Bennet. And I don't think everything out here is a joke, just most things. And shouldn't Moreland know my name by now anyway? I mean…he had just made me squad leader a few days ago because of my ability to perform and lead. Had he forgotten my name that quickly? I also thought drill sergeants were perfect and didn't make mistakes because in war mistakes kill. But here clearly Moreland had made the mistake of calling me by the wrong name. And that insulting mistake cannot go unrecognized by someone with my caliber of ego in this caliber of situation. Moreland had to be corrected this time if it weren't purely for the purpose of motivating my comrades by showing everyone once and for all (even the moron in the window still standing there with a yellow cord wrapped around his throat) that we are all human and even the best of us makes mistakes every now and again, even the Mighty Moreland! And I knew the perfect person to expose this baboonery right at this current moment. Me!*

So I sassily broke from formation without permission, whipped my head around and looked Moreland dead straight in his eyes and confidently but defiantly said, "My name is not Bennet! It's Benson! My name is Benson, Drill Sergeant!"

And that's when it happened. It had been a few months since I'd seen a man get so angry that his veins popped out of his neck in hopes to help the boiling blood inside of them escape. Moreland's face tensed up. It was obvious that he was balling his fist together to keep his fingers from wrapping around my neck. I didn't know if it was me breaking formation, me speaking out of turn, the kid poorly trying to kill himself or a combination of all three that had driven Moreland over the edge, but I was hoping that whichever it was wouldn't also have him drag my life out of my body and over that edge with him.

"Oh, your name is Bennet." Moreland whispered sinisterly as the eerie laughter in his tone made the hairs on the back of my neck salute. Then his words began to slowly rise like a vampire from a hidden coffin until they eventually exceeded all his other previously known screaming levels. "Hahahaha, your name is Bennet. OH…it's Bennet. It's Bennet, Bennet, Bennet, Bennet, MUTHAFUCKIN' BENNET, BENNET, BENNET, GOT DAMN MUTHAFUCKIN' BENNET TO THE 3RD MUTHA-

FUCKIN' DEGREE BENNET! Your name is Bennet and will be Bennet from now until your RAGGEDY BENNET LOOKING ASS IS ON THAT GOT DAMN BUS CARRYING YOUR STUPID LOOKIN' ASS AWAY FROM ME AFTER GRADUATION NEVER TO BE SEEN BY ME AGAIN. DO YOU UNDERSTAND THAT YOU PUNK ASS BENNET???!!!"

Knowing that my life was quickly flashing in front of my eyes I eagerly turned back into formation and gratefully responded "Yes Drill Sergeant! My name is Bennet Drill Sergeant until I leave Drill Sergeant!" We all knowingly would throw "Drill Sergeant" on the end of all of our statements as the ultimate sign of understanding and respect, especially when we had fucked up greatly. And I certainly had fucked up. Moreland just turned around and walked inside of the building. He left us outside cooking in the hot sun for over an hour. Without him dismissing us from formation we knew we had to stand there at attention stiff as boards until his return. He had done this to us on many other occasion, but not for the span of an hour. When he did return he brought the dumbo that tried to kill himself with him. I thought the kid would have certainly been taken to psychiatric care for evaluation, but Moreland had different plans. He just put him in formation but stripped him of all clothing that the kid could use to choke himself with. So now the kid had no shoestrings in his boots, no belt and no long sleeved shirts. He would have to continue through and finish basic training that way, with his boots flip flopping all around dangling off his feet whenever he walked, using one hand to hold his pants up over his waist and his other hand to salute VIPs throughout the day. It was one of the most embarrassing things I have ever seen but surely worked in convincing the rest of us that attempted suicide was probably a bad idea considering that if you failed to kill yourself you'd still have to go through basic training and complete all of your duties just like the rest of us, except in the end once basic training was over you wouldn't receive a certificate of graduation. *So you'd have to complete all the tasks, do all the physical and mental work, and become a soldier without truly becoming a solider? If that's not the ultimate dumbest, most brutal punishment ever invented, there is none.* Moreland just threw the half dressed kid back into formation and punished all of us with extreme physical exercise for the rest of the day. I watched the poor kid do jumping jacks with one hand holding up his trousers and the other hand clapping an imaginary hand over the top of his head. That night in our dorm room I went over to console the kid because I truly felt sorry for him. I also thought that he may try to kill himself some other way while the rest of us were asleep and I didn't want Moreland trying to hang that on me. I asked him why he even joined the Army in the first place since he didn't look to me to be the type to want to fight in any war at any time. He agreed with me and told me he only joined to get away from his rich parents and to prove to them that he didn't need the "family business" to survive. I told him he was stupid and he should be grateful to come from a rich family. I told him what is was like growing up poor and hopeless and that I'd trade places with him in a heartbeat. And though the kid was pretty sad and had been so since the first day of training, that conversation that we had was one that enlightened him, so he promised me that he wouldn't try to kill himself again if I promised to come back and speak with him each day. So in an attempt to help us all sleep well every night from thereon and to keep us out of harm's way with Moreland and the other drill sergeants, I agreed.

Chapter 15
Sorry Bobby

"Turn your bibles to Ecclesiastes chapter 5 verse 12 where the good book says the sleep of a laboring man is sweet, whether he eat little or much: but the abundance of the rich will not suffer him to sleep…" Pastor's voice rang out with the triumph of a civil rights leader.

The congregation was backing his every word right on queue, "Amen!" I thought to myself, *here we go again with the riddles, the riddles, the riddles. This is worse than listening to The Riddler from the Batman comic book series. At least with The Riddler he'd put you out of your misery at the end by killing you!* I looked to the right of me and there my mom was 100% captivated by Pastor's electric words like a dead robot begging for a recharge. I liked Pastor. I was impressed by his ability to move the crowd, but was unimpressed by how many people in his congregation actually believed their lives would be different if they simply went to church as much as possible. From what I could tell their lives were getting worse and their wallets were getting smaller and smaller by the hour. It often troubled me how the poorest people on the planet could find ways to come together and make financial contributions to causes other than their own. So while Pastor was busy word conducting the choir of the damned, I was busy making friends with the other church kids who happened to be there for the same reasons I were, entertainment and camaraderie. Going to church service was like a daily vacation for me. It was the only time I could peacefully get away from Him and school, as those two lives were on a collision crash course destined to explode on impact. But my church life was on a path of its own, one filled with joy and laughter, ridicule and intimidation, all orchestrated by me and my boys! Day in and day out we were the talk of the threshold, whether positive or negative. Either we were being subtly reprimanded by Pastor's sermons or viciously attacked by his loyal staff, both of which we devilishly enjoyed. Or we were making wise cracks about every single person there without remorse or filter which also for some reason we highly appreciated and loved! And for these reasons it was at church I felt the most empowered, admired, and most of all in control of my own existence. Since I went to church nearly as often as I went to school, the friendships made under the angelic stained glass windows of Pastor's cathedral were eternally real. Missionary Johnson stood up and gracefully walked up the isle with one finger raised above her head pointing to the sky, a way church folk often signaled as asking to be excused, knowing their movement could be causing a distraction during Pastor's message. But what she saw as respect we easily saw as a chance to inflict punishment for her having the nerve to walk past us without permission.

"Is Missionary Johnson's finger pointing up to Jesus right now booty?" I jokingly said just loudly enough for her and everyone within five rows of us to hear.

Right on queue my crew responded aloud, "It's booty!" "How booty?" I could barely say the words without

laughing.

"Oh, it's booty, booty, booty booty, booty!" My crew responded as we all just busted out laughing. Missionary Johnson embarrassingly just kept going but hurried her walk in order to save face.

"Shshhhhhh!" Someone visiting from another church turned around with her finger pressed up against her lips trying to encourage us to be quiet. "I'm trying to hear and all ya'll been doing is joking and jiving this entire time. Ya'll gone' bust hell wide open, watch and see!"

Oh no! I felt sorry for this newcomer. She obviously had no idea what she had just done. *Did she just shhhh us? Did she just talk shit to the baddest, most disrespectful church kids every created?* I knew my crew would have no mercy on her especially since she was not an original member of the congregation. Had she more tenure under her belt maybe they would have given her the lighter version of disrespect. But as a newcomer I was pretty sure they would give her the max penalty for her unwarranted conversation. And her punishment would be death by verbal persecution.

"Lady, your one finger is so ashy that when you shushed us small flakes of knuckle dandruff blew into our eyes!" Prince started rubbing his eyes to heighten his joke. He was the true knucklehead of our group.

"Yeah, you better take that K-Mart manicure kit back and get a refund because you got some Rumplestiltskin looking fingers. Look like you been spinning yarn into chalkboard dust, girl!" Ray cracked. He was the oldest of our crew sitting at 14 yrs. while the rest of us were just flirting with 12.

"And you came in here smelling like bug spray. Your perfume done killed about four roaches that was praying for forgiveness under your seat. The bible says thou shalt not kill so if anyone's about to bust hell wide open it's you, them four roaches you done killed and that Toilet De Raid you done sprayed around that goose neck of yours! Pastor done already said hell is hot, so you better wipe that junk off your neck because bug spray is flammable and your head's going to explode!" I said so slobbery with laughter that my chewing gum flew out of my mouth and landed on the collar of her stiff ass blouse. She was so embarrassed and distraught that she tripped over the feet of some other guest as she stormed her way out of the sanctuary. I'm sure someone else wanted to reprimand us for our behavior, but after that last display nobody had enough guts to try. Soon after she left the crew got bored with the service overall, so we went down to the basement to play some basketball. Upstairs the congregation was clapping their hands and stomping their feet in congruence with Godly praise, while we were downstairs clapping our hands and stomping our feet in congruence with strategic basketball plays. The contradiction between the two was unheard of, but we enjoyed every minute of it!

But what I was beginning to realize about my life so far was that if it gave me joy, sooner or later it would try to even out that joy by giving me some sort of pain, in spite of pain already overwhelmingly outweighing my joy by a ton. Though I loved that church, there was something I hated about it as well. It wasn't the arrogance mixed with a holier than thou aroma that you could easily smell when first entering the premises. It wasn't the hypocritical stares I received from sanctimonious deacons and missionaries from my attire not being as clean or fashionably up to par for their intense Christian standards. It wasn't the condescending tones used during bible workshops or Sunday school class sessions being taught by members who could barely read a newspaper let alone read the ancient spiritual texts of one of the most popular books ever written. No, all of those things I could handle as I had been subjected to far worse things in my lifetime. But it was the attention and consistent care that my mom continually gave in financial contributions to the church's ongoing objectives that sowed a seed of hate deep down in the bowels of my soul. While me and my siblings suffered for adequate food and clean clothes my mom was giving much of her money to offerings, fund raisers and church initiatives that always had no end in sight. When I compared Pastor's family's life to ours, the comparison was obviously unequally yoked! Pastor lived in a beautiful suburban neighborhood while we struggled to survive in the middle of death's valley. Pastor's children always wore nice clothes and shiny shoes while our clothes were just shiny because they needed a good cleaning and our shoes had holes in them, not for cooling purposes. And Pastor drove his family to church in a new Mercedes Benz while we waved at them when passing us by, as their car splashed water on us as we walked the green mile to God's house in the middle of a rainstorm. That's what I truly hated. That feeling of being lower than the lowest of the earth. I hated that feeling and it was following me, tagging along with me everywhere I went. It was like a looming shadow hugging my body from the sun shining steaming rays of poverty on my head with no clouds or trees to block its radioactive glare. That sun was the only thing I hated about that church. And my mom was not making it any easier to love her while she enabled those rays to burn me alive!

The world was not being kind to anyone from my neighborhood and it was on an aggressive long streak. My schoolwork was flawless as usual, but my school life was drowning in the deep end. More and more students were beginning to either be suspended from school for their bad behavior or they were going to juvenile jail for much of the same. Inside school doors I was trying to go unnoticed like a small fly on a wall. I just wanted to do my schoolwork and maintain my college scholarship. To fully receive the

O.S.U. scholarship I had to keep an honor roll average throughout Jr. High & High school. That was the plan and with Grandma's voice in my head I knew I'd be ok. But between His psychopathic physical, mental and emotional abuse at home, my mother's idiotic antics at church and the unfortunate inevitable happenings at school I was in a three way war to keep my sanity at all times. On a positive note I was starting to make some new friends to go with the few I already had. But for the most part I was just trying to stay out of harm's way by any means necessary to literally stay alive. With Manny and Leslie being at the neighboring High school and Reggie moving across town to a different neighborhood and school altogether, once again I was out there alone to fend for myself with no family backup to be found. Kids were starting to die in my neighborhood more often due to the increase of drug and gang related violence that was now taking the city by storm. That's when I met Bobby. Bobby was different from anyone I had met before and we immediately became good friends. He had his own demons to battle each day. Some of his demons I weighed against my own and at times I was grateful to not to have to fight in some of the wars he was battling. Bobby was a very smart kid who loved super hero comic books and fantasy movies. I believed he used them as a way to escape the real life he was living. Before Bobby I didn't even know what a comic book was. I met him one day at breakfast in the cafeteria where he was scientifically focused, rummaging through multiple of his comic books arguing with himself about which super hero could defeat the other. Finally I had met someone who talked to themselves more than I did and with less cautiousness. I was actually impressed.

"Hmmm, I don't know. Archangel got them wings and their so deadly. Them bad boys be shootin' out razor sharp knives and everything. He'd be tough to deal with. But then again Wolverine got them blades that can cut through anything. And on top of that his healing power is insane. So Wolverine would most likely end up kicking Archangel's ass. Yeah, it's final…I'm going with Logan on this one!" Bobby sat across from me having a full blown conversation with himself.

I was looking around but no one else was sitting at the table. Bobby had his head down focused on his collection of comics and because I was the only one siting at the table I just assumed he was talking to me.

"Ummmm, I don't know either of those people but you gone' eat that donut? If not, let me get at that." I pointed towards Bobby's unopened donut just sitting on his breakfast tray.

Every day I'd go around seeing if I could get a few people to give me their donut for breakfast. That was one thing I did like about going to school early. Lunch sucked ass, but breakfast wasn't so bad since I had a sweet tooth anyway. Bobby never looked up from his comics. He just pushed me his donut and continued reading, sometimes aloud and then sometimes to himself. Then out of the blue he looked up and said,

"You really don't know anything about Wolverine? Red Skull? Juggernaut?"

"No. No. And no. Who are they and why should I know them?" I condescendingly asked.

"They're Marvel comic book characters! How do you not know about these dudes?" Bobby slapped himself in the forehead and gave me a look as if I was from outer space. "Gambit? Magneto? Captain America!?!"

He was throwing out names of comic book characters like they were common household names you'd give a newborn baby. I started laughing because I didn't know any of them until he got to Captain America.

"Oh yeah, Captain America. I like Captain America. And Batman. And Wonder Woman's hot as hell. I love her sexy ass!" I thought I was on a roll with the name dropping but Bobby looked at me as if I had said something very insulting. He slapped his head again,

"Batman and Wonder Woman are D.C. not Marvel! I hate D.C. comics. Don't tell me you're a Superman junky?"

I stared laughing even harder. Here this nerdy little kid was sitting across the table from me giving me shit about my ignorance of comic book characters as if I were the odd man out. Yet when I was looking at him he was clearly the odd ball. Then again, maybe he wasn't. Maybe he was on to something. So far my life was being dictated by a psychotic murderer who just 30 years ago had killed His wife in a fit of rage and now was playing stepfather of the year to me, with a mantle of broken trophies to match my broken heart. Maybe I was the odd ball, not Bobby.

"Well, I wouldn't say I'm a junky but I think Superman is pretty cool. I never really took the time to evaluate my liking of any of them because they're make believe. You know, fictional characters? Now that donut you just gave me…that's what I think about because that's real and I'm not going to be hungry now for the rest of the day, so thanks!" I got up from the table because the bell was about to ring for all of us students to get to homeroom. I stuck my fist out for Bobby to pound it in friendship and he agreed.

"No problem man. Hey, if you want to know more about comics meet me here after school and I'll put you on to everything!" Bobby excitedly said while carefully gathering his comics together, but then recklessly throwing his schoolbooks in his backpack. It was so obvious that he cared more about Wolverine than he did about Social Studies. "I'm Bobby by the way."

"And I'm Jesse, Bobby. Nice to meet you."

"Hello Jesse Bobby!" Bobby joked. "Talk to ya' later!"

And that was how it started with me and Bobby. Come to find out later that Bobby lived in Westlake just like me. In fact, when walking home together that day I realized that he only stayed a few units down from me. I wonder *why I had not noticed him before? Was it because he was always inside of his home fighting his own demons? He did have a few of his own to deal with. Or was it because He had cut me off from the world so deep that I never noticed Bobby because I never wanted him or me to have to deal with the aftermath of what friendship with me consisted of?* Having friends at church or at school was one thing, but having a true friend that I could share the burdens of life with in Westlake was an entirely different and too dangerous of a story to entertain. But nonetheless, entertain it I did. My friendship with Bobby grew pret ty quickly. I'd leave my house early every morning just to watch G.I. Joe or other cartoons with Bobby. Bobby's mom was never home and when she was home in my eyes she was barely in good enough condition to be a productive mommy. So Bobby would often have to get his younger siblings ready for school. Then we'd walk to school and talk Marvel comics all the way there. I assumed Bobby's mom had a drug and alcohol addiction, but we never spoke about it. Just like Bobby never spoke about Him beating me or embarrassing me every chance He got. What's understood between good hood friends never has to be said! And what I truly liked about Bobby was that he was the only person that I had met so far that I had to question if I'd ever trade places with and walk a day in the life in his shoes. Some days the answer would be yes. And other days the answer would be absolutely not. There were some demons that Bobby had that I didn't want to fight and others that I had that he didn't want anything to do with either. But together as good friends it seemed a lot easier for both of us to cope as long as we used the other's problems as a way to appreciate our own.

"I seen your monkey ass walking home with that smart ass little boy today! You think you slick don't ya? You think ya' can get over on me huh?" He had His hand around my neck pressing the tip of the knife blade up against my throat while spitting on me from the aggressiveness of His words. I could smell the hint of denture cleaner mixed with barbecue potato chips lingering from His mouth as He hovered over me like a crazed bear. I could tell that today He was on one of His crucifying missions and I was the perfect Jesus for today's persecution. "I told ya to stay away from his crackhead mama and her crackhead son. You ain't bout to bring none of that drug bullshit into this house. You think I's don't know, but I knows you stupid ass nigga! I ought ta' cut your head off right now and throw it right through their got damn window! If I see you and him walkin' home together one more time I'm going to stab holes through both ya'll dumb asses!"

And just as fast as my friendship with Bobby had begun, it had ended. It wasn't a true ending as even today we're still friends. But the childhood friendship was completely over because I couldn't risk Bobby being killed over my liking G.I. Joe or Wolverine. And I knew He was very serious about killing us both. Bobby had his own game of life to win and I surely wasn't going to allow His crazy ass to be the super villain dice that would end up rolling Bobby out. He was my burden, not Bobby's. So for the sake of Bobby's life I just stopped talking to him, cold turkey. I'd leave for school all different types of times never stopping over Bobby's house to pick him up. I stopped sitting with him at breakfast and lunchtime during school, and never waited for him afterwards to walk him home. Every time Bobby would try to talk to me I'd just ignore him. I could tell it was bothering him because he and I both knew he had done nothing wrong to deserve such treatment. But more than it bothered him, it was killing me. And though on the outside no one could tell the difference, on the inside I was slowly turning into something dark. There was something very cold brewing inside my heart, inside my soul. I could feel it festering, but I couldn't stop it from becoming. I couldn't stop me from becoming, this necessary evil just to survive! *I'm sorry Bobby. Till this day I'm truly sorry.*

Chapter 16
Beat Your Face

"Sorry ass numb nuts, it's go time!" Drill Sergeant Moreland's go time voice interrupted my thoughts about Bobby.

Moreland had been all over us since that morning prepping us for a major inspection that his lieutenant had scheduled with us for later that evening. Moreland said it would be one of the biggest inspections we would ever have and failing it could set us back in graduating basic training. None of us wanted any parts of being in basic longer than we had to be especially with Christmas right around the corner. If all went as planned we'd be graduating one week before Santa rode his reindeer into town. *Maybe I could catch a ride with him back home? Then again Santa never visited our house because Santa in the Projects would be a disaster just waiting to happen. Not even the fake Santas would come through Westlake!* Moreland put me in charge of the preparations for the inspection. He gave each of us the same pamphlets to follow to ensure that every locker we had was identical to the next, so his expectation for us was perfection with zero errors. But to make things even more stressful for me in particular he put me in charge of everyone being on the same page. Everyone's lockers had to be identical from the hanging of our BDUs (battle dress uniforms) to the amount of items in our dresser drawers. The shirts had to be right. The boots had to be right. And everything had to resemble what was in the pamphlets with 100% accuracy.

So basically this was an inspection to inspect our ability to do things accurately with extreme attention to detail. We had been through these same types of test for over two months, so you'd think we'd have the shit down by now. But with more than 50 men living under the same roof the task would prove to be more difficult than we could even imagine. And knowing that Drill Sergeant Moreland had probably placed me in charge just to embarrass me when things went awry, I decided to give it everything I had to have us all prepared to pass the inspection with flying colors. Since my battle buddy's and my locker would be the first one to get inspected I told everyone to follow our lead and to make sure that their lockers and belongings inside matched our lockers flawlessly. Avant was my battle buddy for a lot of activities simply because his last name started with the letter A and for many things we were matched up based off of the alphabetical order of our last names. And since my last name was Benson, Avant and I were matched up for plenty of things, this inspection being one of them. I liked Avant. He was this short, stalky, muscular guy with a big heart. Even though he was stronger than most guys in our unit he never exploited that truth. He was just this humble, short giant that only cared about one thing… graduating basic training and being able to walk down the isle in his dress suit uniform in front of his family during the graduation ceremony. That's all he used to talk about. He was so obsessed with graduating in his dress uniform that he'd shine his dress shoes every day even though we never wore them. He would also place his dress shirt and pants underneath his mattress every night in an attempt to pressure iron his clothes with his natural body weight by sleeping on top of them. Since we couldn't use electrical equipment like irons and didn't have ironing boards or steamers, I thought his concept was pretty ingenious.

"How do I look?" Avant proudly asked me knowing that the answer I'd give him today would be no different than the one I gave him just the day before. He was in full dress gear today. His green sailboat hat sat atop his bald head like a frog on a Lilly pad.

"You look like a big, built ass Yoda in a little ass leprechaun suit!" I laughed. "Don't you got a pot of gold to be looking for to help Luke Skywalker out with his fight against the dark side? And better yet, don't you got a locker to be getting ready for this massive inspection? Moreland's going to have our asses in a meat grinder if we fail. He's so nervous about this inspection. I can see the anxiety in his eyebrows!"

"Alright, alright. Don't get your panties all in a bunch. I'll get right back on task right after I shine these dress shoes. Your boy gone' be looking like a million bucks on graduation day. Just you watch and see!" Avant sat down and started shining his already shiny shoes. I was too busy to get into any arguments with Avant about getting ready for inspection because I had to get my own locker ready first. Since everyone else in the platoon was waiting for Avant and I to complete our lockers before they were to complete theirs I decided to get moving on mine. I didn't want to be the reason we failed the inspection. I didn't think Moreland could take much more of our shenanigans. Everything inside of our lockers had to be congruent with each other from the way our clothes were hung all the way down to the spaces in-between them. My plan was for my locker to be perfect and then for Avant's to follow my locker, so forth and so on until everyone's lockers were completely identical. It seemed like a good plan at the time. I looked over at Avant and even he was well into getting things squared away. I started walking around our dorms and everyone was on task. Floors were clean as they could be under the circumstances. Beds were tightly made. And everyone was well into their pamphlets working together to complete their lockers correctly. I stood there proud knowing that within a few hours we'd be having an inspection and most likely passing with flying colors since everyone was participating like expected. Even the area of the kid that tried to commit suicide was looking good.

He was packing things into his locker as well. He saw me looking at him from afar and gave me an "it's all good squad leader" wave of the hand. I smiled back and thought to myself, *good job Bennet...today could actually go as planned with zero hiccups! Maybe now Moreland will get to see that he did the right thing putting you in charge. Maybe now he'll stop calling you Bennet and let you have your original name back? Probably not, but at least you'll get your due respect!*

When she came into our room I hadn't noticed her the way that I should have. I was blown away that there was a woman on our floor since Fort. Knox didn't have any units with females in them for basic training. In fact all we had seen on base for the past few months were men, except for some instructors and the lunch ladies in the mesh hall. A lot of those ladies certainly reminded me of men! But this girl was a good looking lady. She was slightly tall and you could tell she was in great shape even through her BDUs. You could also tell she had long hair by how big she had her bun wrapped in the back. I figured she was majorly lost, probably in the wrong wing of the city and would figure it out sooner or later that she was in an all male basic training unit. I couldn't care less what she was up to anyway. I was completely focused on the task at hand. Moreland had already informed me that the Lieutenant could pop up at any time, unannounced and that I would have to call everyone immediately to attention as soon as the Lieutenant's boots crossed over the threshold of our doorway, no differently than what we did when any Drill Sergeant entered the room. My calling the team to attention would be the start of the inspection. *So I didn't have time to gawk over some lost girl playing soldier dress up, no matter how good she looked. Moreland was expecting greatness and I was here to give it to him.* After standing in the middle of the room for a few seconds and looking confused, as expected I assume the girl realized she was in the wrong place as she just up and left. *Where was Moreland and this Lieutenant?* My patience was wearing thin. We had been working our asses off all morning and now it was late afternoon. Soon we'd be late for dinner and that just wasn't going to fly. The anxiety was killing us all. We were all sitting on the floor next to our bunks because we didn't want to mess up our freshly made beds. Part of the inspection would be how tightly wrapped our bedding was and everyone knew that bedding would be an easy part of the inspection to pass since making our bedding tight was something we had to do every day. Then I saw Moreland standing outside our doorway and he looked pissed. When his feet crossed the threshold I yelled out "Attention!" Everyone hopped to their feet and stood like statues with their hands to their sides and faces front. Moreland walked right over to me. I could feel the intensity in his walk as he stomped over. Each step he took his boot would hit the floor with just enough pressure to clear any misunderstanding that he was or wasn't pissed off. By the time he made it over to me his feet had said a thousand words and they weren't words of endearment.

"What the fuck is wrong with you?" He whispered the words into my ear with enough passion that it felt like he was screaming even though he wasn't. "The fuck, the fuck, the fuck, the fuck, the ffffffffffuck? What the fuck is the reason you exist? You mother fucking Bennet you! You call the team to attention for me, but you don't do the same for my Lieutenant? You don't do the same for someone ranked higher than all of us?" Moreland whipped his head around to motion back to the Lieutenant standing in the doorway behind him. OMG, it was that girl! *What the fuck is wrong with me? The entire time I was expecting a man to come through in his Lieutenant dressed up type uniform for inspection purposes. It never occurred to me that the Lieutenant could actually come in BDUs and it certainly hadn't crossed my mind that he could be a she. Damn that was stupid of me! I never even noticed the silver bar on her collar that was clearly in view now. Oh wow, fuck me!* "We're going to try this again, the right way. And if you fuck it up this time I'm going to take your head and stuff it up my own ass and then take a shit in a lava pit! You feel me?" Moreland whispered and then yelled out "At ease," while walking back out of the room. And that's when I realized that this wasn't going to go as well as I had originally thought considering the start. The Lieutenant stuck her boot back over the threshold of our doorway and I yelled out at the top of my lungs, "Attention!" *Here goes nothing!*

"Private Benson, Bennet…no wait Benson from Youngstown, Ohio…4th Platoon ready for inspection sir… no I mean ma'am!" *Oh no! Did I just call her a sir?!!! Oh fuck. Moreland's going to kill me. This shit is terrible! Fuck me!* I stepped to the side so that the Lieutenant could start her inspection of my locker.

"Youngstown, Ohio huh? Sergeant Moreland aren't you from somewhere over that way?" The Lieutenant said with a smirk on her face indicating to Moreland she understood why things were starting off rocky since him and I may be from the same neighborhood. *Was Moreland from where I was from? Naw…he was too much of an asshole to be from my neck of the woods!*

I quickly glanced over at Moreland to see is he was already losing it and after seeing the expression on his face I immediately placed my eyes toward safer scenery. The Lieutenant was moving her hands through my locker inspecting clothes ensuring that everything was accurate. She had the diagram in her hand and was intensely looking at it to make sure she didn't miss anything. Everything had to be in perfect order. Our shirts had to be hanging on hangers buttoned up to the top button with all buttons facing to the right when hung. When she unbuttoned our shirts our pants had to be hanging on the hanger with the pants legs on the left and the waist band hanging to the right with the zippers facing front. Also the zippers had to be zipped and the pants buttoned. If any of this was not complete, then the inspection in regards to our clothes would be a fail. That's the degree of attention to detail this inspection had.

"So far, so good." She looked at me and gave me a wink that made me think that was an indicator that she was rooting for me. Boy was I wrong! She started feeling around the pockets of one of my coat jackets intensely.

"What's this Private Benson?" She pulled out a folded up piece of paper that was in my pocket and handed it to me. Our pockets were supposed to be empty and I had no idea what the paper could have been. "Is that supposed to be in there?" she asked.

I looked at the paper and realized that it was a layout of instructions that the army recruiter had given me three months ago before I officially joined the service. Since it had to do with the military I figured she'd give me a pass on having it in my pocket. Wrong again!

"Oh this? These are just some instructions that the recruiter gave me months ago to ensure that I got to the airport on time and etc so that I didn't miss out on getting here ma'am." I proudly said with the confidence of someone knowing they're wrong, but trying to be right.

"I didn't ask you any of that Private. I asked you is it supposed to be in your pocket? It's good to know that if you got captured by the enemy at least the enemy would know that you can follow your recruiter's instructions but not your commanding officer's." She arrogantly held my coat up and dropped it on the floor as if I had insulted her with my explanation of why the paper was there.

"Let's see what else is in the wrong place at the wrong time, shall we?" She bent over and started going through my drawers.

All I could think of at that time while staring at her ass was *this girl has a nice figure for a army grunt. I wonder why she's in the military and not on television or in a magazine somewhere. Oh yeah, she's kind of bitchy, that's probably why. Movie producers and magazine execs hate bitchy chicks. Should I tell her about herself? Hahaha, yeah right. Her and Moreland would have my ass for dinner!* That's when I could feel Moreland's eyes beaming at me with the message of "STOP LOOKING AT HER ASS, DUMBASS!" My eyes widened and returned a glare of "Yes sir! Right away sir!"

Just when I thought I was on a roll and the inspection would go through with flying colors, she hit me hard. She questioned everything in great detail about my drawers. She asked me why I had my toothbrush lying on its back in my drawer instead of lying on its side with the bristles facing to the right as the diagram displayed. *Is she serious right now? Who wants their toothbrush lying on its bristles in a dirty drawer that has been shared by whosoever thought year after year?* Just like my coat, if she thought that I had missed something, then she dumped the belongings on the floor in front of me. By the time she got through with my locker half of the items were still hanging up and the other half were all in a pile on the floor in front of my feet. I thought the entire process was disrespectful considering how much work went into getting the locker prepared for the inspection. What took hours to put together she had destroyed in minutes. *What was worse was that if my locker passed on a scale of 50/50, and I was one of the sharper tools in the shed when it came to our platoon, what would be the end result of the entire inspection? I mean, everyone was following my lead and I just flopped. So I could already imagine what was about to happen to everyone else.* Avant was up next so he at least should get a 50/50 split in perfection like me since he was right next to me? Wrong a third time! While we were failing inspection Moreland was pacing back and forth like a rabid dog waiting for the right time to pounce on some roadkill in the middle of a busy highway. He was already over the top and the Lieutenant had only inspected two lockers. We had more than fifty to go and at this rate I knew Moreland wouldn't make it past ten. The intensity was so high you could hear a pin drop. Avant proudly stood to the side as if his locker was going to do so much better in the inspection than mine. His shirts weren't even buttoned up so immediately the Lieutenant started throwing all of his clothes on the floor. She seemed to be having fun with trashing Avant's locker. In fact she was on a roll. By the time she got done with Avant's locker everything was on the floor and it was empty. Then she just carried on to the next set of Privates' lockers behind ours which so happened to be my good buddy Ahmad's. I was so glad not to be standing by him during the inspection because I'm sure if I had been we would have already been getting reprimanded for laughing at the situation, especially since we were all still standing at attention. We could't talk, laugh, smile or move while at attention. This was just the military way. While the Lieutenant was off inspecting Ahmad's locker Moreland stayed with us to show his lack of appreciation of what had occurred thus far. His veins were pulsating out of his neck and I thought *he's turning into the Incredible Hulk! It was as if at any moment he was going to bust out of his clothes and turn inadvisedly green.*

"Oh…you two fuck wads within the span of 5 minutes have literally ruined us! You have fucked up something that I thought was unfuckable! Why your parents birthed you I have no idea but I'm going to try to reverse your births. I'm going to ask your mothers to suck you back up into their vaginas and then I'm going to ask God to rethink his positioning on your existence. I'm going to beg him to allow Mars to be your place of origin instead of here!"

Right when he said that I saw him look down and in front of him on the floor was Avant's dress uniform that he had been sleeping on between his mattress every night to ensure it was pressed with no wrinkles. Earlier when the Lieutenant had threw Avant's suit on the floor I could tell he wanted to immediately pick it up and dust it off. But he couldn't move because that would have been a violation of protocol while standing at attention. I could also tell that every minute it remained on the floor was another minute of hell Avant couldn't bare. Moreland must have recognized the same thing because he just stood there silently staring at Avant's suit. And as soon as he heard the Lieutenant say something was wrong with the next lockers he let out a battle cry and punted Avant's suit out the door and down the hallway. Moreland kicked Avant's suit like he was in the Super Bowl trying to end the game with a winning field goal with no seconds left on the clock. If there was an upright Avant's suit would have split them right down the middle for the game winner, along with his recently shined shoes as both made their way down the dirty hallway we hadn't cleaned. I guess that sufficed Moreland for the time being as he went to join the Lieutenant in the other isle behind us. I turned my head to look at Avant and as expected he was devastated. Here stood this muscular, rhinoceros type build of a man with his chest poked out and his hands to his side, strong in statue, short in height but mighty nonetheless…and there he stood on the verge of collapsing because the suit he had been taking so much good care of since day one of basic training had just been kicked down the hall like an old teddy bear some spoiled child was no longer interested in once some new bigger and brighter toy had arrived. And at first I was ok. I was ok to look at him with compassion and was even inspired to maybe have a consoling conversation with him, after all was said and done that day. But then it happened. I wish it hadn't, but it had. I saw a drop of a tear trying to hang onto his tiny eyelashes for dear life. I watched that tear dangle beneath his eye swelling up second after second until it was entirely too heavy to hold onto any longer. And it just let go. It landed on his cheek like a wannabe olympic diver entering the swimming pool with a crooked spine and a fat boy's summersault. It was bound to make a splash. Another tear leaped out following suit soon after the first. And before I could turn away there was a full stream of them running down his face making a hard right turn into the corner of his tightly drawn lips. I tried to turn away before the image could be burned into my head but it was too late. All I could see now was this little Hercules of a man silently crying over his now dust engulfed suit and the image was too much for my insensitive brain to handle. An air bubble was trying to sneak its way up my throat and out of my mouth but I squeezed it off by holding my breath. I closed my eyes in an attempt to concentrate but that just made matters worse as the image of Avantcules just pounded through my mind. As I thought to myself, *if only Ahmad was up here right now to see this with me instead of having his own stuff thrown on the floor too from a failed inspection, this would be the perfect laugh for us.* And once my mind and breath could hold it no longer the image forced its way out and the laughter pushed itself all the way through my throat up to my nose. It was one of those hysterically long snorts that comes out of your nose in sections when you're desperately trying not to laugh and silence is of the essence. That snort was so loud that even Ahmad knew it was mine and I heard him let one out even though I knew he couldn't have known what I was laughing about, but he had to know it must have been severely funny for it to come out in the form of a snort. *And if Ahmad knew it was me, so did Moreland! Fuck me!*

He came back over to our side of the room like a raging bull with its balls in a clamp, pepper sprayed with crack cocaine! By that time I had gathered myself and was standing back at attention. But Moreland's animation would certainly take me back off course.

"Who did it? Who the fuck has Goliath size bowling ball balls over here, huh? Who thinks this shit is funny, huh? Who thinks we're having fun, that this shit is all fun and games?"

Moreland was furious! No one answered him but I knew everyone knew I was the culprit. We were a tight crew. No one would ever rat out anyone else. It was always an us against them mentality that even Moreland's fear induced tactics couldn't break. But I also knew that if someone didn't fess up soon, Moreland would take his anger out on everyone and that was something I just couldn't allow to take place.

"It was me Drill Sergeant. I'm the one that laughed." I said it timidly hoping that he would have mercy on me. But of course he wouldn't.

"Oh I knew it was you Bennet." Moreland somehow whispered loudly. "I knew it was you even before you knew it was you. I knew it was you before your raggedy ass parents even thought up a you. I knew it was you even before it was a you! Ohhhhhhhhh, but I got a trick for you. I got a trick of a trickster's trick for your incompetent ass. You're with me now Bennet. Ohhhhhh, you're with me for the rest of this inspection. You're going to stand right next to me and every time the Lieutenant finds something wrong with one of these lockers you're going to get down and beat the hell out of your got' damn face!"

"Beat your face" is a military term for "start doing pushups." Drill Sergeants would say it to us all the time as pushups and etc were often used as forms of discipline or punishment. It was one of the ways the military would get its soldiers into great physical condition. And with as many mess ups we had going on there were plenty of "beat your face" directives. I felt good about taking responsibility for my actions but also knew with about 40 + more lockers to inspect, it was going to be a long and painful night for me. I reluctantly followed Moreland and the Lieutenant around like a lost puppy. Each locker had item after item constantly in the wrong position or place. And each time that happened I had to beat my face. It didn't take long for my arms to feel like they weighed a ton. I wanted to cut them off and throw them away, that's how heavy they felt. But like in all stressful situations I always found a way to keep myself amused. So I would mess with Moreland by prematurely getting up from the ground while doing the pushups and stand on the opposite side of his shoulder. When the Lieutenant would find and item wrong Moreland would turn over to his right shoulder to see if I was still doing pushups. I'd of course be recovering standing behind his left shoulder at attention knowing that was not where I was supposed to be. And of course Moreland would become extremely animated, stare at the empty spot on the floor and then turn to his left shoulder and scream, "Didn't I say to get down and beat your stupid looking face Bennet?"

"Yes Drill Sergeant!" I'd reply looking at him as if I didn't understand.

"Then get down and beat your stupid looking face!" Moreland was relentless.

This would go on and on, back and forth for hours. Every time I had to do pushups I would prematurely get off the floor and stand on the opposite shoulder of Moreland's, standing at attention. And every time the Lieutenant would say something was in the wrong place in someone's locker, Moreland would look over the shoulder that I should have been doing pushup behind, stare at an empty space on the floor for about 30 seconds, turn to his other shoulder to see me standing there all dumbfounded and then he'd scream out, "Didn't I say to get down and to beat the hell out of your stupid looking face?!!!"

And I'd reply "Yes Drill Sergeant!"

Finally there was only one more locker that needed to be inspected. The game between Moreland, the Lieutenant and myself would finally be coming to an end and fortunately for me because I was extremely exhausted.

"Just one more to go and we can call it a day. I bet you're happy to hear that huh?" The Lieutenant compassionately said to me giving me a look implying that she was going to give me a break on the last locker.

Moreland gave me a look that implied if this last locker resembled anything close to the others, he wouldn't be giving me no sort of breaks! *And whose locker was it? None other than suicide boy himself!* I thought to myself, *come on man. I'm exhausted here. Please just have your shit on point so that I have an opportunity to keep my arms.*

I like my arms very much and they can't do not one more push up! But then I noticed something that in all of the commotion even the Lieutenant didn't notice. Not only did suicide boy not have his bed made, he didn't have linens on his bed at all. *Oh fuck me! Where the hell is this kid's shit at?*

"Private Timothy Busby from Dickinson, North Dakota…4th Platoon, ready for inspection ma'am." Suicide boy saluted the Lieutenant straighter and more accurately than he had ever done any other time that I'd witnessed him in action. So I began to have a glimmer of hope that may be this time things would go a lot smoother at his lock er than the others. But as soon as he stepped aside and the Lieutenant opened his locker any hope that I had of things going smoother slowly vaporized into thin air like the white smoke of jet planes when they streak across a cloudy sky. As soon as she pulled his locker door open a pillow and blankets along with a severely stuffed duffle bag came tumbling out onto the floor. Nothing was in his locker. No shirts. No pants. No shoes. Nothing. The only remains in his locker were the empty hangers that should have had clothes attached to them. Obviously Timothy had all of his clothes packed tightly in his duffle bag as an indication that he was ready to go home, despite the fact that we still had many weeks of basic training left to complete. *Now this fool could have picked a better, more efficient way to express that he was well ready to go home. He could have wrote Moreland and the other Drills a letter. He could have went to see the Captain and made his request known there. He could have even just went to the bus station and bought himself a one way ticket back to Dickinson, North Dakota. Anything would have been better than allowing his packed bag and bed linens to fall to the feet of a Lieutenant during an inspection with Moreland present.* The Lieutenant quickly covered her mouth with both her hands and hysterically ran out of the room. Moreland whipped his head around to me and before he could utter one word I dropped to the floor with new found life and started beating my face! Moreland ran out after the Lieutenant. I was sure that he had plenty of explaining to do. I was hoping that he would explain himself quickly so that he could come back in and tell me to recover from doing pushups. Until then I would just have to struggle on that cold floor trying to do something like a push up while looking up at Timothy from time to time with total disgust written all over my face. *He needed to know that at that moment I kind of wished he had succeeded at his earlier attempt to end his own life. Better him ending it than me!*

I had to find Moreland and ask him for permission to recover, but I was afraid. Timothy had probably sealed my fate with that last stunt but I had no choice but to find Moreland because I'd rather ask him for permission to recover vs. him coming back and seeing me just lying on the floor doing nothing. It had been at least 30 minutes since both him and the Lieutenant had left the room and I was determined to put this entire debacle behind me, at least for my arms' sake. *Where should I look first? I'll try his office.* Before I could reach Moreland's office I could already hear him and the Lieutenant, but what I heard was not what I expected. I heard extreme laughter and an unexpected amount of joy coming from a room that I had anticipated to be full of reprimanding and grief stricken paraphrasing. I was blown away. We had obviously just failed a major inspection, yet the atmosphere in Moreland's office was one as if we had passed. And with me having to be punished locker after locker with no mercy in the dosage, I was no longer intimidated to interrupt whatever this was in front of me.

"Excuse me Drill Sergeant Moreland, Private Benson requesting permission to recover, sergeant?" I said after giving the door a couple of excuse me knocks.

"Bennet, get yo' tired lookin' ass up in here and let me kick it wit' you for a minute." Drill Sergeant Moreland laughed while the Lieutenant followed suit.

"Yes, come on in here. Please come on in. This should

be a very interesting conversation because that show out there was the funniest thing I have ever witnessed in my entire life. It was so funny I had to cover my mouth and run up out of there just to keep the inspection respectful!" The Lieutenant could barely finish her statement without laughing terribly.

"Shut the door behind you Bennet and have a seat." Moreland laughed.

I was floored. *What was going on here? Was I in trouble? If I was in trouble these sounds of laughter preceding the punishment to be inflicted were new to me. I was used to sounds of anguish and despair being strummed before the lashing at home. Why were these two in such good spirits? Hadn't we miserably failed the most important inspection of the year? Wasn't I the worst squad leader Moreland had ever seen in his entire career?* I was truly confused and had no idea of what to expect next.

"Bennet, I'm going to ask you something but I want you to truly think about your response before answering me. Why are you here? Out of all of the things you could have done with your life...out of all the places you could have gone...why did you decide to join the United States Army? When I think about it and look at the situation it doesn't make sense to me."

The way Moreland was talking I had never heard him speak this way before. He was actually using a normal tone and speaking like a regular human being. The Moreland I knew was not a regular human being. The Moreland I knew and feared was a massive mechanical monster intended to make life for me as hard as it could possibly be without drawing blood. This new Moreland seemed less massive, less ginormous. He seemed regular.

Moreland continued,

"Why are you here? You certainly didn't need to join the Army because you're not that bright and couldn't have went to college. I've seen your test scores and they're through the roof. You're probably smarter than me, Lieutenant Smith and everyone else here. So why are you here? You're athletic. You're the fastest guy on base. You should be on some football field or running in the olympics or something. I seen the picture of the girl you left behind to come here. If I were you I wouldn't have left her behind to join anything for any amount of money, that's how fine that girl is. But you left. Why? You're passionate. People want to follow your lead which makes you a natural born leader. They look up to you. The entire platoon looks up to you. Shit, some things come so easily to you that even I look up to you too! Yet all you do is joke, play around and try your hardest to make people believe that you're the dullest tool in the shed and don't understand a got damn thing at all. But why? Why do you do that? And with so much potential to literally be able to do anything that you set your mind to, why did you set it to come here?"

And for the first time in a long time I was stunned. No one had ever given me an accurate evaluation of myself the way Moreland had just done and that threw me for a loop. *Why was I here? What was I truly trying to accomplish? And what events led to me deciding to join an organization that my religion just flat out forbid? Let me think...*

Chapter 17
a Coward and a Quitter

It never transparently presents itself. Life sneaks up behind you butt naked wearing a pair of cotton soled tennis shoes and a feathered belt with a spiked baseball bat in one hand and some cheap paper towels in the other for clean up. But I was tired of it sneaking up behind me and bashing me against the wall. So I decided to do something about it. I mean, my home life wasn't getting any better. No matter how well or how many times I cleaned up the house the roaches wouldn't leave. In fact one day one crawled in my ear while I was asleep and would have probably reached my brain had it not been making so much noise running around deep in my head. My mom poured some blessed oil down into my ear in hopes of praying the roach out. She had bought the oil off T.V. from some television evangelist who claimed it was miraculously powered by the hands of God. She went into some type of trance like, speaking in anointed tongues type of state and started shaking my head around like it was chicken legs in a bag full of flour. But eventually that roach did just somehow slide right up out of my ear. *Maybe my mom was on to something? Maybe the power of God was somehow injected in that overpriced bottle of blessed oil, transcending from the hands of God himself and into my ear causing the bedeviled beast to rid itself of my head? Maybe mom could pour some of that oil down the throat of my stepfather so that whatever demons lurking in His soul causing Him to hate me so much could slide out of His ass so I could flush them down the toilet never to be seen again? Naw, probably not because not too many months later that same television evangelist that sold my mom the miracle oil came on national television confessing his sins of cheating on his wife with some crackhead prostitutes. How could the power of God be expelled through his adultery stricken hands into a bottle of oil to help little ole me, but yet not be miraculous enough to be used on his penis to prevent him from cheating on the very wife who stood behind him every Sunday on that massive television program?* After that I asked my mom how come the blessed oil was only strong enough to work on house roaches and not church roaches? She got so mad that she put me on punishment for a week. So life at home wasn't getting any better, while life at church continued to be a huge contradiction. Everything morally that the church taught and stood for either was never practiced full heartedly by its members (which for me was so obvious that it hurt their reputation) or never worked at home to help change Him from tormenting us, so I was quickly growing uninterested in the church's political agenda week after week. However, life at school was starting to show some serious progress. My grades were flawless. Intelligent teachers loved me. It was only the rare and stupid ones who hated my guts. My O.S.U. scholarship was well intact. And I had this great idea to try out for the school's Track & Field program. This was going to be my way of not allowing life to sneak upon me to beat me down. This was my way to fight back! I knew He wouldn't allow me to play any sports at school. When I brought applications home for permission to play football and basketball He beat me viciously each time. But the school's Track & Field program was so far under budget and under the radar that you didn't need your parent's permission to join that team. You just needed to have strong legs and I had those. I loved to run. Since my family didn't own a car I often found myself running back and forth everywhere on foot as my only means of transportation. I used to run to different sides of town just to hang out with the few friends that I had. My best friends used to talk about how musty I'd smell from walking way across town just to play with them. I didn't mind any of that because my freedom and their friendship was more important to me than a few good hearted jokes! And because He told me I wasn't allowed to have any friends (and would come up and beat me in front of them any time He caught me with them), it was a lot safer for me to have friends way across town out of His eyes' reach. So the constant running back and forth across the entire city just for leisure purposes became great conditioning for my legs. And since Track & Field uniforms were free and the practices and track meets were the same times as some of my after school learning programs, secretly pulling off being on the track team was becoming an easy thing to do. Or so I thought!

I couldn't believe how well I was doing at track. I was a true asset to the team. The idea in track is to ultimately end up with the most amount of points at the end of the day. The more times you and your teammates rank 1st, 2nd or 3rd in a race, the higher the points you'd receive. Then at the end of the day all points are added together for a grand total. Our school had some really fast runners, but we only had sprinters. Other events like high jump, long jump and long distance running we truly didn't have people to participate in those events. So we'd often lose because we'd get minimal to no points in those areas. But that was before I joined the team. Once I joined we started winning meets because I started running in the long distance races. The long distance events came natural and very easy to me. It was no different than me having to walk two or three miles to the store or the laundry mat. The only difference was I got to run without a ton of clothes in a pillow case on my back or a gallon of milk in my hands. Track was a piece of cake! And I was coming in first place in all my events. At 5 points an event and running a minimum of four events I was bringing in 20 points all by myself. Often the scores in track would end up around 50 60 points so I was contributing to at least a third of the total score rendered every time. I started making new friends from the track team. Everyone was happy I was a part of the group. Every morning at school they would announce our wins over the loud speaker. Before they couldn't announce anything because we barely won any meets. But now our team was being congratulated all the time. The principal would call out the names of the students that won their specific events and everyone in the class would clap and cheer. My name would come out four times and everyone would applaud. It made me feel like a champion. It made me feel proud. It made me feel like I belonged. I finally felt that my life was going in a direction that may end up bringing me joy and peace of mind. Even the teachers that didn't like me started treating me better in class. Students that hadn't spoken to me all school year started waving at me in passing in the hallways or sitting next to me in class and striking up random conversations. I was becoming a popular kid and I fell in love with everything that came with that title. It was all working out until one day I came home from school. We hadn't had a track meet that day and practice was cancelled so I came home early. I knocked on the door because at 12 years old these guys still wouldn't let me have a key to the house (super ridiculous). My mom would usually open the door. I'd come in and just sit down on the couch and pray for a normal end to the evening. But this time He answered the door. As soon as I looked up and seen it was Him it was too late too react. He grabbed me by the neck and started choking me.

"You think you're slick don't cha? Thinks ya can out smart everybody, don't cha?" I could smell the hate coming from His throat.

"No sir!" I had to respond but could barely get the words out because He was choking me up the stairs.

"Yes you do. But you ain't as smart as you think you are. They done hyped your head up. You's going to that college every year. You think you gone be somebody. You's ain't gone be shit bitch!" I could tell He was really upset because He was on a tangent and cursing more than usual. *But what had I done? I was very good at making sure I did the same routine day in and day out so that my life could run as smooth as possible. Let me think...did I take out the garbage that morning? Check. Did I make sure the door was locked when I left for school? Check. Did I go to school? Check. Did I make sure that no one was next to me when I came into my neighborhood so that He wouldn't think I had any friends? Check. I was dumbfounded. What could it be this time? All things are checked off as a success, so what could have Him all up in arms?* He dragged me into my bedroom and opened up my dresser drawer. *What? Did He want to borrow one of my too small shirts or dirty socks? Shit, take em! Anything to get Him the hell out of my face!*

"So you thought I wouldn't find out about this, huh nigga? You thought you could just bring some shit into this house without me finding out about it? Got this shit hid way down at the bottoms of the drawer. But I's checks everything nigga, even the bottoms bitch!" He was laughing at me and holding up my track uniform.

And that's when it all made sense. I had been doing it so cautiously well that I had forgot that it was even something that I had to be worried about. *The gig was up. The Monster had realized that I was on the track team. This was not going to go down well.* I tried to reach out and grab the uniform out of His hand but it was too late. He just pushed me to the floor and started ripping my track jersey in half. The shorts were too thick for Him to rip so He took out one of His knives and shredded my shorts into tiny pieces. He was so excited to destroy my uniform that His eyes were shinning. This may have been the happiest that I had ever seen Him. I just sat there on the floor looking up at Him with hate. Starring at Him with the passion of someone ready to rise up and revolt against their oppressor. He must have noticed hope rising up in me because He very quickly grabbed an extension cord and started beating me. He beat me to where I had to turn my backside to Him to protect my face. I couldn't go to school with welts all over my face. That would be too embarrassing. So my back and my legs had to be sacrificed for the greater good. And sacrificed they were. He wouldn't let up. At first I was crying but then after awhile I just lay there, still…emotionless. Once He realized that He had beat all hope of rebellion out of me, He stopped.

"Every time you come home late from that damn school for anything other than schoolwork, that's your ass little nigga! I will beat the disobedience out of you for the Bible says to honor thy father and mother so that your days are long upon the earth. I will ensure that your days are short for disobeying me boy! Now try me bitch!" He threw the ragged uniform on top of me as in a final insult to my manhood. My back and legs were on fire. But there was a larger pain than the beating brewing inside of me. My heart was in shambles. My mind was in a state of undeniable confusion. And my soul was penniless, poorly broken down from a rising river to a drizzled stream. Just when I thought I was getting a portion of my life to resemble something normal and long ago remembered, He once again stepped in and cut it off. Strangling all hope of me becoming a productive young human being. I was back to being a hopeless, shamed animal. I fell asleep in the same spot that I had been beat in that night.

The next day in school everything was back to normal. I had went through my day no differently than any other until we got to gym class. I usually always participated in gym but today I would not because I couldn't take the risk of getting dressed in the locker room and everyone seeing the welts and bruises on my body from the beating I took last night. After school I had a choice to make. I could either go to track practice and take a beating when I got home or just go home and most likely avoid a beating. I went with option A and decided that I would no longer allow Him to dictate my life. I went to track practice and took the long way home afterwards. When I got home, He beat me. The next day I went to track practice again. When I got home He beat me so bad that I wished I hadn't went to practice. This went on for weeks and each time I went to practice the beatings got worse and worse. But there was a reason why I needed to practice. We were getting to the end of the season and we had one meet left that would determine if we could go to the state championship. Our school hadn't been to the state championship for track for almost 30 years, so this was kind of a big deal. We were not only destined to go to state this year, we were favored to win it. We were a sure bet to win the city competition which would be our entry into the state competition. It was the talk of the entire school because we hadn't went to state for football or basketball. This was the school's last chance to go to the state finals. All day long in school students and teachers were coming up to me wishing me luck as the city finals were to be later that evening. But for some reason that day all of the hoopla about winning city and going to state just angered me. I got so angry throughout the day that I went to the coach after school and quit the team. He begged and pleaded for me to reconsider since the city finals were that same day. He encouraged me to just stay on the team until after we won city and then I could quit. But I told him no. *First of all I didn't even have a uniform. Second of all I couldn't be riding the bus or running around the track field with bruises and blisters all over my body for everyone to see. How would I explain to them what was going on? Would they even care? Would they just make fun of me and push me even lower down the popularity totem pole? I probably couldn't explain it. They probably wouldn't care anyway. And I certainly couldn't afford to go any lower down the popularity pole less I'd end up like Sebastian in the Little Mermaid...under the sea!* So I stood firm by my decision to quit the team that day. I just couldn't take another beating as the next one I thought could be my last. After school I had to walk past the bus that was taking the track team to the city meet.

Teachers and students were outside wishing the team good luck. I tried to slide past unnoticed but the coach saw me and yelled out,

"Jesse, come on son. Don't quit on us now Jesse. We need you on this bus. The team needs you. The school needs you. We can win this thing today! We can't do it without you. The points just won't add up if you're not there!"

Before long teachers and students had joined in on the coach's chant to try to convince me to get on the bus. I had worked so hard to gain the respect and approval of my peers, especially the ones on that bus that each step I took to get away was getting heavier and heavier. It was like my shoes were made of cement. I turned one last time to look at what I was leaving behind. The battle between whether I should just keep walking or turn around and get on that bus was at a deadlock. But then one of the jocks on the bus yelled out the window "Ahhh, fuck him. We can win without him! Let's just go already!" And that was that. I turned around and kept walking. Students started booing. I think even some teachers booed. This made me pick up my pace and before I knew it I was in a full blown sprint home. When I got to the house He was waiting for me. I smiled because I knew I had did what He wanted and was expecting Him to at least hug me and congratulate me on being obedient. But instead He seemed disappointed to not have a reason to whoop my ass again. He simply turned away and went to His room. My mom told me I did the right thing listening to my father. *But He wasn't my father. And deep down inside it didn't feel like I had done the right thing. In fact I felt like a coward and a quitter. And in the neighborhood I'm from what I had done was considered a bitch move. I felt like a bitch. In fact, that's what I am, a bitch! I could have taken one or two more beatings, couldn't I? Of course I could have. I had been taking them my entire life! Why was it such a big deal now not to take one? Ah man...I had made the wrong choice and it was too late to reverse. And what the fuck would be in store for me tomorrow?* I just went to my room and cried myself to sleep.

And as expected the next day at school was a nightmare. We didn't win the city track meet. In fact we had lost by only 10 points. With the four events I normally ran in we would have easily gotten those 10 points with another 10 more on top of that to spare. The announcements that day congratulated the athletes that won their events on having a great season. Someone in homeroom yelled out,

"If someone would have just ran yesterday we would be going to state right now!"

Everyone knew she was referring to me and everyone knew she was right. Even I knew that! At that time nobody in the entire school liked me. The students shunned me that week. The friends I had made on the track team all abandoned their friendships with me. The teachers that hated me went back to acting like they hated me. Even the teachers that loved me told me they were disappointed in my decision to quit the team the day of the city meet. One of my teachers that was going through a divorce said that my actions were those of typical male behavior, alway prematurely quitting something that they've previously committed to. The track coach filed a citation on me with the school complaining that I never turned in my track uniform. The school informed me that if I didn't return the uniform they'd hold me back from graduating to the next grade level at the end of the year. One kid spit on me in the hallway for making us lose the city meet. Even He wouldn't spit on me when beating me so I certainly wasn't going to allow some punk ass bully to do it to me at school. So we fought and I got suspended, which also got me another beating at home. *What the fuck is my life right now?*

I thought that everything bad happening was because of me quitting the track team, but it wasn't. People soon forgot about the entire track incident but things in general weren't getting better, they were getting worse.   The drug game was at an all time high in my neighborhood. Crack cocaine was a huge success. A lot of people started smoking it. A lot of kids started selling it. And a lot of us started dying over it. I started seeing Manny hanging out on the street corners with some of the older guys. They never asked me to hang out with them but they'd always ask me,

"Hey, ain't you Crazy Joe's kid?" *Great! Now He has a neighborhood name. I didn't even have one of those. Or maybe I did, "Crazy Joe's kid?" Fuck me!*

One day I came home from school and there was police caution tape all over the parking lot near my house. There was blood all over the ground and chalk drawn around where the crime occurred. The police detectives were there making their assessments of the situation while neighborhood spectators either gawked or cried in disbelief. The paramedics already had the dead body on the stretcher getting ready to put it in the ambulance. Somebody had gotten shot. It was probably over drugs, money or both. *But who was it this time?* Shootings were beginning to be very popular in my neighborhood. I'd hear gunshots nearly every day. Someone would end up receiving those gun shots at least every week. And somebody would die from them it seemed every month. He was standing on our porch clapping like He had just heard the last of a wonderful performance at the opera and was requesting an encore. Someone in the neighborhood yelled out,

"Go back in the house Crazy Joe! What the fuck nigga?"

I was happy someone was saying what I was already thinking. He just laughed and clapped louder. I ran over to the paramedics just in time to see who they had on the stretcher. Whoever it was he was certainly dead by the amount of blood on the ground. And when I saw who it was I was blown away. *Oh my God...it was Tori! The same boy who had pulled the gun out on me when we were just tiny kids was now dead on a bed.* Someone had shot him multiple times. Tori had kept his word by me. He had looked out for me plenty of times in the Projects when he was around. He always would wave at me from the corner when he saw me or say "what's up" to me when passing by. We were far from being best friends, however I knew that if he ever saw me in trouble anytime he'd be quick to lend me a helping hand, even if that hand would most likely have a gun in it. And now that hand wouldn't have anything in it because it was dead. Tori was only 14 years old. But he wasn't alone. There were plenty of others, some younger some older who would acquire the same fate. One of my friends in school received a 25 years to life prison sentence for killing a guy over a drug deal gone bad. He had just hit me in the head with a basketball a few days before so at first I thought, *good riddens.* But after about a week I was pretty sad that he had got caught up that way. Manny was also getting into a lot of trouble all the time. He was in juvenile jail for skipping school and selling drugs too. It seemed like the world was getting smaller and smaller. *But why couldn't my immediate world get smaller?* I would go into our living room closet each day for hours and pray that the next dead body popping up would be His. I would beg God for hours to strike Him down with a lightening bolt and end His life. If God didn't want to do that he could just erase His memory so that He couldn't find His way back home from wherever He was. Sometimes He'd be gone for days and I'd think that God had finally answered my prayers. Nope, He'd always return about day six or seven just in time to hurt me some more.

a Wheelbarrow to Heaven

Life to me was like a private portrait hanging on the walls of the cellar of some abandoned warehouse anticipating a long awaited demolition that was never to come. There it was frozen, unchanging and only visible to those brave enough to venture down there to see it. It was like I wasn't even a part of my own existence. I was just watching it all take place from outside the frame without any say so in what the poses or lighting would be. Shadows looming over my crooked body seemed normal even though I knew better than that. The only light in the background was Grandma who I knew was watching over me directing my every move, my every play. King me Grandma! This man is trying to wipe me out and take all the pieces of joy that I have. And I'm not sure how much more of this game I can withstand, so king me! She would not let me down. I could feel her in my soul. I could hear her in my mind. I could see her in my heart and she stood strong there. And so I pressed on. I was getting older. Wiser. Smarter. But I was also getting restless. *When would I get to live the life that I knew I was meant to live? Where would my revolution come from?* It couldn't come from the church as it was too busy sucking us dry financially. In fact, mama cared more about supporting the church's building fund than she cared about paying rent. She cared about tithes and Pastor anniversary donations more than she cared about clothing her own kids or putting food on the table. I was a freshman in high school now and this was going to be a rough year.

The gang violence in the schools and neighborhoods was at an all time high. People were getting killed every other day it seemed. And you'd be hard pressed to find anyone around us happy for more than a day or two. All I knew was that I needed to be focused to ensure that I kept my scholarship to O.S.U. Having poor grades would certainly make me lose it and losing that scholarship would be suicide! I couldn't see any other way of getting out of this rat trap without going to college and getting out was a matter of life and death. My life was being broken down into three distinct pieces home, church and school.

My home life was detrimentally silent and lonely. I didn't truly have any friends at home. I just had understanding constituents, partners that understood what living in the Projects meant and poor people simply going through some of the same bullshit I was. This was more of an understanding by association type of community than anything else. The Projects had a life of its own. It breathed deeply and aggressively. It was still when it wanted to be still and it moved whenever it wanted to move. And we the people were its soul and heartbeat. But we weren't in control of anything so someone else was the brain. The brain was far off somewhere on the outside looking in. And it didn't mind what was going on with its body. It didn't care if we were struggling and dying each day. And we all knew that, yet we couldn't do a damn thing about it. And that's what broke the Project's heart. That's what drowned the Project's soul. The homeless shelter was at an all time high of temporary residents. People's apartments were being broken into so someone always had to be home to stand as a human guard dog to watch over the little property they did own. Drugs were pumping through the Projects no differently than drinking water. The street corners were full of young motivated thugs just waiting for their chance to make a quick buck or become the next big thing talked about at the kitchen table of neighborhood gossip. And bullets flew. They flew like crazed pigeons. And where they landed had no guaranteed predestination.

Funerals were often. Graduations were few. And the future was about as bright as all the busted taillights in the parking lot. However, there was a small glimpse of hope dangling in redemption's wind and that was the hope that we'd soon be moving out of the Projects. Mama kept talking about this city program called Section 8 which was supposed to help us get out of the Housing Projects and into our own home. She kept saying that we'd end up in some nice neighborhood where we wouldn't have to worry about crackheads and wino legends.She said that we were moving on up the waiting list and that any day we should get word on where we'd be going. *Yeah, ok. We've been on that list for over ten years now. They couldn't still be counting down on a ten year list. I mean, by now someone had to have lost count of our place on that dusty ass list right?* But I'd just smile at her and raise my black fist into the air and quote Jesse Jackson's "keep hope alive" spiel. In the meantime I'd be trying to figure out how not to get killed when inside or outside the house. He was on the inside terrorizing us day in and day out, business as usual. I was becoming truly numb to it all. What could one expect after being haunted over and over for almost a decade. The first few years when you hear the spooky moans and groans you run from the ghosts and hide under your bedding sheets. But after awhile you stop running all together and beg those mother fuckers just to come out and fucking kill you already! That's where I was beginning to be with Him. I became immune to the beatings since I was getting them every night. I was being beat now for screaming in my sleep. I couldn't control it and didn't even know I was screaming at all until I would be awaken out of my sleep to a whip being cracked against my back. And I could never remember the nightmares I'd be having which would make me question if I was actually screaming in my sleep at all. For all I knew He could have just been making the en tire shit up just to give Himself justification for wanting to come in my bedroom and beat my ass. Lijah and I shared a bunkbed and sometimes he'd roll out of the bed in his sleep and crash to the floor. Those would be the times that He'd beat Lijah's ass for making noise so late in the night. *Lijah had the top bunk so you'd think someone would be more concerned if he had rolled out the bed and hurt himself from the fall to the ground, but nope.* He was crashing to the floor and getting beat so often that I decided to switch bunks with him. I felt if I hadn't either the fall would have killed him or He would!

"Praise God. Turn your bibles to Matthew Chapter 4 verse 7 and it reads: But he answered and said, It is written, Man shall not live by bread alone, but by every word that proceedeth out of the mouth of God. 5Then the devil taketh him up into the holy city, and setteth him on a pinnacle of the temple, 6And saith unto him, If thou be the Son of God, cast thyself down: for it is written, He shall give his angels charge concerning thee: and in their hands they shall bear thee up, lest at any time thou dash thy foot against a stone. 7Jesus said unto him, It is written again, Thou shalt not tempt the Lord thy God. 8Again, the devil taketh him up into an exceeding high mountain, and sheweth him all the kingdoms of the world, and the glory of them; 9And saith unto him, All these things will I give thee, if thou wilt fall down and worship me. 10Then saith Jesus unto him, Get thee hence, Satan: for it is written, Thou shalt worship the Lord thy God, and him only shalt thou serve." Pastor read from the good book with such conviction in his voice. I loved to hear him speak. His ability to hold the attention of the crowd was second to none, maybe not even to Jesus himself! He continued with his sermon,

"You see, even the devil knows the word of God and he knows it even better than you and I. He's smart. He's cunning. He's conniving. He'll speak truth to you while still being the father of all lies! If he had the audacity to tempt Jesus to go against the will of his own father, what in the world would you expect him to do to you and I to get us to go against the almighty?" And as usual in unison half the congregation yelled out "Amen! Preach Pastor!" And while all of this was going on all I could think of was *I wish they would quit interrupting his speech with this chant of amen all the got damn time. Maybe if they wouldn't yell it out so often church service would end at a decent hour. I bet if you subtracted out all of the amens and preach it pastors from these presentations church services would end at least an hour earlier. Who was the first person to say amen during a church speech anyway? Whosoever that was we should have banned them from all church services for life! I bet you the multitude that followed Jesus everywhere wasn't interrupting his speeches with amens and hallelujahs every five seconds. If they would have done that there would have been a lot more than three people being crucified that great day Jesus took an L, I bet you that. I wish they would just get to the announcements already because I'd really like to know if Missionary Talley's famous chocolate chip cookies are being sold after church? I ain't got no money but knowing her she'd probably give me some cookies for free today because I was the only one paying attention and got some answers right earlier this morning in Sunday school. But then again she might not even remember that because it happened five hours ago! Why church ain't got no recess anyway like in elementary school? Don't they know somebody about to catch a leg cramp sitting here like this so long? And why these church benches so close together anyway? Man they got less leg room in this sanctuary than they got on the city bus. But bus fair way cheaper than these church dues. My family is going to have to ask this bus driver to let us off this mother fucker until they come up with some bus passes you can get on lay a-way. Fuck it, this is my stop right here Pastor...let me off this bitch, got damn it! This church is on Elm Street too and this is just like the movie Nightmare on Elm Street. That can't be no coincidence! If they ain't have all of this colored glass stained up on all the windows in here somebody could open a window in this mother fucker. The way Pastor talk about how hot it is in hell I can assume it ain't as hot in here as that, but we certainly giving them mother fuckers down there a run for their money. Turn the A.C. up in this bitch! We done took about ten offerings today alone and you mean to tell me ain't none of those offerings going toward the air conditioning up in here? Deacon Tony's S Curl is starting to drip all over the floor. The next person to holy dance over there by Deacon Tony might just slip and break an ankle. Somebody better put a "Caution Wet Floor" sign up over there before we get sued. But whosoever sue us is going to hell cause they know they can't be suing no baby Jesus. You cannot be gettin' no workman's comp from the Lord got damn it! And why the Pastor and that dude sitting next to him the only two people in this entire room that get juice brought to them in that pulpit? I'm sitting here more parched than a bitch. I know Sister Johnson's always amening ass has got to be thirstier than a mother fucker in here. Pastor, give Sister Johnson a small swig of your orange juice before she be done passed out in this bitch please. Lord knows if she do pass out you all will be throwing one of those big ass bed sheets around her body to cover her already head to toe covered up ass, which probably contributes to her passing out every service anyway. Knowing ya'll don't need no blanket to cover her up because she already in a full blown Pilgrim dress as it is, looking like a foot soldier from the movie Glory! Please let her have some of that anointed orange juice for Christ's sake. Shit, I'd become a super minister tomorrow if ya'll would just promise me I'd get first dibs on that orange juice every Sunday, Amen? And why everybody in here waiving these tired ass church fans with the "I wish these were the members at our church" looking ass mother fuckers on the fronts of them? As if them shits is really working right now in this hell hole! All them fans is doing is pushing around hot ass sinner breath mixed with fake ass Mary Kay cologne these dudes done picked up at the flee market and sprayed on their sweaty ass balls before coming to church today. And the models they use on the fronts of them fans certainly don't go to our church. They are too damn good looking to be members of Freddy Krueger's Temple. All ya'll doing is getting these old ass deacons' hopes all up for something that ain't never bout to walk through them raggedy ass doors. Besides ya'll don't want none of those she devils in here anyway cause I swear I just saw two of them fan models on a new rap music video that came out on B.E.T. These chicks all in their bathing suites shaking what baby Jesus gave em' for Tupac Shakur! But I guess that's really no different than what some of these chicks in here shaking for these wanna be Tupac baby Jesus thugs. Is they selling them chicken wings after church or what? That's all a brother wanna know! And please father God forgive me for saying the words balls, ass, shit and mother fucker in my mind because I heard that the bible says what's in your mind is also in your heart and Lord knows my heart ain't got no bullshit in it. And now I'm sorry for thinking the word bullshit. Shit! Damn! Sorry baby Jesus! And sorry to you too Tupac!*

Just when I thought the day couldn't get any more interesting than the thoughts pounding through my mind about the service coming to a close, here comes my mom walking down the middle of the church isle with some type of wheelbarrow in hand. Today was the Pastor's anniversary church service so all kinds of interesting things could happen on that day. The pastor's anniversary would come around once a year. A lot of churches will do this from time to time. We would invite all kinds of visiting churches and guests to our church once a year to celebrate the anniversary of the church becoming a church or the pastors being married to their wives as leaders of the church (I could never remember which one it actually was). This would be a week long event that would have the ending season finale happen on that following Sunday. Each day there would be different guest speakers and seminars throughout the entire week. Different churches would come and celebrate God delivering their perspectives on why as humans we were on this planet and what our purpose for existence actually was. There would be singing and dancing each and every service all in the name of Jesus. But most importantly every single day these churches would participate in offering ceremonies where all the funds raised would go to the Pastor and his family's pockets. The entire event was pretty nostalgic. It was one of the most exciting times of the year for our church. My crew and I liked it a lot because we would get to hit on all the visiting churches' girls when they'd come to visit. It would be like playing baseball and the idea was to see which one of us would get to run all the bases before the game was over. First base would be getting a girl just to entertain you talking with her for longer than five minutes for you to get her phone number to give her a call at a later time. Second base would be somehow getting that girl to kiss you before anniversary was over. Third base would be for you to get to squeeze that girl's ass and/or breast while kissing her. And fourth base would ultimately be if you could go all the way and have sex with the girl before she left. None of us would ever get to fourth base but plenty of us would eventually get to third, which was certainly fine by me! So you can imagine something completely weird would have to be happening to draw my attention away from the ultimate task of being the first moron to get to fourth base with one of the visitors. *And my mom sashaying down the isle in her on sale at The Goodwill, baby blue, snapping tortoise neck, they'll never make me a missionary or mother of this damn church, tweed ass donkey sweater was just enough nonsense to get my full blown attention. What the hell was she up to anyway? She need to sit her dumb ass down right now before my crew have added ammunition to start shooting joke slugs at me with. It's not like they already didn't have enough material as it was. She's about to make it hard for a church pimp like me out here! And what the fuck is in that damn wheelbarrow? Sorry about the mind cussing baby Jesus!*

I couldn't tell what was in there yet but I knew it couldn't have been anything sensible. Wheelbarrows belong in the field, not rolling down the isle of the church. When she made it to the front of the sanctuary you could hear a pin drop in that place. I wasn't the only one anxious to solve this mystery. That's when Missionary Clark stood up and walked over to the podium.

"Oh what a friend we have in Jesus." She said motioning over to my mom who quickly decided to leave the barrow where it was and took a seat.

"God is good isn't he saints?" Missionary Clark sang out.

"All the time." The congregation replied.

"And all the time God is good." She continued.

"I'm so excited about what Sister Jackson has indulged us with this afternoon." *This afternoon? It's about to be 4:00pm and where I'm from that's right on the verge of being considered evening time. I know I'm not in here missing the football game over some misplaced wheelbarrow that my mom accidentally rolled down the isle. Crucify this chick already!*

"She is such a good and faithful servant. God has certainly blessed us with her joining our church family. Amen. And God is certainly going to bless her thirty fold for her contribution here today." Missionary Clark removed a cloth covering the top of the wheelbarrow revealing something that had eluded my family for years…money!

This wasn't just any type of money either. These were mainly silver and gold coins and there were so many of them that you could tell the barrow was quite lucrative. Everyone's mouths gasped in awe of the spectacle.

"This is for you Pastor. God has moved Sister Jackson to bless you and your family on this wonderful anniversary. Isn't he a glorious and magnificent God? He may not come when you want him but he's always right on time, isn't he saints?" Missionary Clark continued singing the praises of my mother's generous contribution while the congregation clapped and cheered with glee.

What the fuck is going on here? This bitch is crazy.

I mean, I love her but has she lost her got damn mind? Last Christmas I thought she had went into bizarre heaven when she got all the missionaries, mothers, deacons and ministers of the church Christmas gifts. It wasn't the fact that she got them gifts that made me angry. It was the fact that my mom literally got us nothing for Christmas that same year. In fact, she hadn't gotten us anything for Christmas, birthdays or any other holiday since that time. *So why in the world would she get the wanna be Jesus freaks gifts and not her own flesh and blood? Most of the Jesus freaks didn't even like us. We had to walk to church often because we didn't own a vehicle. Some people were kind enough to pick us up for church, but most of them didn't want to come to the Projects. That was too big of a risk for them. Besides our house smelled like roach shit anyway so who'd want that riding around in the backseat of their beatdown station wagon? I understood completely. They only needed to be Christ like when it smelled convenient. Even Jesus wouldn't have picked our dirty asses up on the way to Damascus. Or would he? Hmmmmmm.* The amount of money in the wheelbarrow had to be more than a few thousand dollars. This was beginning to be an epidemic. My mom was starting a trend of providing for her church family instead of providing for her real family. *And where in the world was she getting all this money from? Was she really trying to buy her way to heaven? And if so, was she spending enough money for all of us to get through those pearly gates or was this just enough for her to have VIP tickets and for me to stand outside trying to figure out how to sneak in backstage?* In any case, this was some pure bullshit!

Speaking of bullshit, school was killing me now. I couldn't make it through most days without being ridiculed by some asshole trying to make a name for himself. Manny couldn't protect me because he was in and out of juvenile jail so much that I hadn't seen him at school or in the Projects. I would visit Aunt Lorene and Leslie at their house just to sneak into his room and steal some of his school clothes. Without his hand me downs the torture by the students would have been every day instead of every other day. Leslie was out of high school as she graduated on time. Manny on the other hand was way behind and now officially in the same grade as me. I was happy about his failure because I missed him a lot. I needed him to be in the same grade as me because I wasn't sure if I could make it through high school without him. But so far I was making it without him because he wasn't there. Manny had this nice, thin, Miami Hurricanes college football team, Starter trench coat that was really cool. I of course borrowed it (without permission). Starter coats were the most popular coats at the time. They were rather expensive and where I'm from the more expensive your clothes, the more popularity you received. People just treated you better when they knew your apparel cost more than theirs. I really didn't have enough clothes to wear to school so I had to improvise. Our school didn't care about dress codes and such, so I'd wear that Hurricanes coat all day, every day just to hide the clothes I had underneath. Then I decided to start wearing it as a coat one day and then tuck it into my pants as a shirt the following day. It took a few weeks before students caught on, but when they did the gig was up! The ridicule from the students was getting so extreme that I had to start walking home from school alone as much as possible just to avoid getting into fights with jokesters. And with a 45 minute hike back and forth to school every day the school year was becoming volatile to my existence. I was seriously starting to contemplate getting into the drug game. Manny had already started his dabble into that life which was how he was getting all of his nice wears, in spite of his mom working full time to buy his clothes anyway. *How come his mom was a hard worker and my mom was a prayer junkie when they both are sisters and grew up in the same household? How do those apples fall on completely different sides of the common sense tree?* Just when I thought I could take no more judgmental punishment from my high school skeptics, resulting in me having to resort to drug hustling, a solution to my problems popped up one morning during English class. A group of older students from the janitorial team was going from class to class passing out flyers for people to come and apply to get a before and after school job working for the school's janitorial staff. The job would pay about $5.25 an hour and you'd get to work about 20 hours per week. They only needed to fill one position and the older students that came around to promote the job looked like some cool guys. They didn't have on dirty clothes like me and the way they talked about working for the school made me instantly want to apply for the job. So that's exactly what I did. Later that week my interview for the job was at 7:30am in the morning with the head janitor. I got to the school at 6:00am and patiently waited outside the janitor's door until it was my turn to interview. I was the first interview of the day. Once the head janitor realized that I had showed up to the interview an hour and a half earlier than scheduled, he didn't interview me or anyone else. He said in all his time of working there no kid has ever come to the job an hour and a half earlier than scheduled so he was giving me the job for being overly impressive with enthusiasm and promptness alone. I gladly accepted the position. I figured if I currently had zero dollars to my name and now had a chance to make about $100.00 a week, that was the chance of a lifetime for me. *Basically someone was going to pay me money to work, which would take hours out of my life daily from being at home with Him. All the while allowing me to save up some money so that I could go out and buy my own clothes and occasionally pay for my own meals, instead of me having to resort to selling drugs and looking over my back every minute so that none of these asshole, fake ass cops or enthusiastic wannabe thugs tries to put me behind bars or worse blow my brains out over a few crack rocks. Hmmmmm? This seemed like a no brainer for me.* Besides, He certainly wasn't going to allow me to get into the dope game without a huge fight. Manny wasn't going to allow me to get into the dope game with him yet either. I had already asked him and he said, "Nigga' you ain't hard enough to sell breast milk to a starving baby monkey, let alone get up in these streets with me. Stay yo' smart, Albert Einstein Project looking ass in those text books and don't lose that scholarship you got and leave this street shit up to me. This shit I'm doing ain't real. You got that real shit all up in that nerdy ass head of yours. Use that shit and figure out how to get the both of us out of this bullshit we in!" So for the meantime it was going to have to be little janitor boy for me. And since being a janitor was giving me more opportunities financially than anything else ever had, I was cool with that!

Life can sometimes hover above our heads like clear blues skies on a bright summer day. But just like weather life is unpredictable and in an instant those same blue skies can become completely dark bringing all sorts of chaos and destruction along with them. Sometimes a rain coat and umbrella will do the trick. But there are plenty of times when no matter what you're wearing or how prepared you think you are, what you end up encountering overwhelms you and worse things happen than wet hair with some drenched clothes! My mom was in good spirits. Section 8 had came through and we indeed would be moving into a new home across town. The new house was in a way better area than ours. We'd be moving out of the Projects and into a real neighborhood with mailboxes in the front yards and picket fences in the back. Wow! This would be the first time we wouldn't have to share walls with neighboring apartments. In fact, we'd have our own porch and garage even though we wouldn't have a car to park into it. We'd have both Black and White neighbors (which I didn't even know neighborhoods existed where both races occupied the same streets), Hispanics and Asians all coexisting in the same radius reminding me of the Gifted Program I used to attend. I couldn't wait to get out of Westlake. The Projects were cool and all but they were also dangerous. I was fortunate to had made it this long without major injury. Many of my peers hadn't been so fortunate and were already dead. There was a significant amount of children that had died before reaching their teens and that bothered me inside. *Why them and not me? I mean there were plenty of times I wished I were dead. Why'd they get to exit so early while I just seemed to inevitably wait for what I knew was a sure thing, death by default based off of location? Why God? Why am I still here? And certainly why is He still here? Based off of your good book, these hypocrites keep misunderstanding that He most possibly can't have a good purpose for still being around. Isn't Mother Earth ready to shit Him out and flush Him down the karma toilet yet? Just pinch Him off already, wipe the slate clean and flush Him down so that I can rise up please! I am having the faith of a mustard seed like last week's Sunday school lesson so when I open my eyes, presto He should be gone. Damn! Nope, He's still here and what a continued disappointment to my faith. What's the difference between me and King David anyway? God used David to kill a giant with just a slingshot so I'm sure God could use me to do the same. But I hadn't had the confidence or enough faith to try so there went that theory!*

"I want ya'lls ta' goes upstairs and packs yas' thangs all up. I's gots the good Minister Snipes comings over wit' da trucks to picks us up and takes us to the new house." Mama was so excited to finally be able to say those words.

Her voice travelled with the confidence of someone who normally fails but finally came through on one of the most important things in our life at the time. She was proud to be moving into a new home and every word she'd say for the next few weeks would have tinkle bells of happiness and flutters of glee surrounding them. They were quickly getting on my nerves and had only just begun.

"Yeah, and hurry ya'll dumbasses up too before I have to take out my knife and skin one of you monkeys before the good minister Snipes gets here. And if he has anything to say abouts' it, his praying ass can get this blade too. I'll skin the curly little hairs off his chinnie' chin chin no different

than any other of these weak negros running around here!"
The conviction in His voice no different saying this than
Him saying pass the salt, so He certainly believed in His
own shit!

I just ignored Him as if He wasn't even there. I knew
He hated when I did that more than anything. But I was
no longer that small nine year old kid He could grab by
the neck and slap around anymore. I was in high school
now, a young man mixing it up with new age gangsters and
distinguished young gentlemen so the tactics used on me
to discourage and implant fear were no longer viable and
couldn't be sustained. And even though I had not yet tested
my new found mental and physical strength on Him, real
recognizes real and He knew His time of terrorizing me was
quickly starting to diminish. Lijah and Halia ran upstairs
immediately to obey His command while I just stretched
my arms out and yawned in obvious disobedience. He
stared at me from afar and started reaching towards His
back pocket. *We all know what's in that back pocket and if
He reaches for one of those knives this time and comes for
me we're going to finally get to see if He is who He has
been saying He is my entire life.* And even though my life
was going so much better with my new job and all, I was
still ready to go at any minute. I was ready to die. Before
when I was younger I was afraid to die because I thought I
had something to live for. But over the years He had ruined
my desire to live, my desire to try and get to the promise
land. Grandma would have been so disappointed but for
some reason she hadn't been crossing my mind this year
like she usually did. Her teachings had always stuck with
me, but He had nearly drained her out of me at that point.
But He was still Him and one thing He was not was a punk.
Mama began to panic as the tension in the air was so thick
that it couldn't have been cut with a samurai sword. And
He would need one of those to kill me today! "Go upstairs
and pack your stuff Jesse!" My mom pleaded.

"What stuff? I can fit everything you've ever gotten me

my entire life into one medium size paper bag."

"What the fuck you say nigga? Who do ya' thank' yous' talkin' to, huh? I will…" Before He could even finish His typical threatening sentence I stood up and loudly yawned again.

"Yeah, I'm out. I know where the house is at so I can get there on my own. I don't need to ride in no truck with nobody. I'll just grab my backpack and I'll meet ya'll later. Just don't bring none of this shit to the new house. It's all roach infested. Don't bring the couch. Don't bring the refrigerator. And don't bring any of this bad energy with you to the new house Mama because if you do it'll be as if we haven't even moved. Leave all of the weak stuff behind and start anew. Ain't that a bible verse? Old things shall pass away and behold all things become new? Yeah, that's it. I believe that means leave all this weak ass shit behind if you want to be in a new environment. You can take these niggas out the hood, but you can't take the hood out of these niggas…especially out of His bitch ass!" I said that last line knowing that would be the line to break the Devil's back and already had my hand on the doorknob twisting it as I said it. He charged at me but it was too late. I just slammed the door and walked off the back porch and with perfect timing because Mook was waiting right outside on the street. We were old enough to drive now and Mook was the first of our crew to have his own car. I swiftly walked over to Mook backwards with my back to him so that I could face the attacker that I knew would be coming out the house behind me. Mook hopped out the car already knowing something strange was going down by my demeanor. He opened the door and cooly walked off the porch. His charge was over because He saw there was two of us.

"What's up Crazy Joe?" Mook raised both his hands to the sky in an intimidating manner and teased Him. "Wit' yo' old weak ass!" I just chuckled as He just stopped and stared at both of us.

"Come say it to my face pussy! You pussy ass bitch! Come and say that same shit right to my face so I can cut your tongue out and mail it to your pussy ass mama along wit' your ears and your dick that Imma' shove down your pussy ass throat!" He calmly started walking towards us. Mook was no fighter. He was just a good bullshitter from the suburbs trying to be a hard ass. And the way He said those words with such promise freaked Mook out. I may have been used to hearing things like that but this was all new territory for Mook. This Dude was more than 20 years older than both of our ages combined but we still had doubts about the dangers of truly getting into a rumble with Him. One of us could get seriously injured or worse, killed. So I just smiled at Him, never taking my eyes off of Him while stepping into the car. That's when He darted towards us and I slammed the door. Mook yelped out a scared little whimper and peeled out before He could reach us. I rolled the window down and stuck my arm out with the middle finger raised high. *Fuck you nigga! I am not that same scared little kid you used to fuck with!*

Things were certainly different now. I was different. I looked at the world differently, with different eyes. I looked at it with eyes that couldn't be distracted by the slight of malicious hands or blinded by the ominous glare of the bigotries of men. The form of innocence I used to know had passed and I was now being molded by the grips of circumstance, its knuckles kneed and hard pressed to break my will to survive by squeezing out the last of the little sanity I had. I was no longer naive to hope's tease of a better tomorrow. But even though I had accepted the torture of life for what it was, I had not yet given up what I knew I would have to do to make life what it had to become. And what it had to become was real again, familiar, warm with a hint of sweet chocolate chip cookie dough wavering in the air. It had to become loving and nourishing holding me tightly, smothering me until I begged it to stop. It had to become soft but stern, caring but strong, soothing but raw. It had to become Grandma! The tragedy of her was long gone but the presence of her still remained, chin on my head breathing confidence down my spine. I can't say that she was living through me, but I could feel her alive within.

Now that I had a job school was beginning not to be so tough. I could buy my own things like clothes and food, etc. It's funny how well the students treated me once they realized I had a pair of Jordans on my feet. It was like joining a private club except I never knew that all you had to do was wear the entry fee and you were in. Then again maybe I did know but just couldn't do anything about it at the time. But now I was old enough to do something about it. Sixteen years old is still an adolescent age for most people but where I'm from if you were male and made it to sixteen, then you were easily considered an adult. Many of us had died well before that time so I considered myself to be pretty fortunate. Now that I think of it, Manny and I both were. I saw him a couple of times on the street in passing but I had yet to see him during school. But then out of nowhere one morning in homeroom he was there. He was such a natural born leader. As soon as he walked into the class he had everyone's undivided attention, even the teacher who was not as pleased as I was to see him. Mrs. Lees was our Spanish teacher and she was the weakest teacher we had. The students hated her, not because she was mean but only because she was weak. No one listened to a single word she said until she began to threaten us with the buzzer. The buzzer was a new teacher assistance system that the city had put in place to help keep the peace in classrooms throughout the day. Teachers could push the button if they felt threatened or intimidated and needed assistance. It was mainly to be used if students started physically fighting each other since teachers and students could be easily hurt during a typical brawl. Us students just saw the buzzer as another annoying instrument teachers could use against us to keep the playing fields unevenly tilted in their favor. To us the buzzer was just a cop out for teachers to not have to take their time building the proper relationships with students to be able to successfully run their classes.

Pushing the buzzer meant that in moments the principal accompanied by police officers would immediately be at your door. Most teachers never had to use their buttons, but the ones who did got little to no respect from us. The buzzers were designed for dire situations. However, Mrs. Lees seemed to find herself in dire situations all the time. *So was that her fault or ours? Whoever's fault is was it looked like it was about to repeat itself again as Mrs. Lees wasn't wasting any time in letting Manny know that she would push that button on him in a heartbeat and Manny wasn't wasting any time either letting her know that he didn't give a damn if she did!*

"Mrs. Lees, I think I should be the one to teach all your classes today and you should just go kill yourself!" Manny gave her a look with his eyes that signified he was in total control at that moment. "But before you kill yourself could you just make sure to add me to your will? Know I don't take no money from nobody if it's under a thousand though!"

The class busted out laughing. They always loved a good show and this would be today's most promising entertainment. Mrs.Lees clearly embarrassed walked over to the red button signaling her intention to push it if the nonsense were to continue.

"Take a seat Emmanuel. You can take it here or you can take it in the principal's office, your choice." Mrs. Lees' hand was overly eager to slam the buzzer like a knowledgable contestant on a TV gameshow. Manny grabbed a desk and spun it around to face the rest of us in the class as if he was running the show. Then he put his feet up onto another desk and started talking to students around him as if he was in his own private office and Mrs. Lees didn't exist. And there wasn't anything that Mrs. Lees could do about it because the rumor was that the principal had given Mrs. Lees strict instructions that she was limited in the amount of times she could push the buzzer. And being that this was just the beginning of the day I guess Mrs. Lees decided to save her buzzer pushes in anticipation of some harder situations that would most likely wield their ugly heads later on in the day. I don't know what it is about after lunch and high schools but if things are about to explode, they often do so after lunch. *Could it be that the stale tasting Sloppy Joe sandwiches were induced with aggressive fight promoting ingredients that would make students want to fight all the time after lunch? Naw, that couldn't be it because none of us was eating that shit, but fights would still break out all the time anyway.* Manny finally noticed after several minutes of him and Mrs. Lees jockeying back and forth for control of the class that I was actually there with him. He smiled for a quick moment before quickly returning back to his dominant disposition.

"Hey yo, everybody listen up real quick because I don't want any of you stupid mother fuckers misconstruing what I'm about to say next." He looked over at me in the corner of the room and started pointing. "You see that little peanut head looking, smart ass nigga' trying to lay low over there in the corner? That's my mother fucking brother over there. So if any of you Kool Aid, heart pumping midgets ever try to put a hand on him in a harmful way I will bust so may caps up in that ass that the world'll think your tailor stitched your clothes with Swiss cheese and bubble gum! Ya'll better treat him as if he was me, period!" Then he stood up and walked out of the room in spite of the class just beginning. Before he made his glorious exit he reached out and slammed his hand on the buzzer and said to Mrs. Lees "Now buzz that, you stupid bitch!"

And from that point on everyday was a good day like that. What I had been wishing for a long time was coming to pass. All I ever wanted was to be in school with my big bro. I had wondered what it would be like, what it could be like. And now I knew. It would be like walking on sunshine beaming off the backs of my enemies warming my ambitious toes as I stick my foot up their asses! Wow. I could certainly get used to that and I did. Manny and

I started hanging out more. He let me sit with him and his crew at lunch. I mean, it shouldn't have even meant anything to me knowing I knew everyone sitting at the table since they all were from Westlake. But it did mean something. It meant everything! It meant acceptance! I had been looking for acceptance for so long, ever since He had married my mom. Once He married her everyone abandoned me. Grandma left. Aunt Lorene and Leslie left. Reggie left. Bobby didn't leave but I had left him. And my best friend and brother Emmanuel had been locked away in jail most of the time. I had my church crew but they didn't live in the Projects and they didn't go to my school. So the only time I got to chop it up with them was at the temple and the temple wasn't giving me any trouble that I couldn't handle on my own. It was my life at home and my life at school putting me one foot into the grave! But now with Manny back in the picture I felt safe at school. After everyone found out Manny was my brother, they all started treating me with respect. He was the king of the jungle and I was the king's sidekick. And being the sidekick had its perks. Girls that hadn't noticed me before started noticing me. Even teachers I didn't have started knowing my name. The only difference in our lives now was what each of us did after school. Because after school since Manny was a drug dealer he would hit the streets, and since I was still a janitor I would hit the broom closet. *Why? Because I still had an academic scholarship to the biggest college in the state and I didn't want to fuck that up. Not to mention I still had to go home to Him every night.* He could barely handle me working at the school. He hated the fact that I was making money being able to take care of myself without having to depend on Him and Mama. I don't know why He cared about that so much since neither one of them was working or ever worked! He just wanted to stab us with knives and she just wanted to give all of our hard earned (or not so hard earned now that I think about it) money away to the church. So most nights I found myself doing the two things I knew how to do well without putting my life at risk, work hard and study hard!

"I told you not to do it didn't I?" I was looking at her with such disgust that my tone didn't need to match. "All you had to do was just listen. So was it worth it?"

"Was what worth it boy? I don't knows what you's talkins' about. But I do know you's bouts ta' gets on my nerves! That's what I's knows!" Mama's tone was not so pleasant as mine was.

"Mama, there's roaches everywhere. I keep seeing them. They're in the living room. They're in the dining room. And they're all over this kitchen! I told you not to bring nothing from the old house. Did you listen? Noooooooooooo! You bring all this nonsense that we didn't even need and now look. This place is just as infested as the last one now. In fact, I think this place has a bigger roach problem than what we had in Westlake! I think the roaches know that this is a better neighborhood and in their happiness have decided to breed more. Depressed roaches don't breed as much. I said leave the couch and you bring the couch. I said leave the TV and you bring the TV. I said leave all this crap there and you bring all this crap here. And I told you it would be a huge mistake and lookeee here, a huge mistake it is!" I was talking to her condescendingly on purpose because I knew she'd only hear me if I talked that way.

"Boy you better leave me alones, ya here?!! That ain't nothing buts the devil in ya' tryin' ta' makes me upset. But you can't steals my joy! Get's thee behind me Satan! Hallelujah!" Mama passionately raised her hands during her rant.

"Oh my God, spare me the sanctimonious yap, yap and do something about these roaches already. You know since we're quoting Bible scriptures now doesn't the Bible say something about cleanliness being next to Godliness? Because if that's the case this house is so nasty that you don't have to tell Satan to get behind you because he already right up in your backyard. He's breathing all down your hypocritical neck at this point. Jesus wouldn't like this house and you know it. He wouldn't have had his last supper here that's for sure. Roaches would have been drinking all the wine and getting drunk. Then they would have broke all the bread before Jesus could have blessed it. You need to baptize some of these critters and make them join the church. You got enough roaches here to start about two hundred million Mississippi Mass Choirs, don't you?" I could barely say the last few things without laughing, but the situation was certainly no laughing matter. Just when I thought I was making some headway with Mama He comes rolling down the stairs in His dingy maintenance looking pants. Me ignoring Him had become common place now so I acted like He wasn't even there and walked into the living room to avoid confrontation.

He opened up the refrigerator but to His dismay there wasn't anything He wanted in there. He lashed out at Mama, but this time He did something that He usually never did. He cursed at her. Normally He'd do all the cursing at us. Being that Mama was a God fearing woman He never cursed at her. But today He was on some new tangent and decided to let Mama have it.

"How come there ain't shit to eat in here?" He slammed the refrigerator door to show his frustration.

"Joe there's a plenty in that frigerator ta's be's eatin.' I's gots that stew in there from this week and cornbread's in there too." Mama timidly replied. I could tell she was trying to keep the peace. *She better tell that Satan to get behind her and back her up because He's worse than Satan.* The thought made me snicker. Maybe He heard my snicker. Maybe He didn't. But for whatever reason He decided to cross a line that I never saw Him cross before, and He called my mom out of here name! "Bitch, I ain't trying to eat that old ass shit! Got damn it! Can't you do anything right?" His words struck me in the ear like a loud siren. And then I lost it! *Who in the hell does this nigga think He talking to?*

"Don't you use the Lord's name in vain in this house Joseph! What is wrong with you?" My mom's voice had an intimidated crackle to it that made me highly uncomfortable and empathetic to her situation. She was undoubtedly afraid and had never been so before. *So why now?* It didn't matter. I was now aggravated and determined to right His wrong. I walked into the kitchen, bent down and made a mad rush towards Him. I slammed my shoulders directly into His waist and hoisted Him up off the ground above my shoulders. He was surprisingly quite light. I had tackled much heavier people during my rustles and bustles with peeps in the street and I just assumed based off of all of His ridiculous gladiator banter over the years that He'd be much heavier. But then again this would be my first time testing out His weight in such an obvious defiant manner. I pushed Him backwards with my upper body and tossed Him ass first into the sink, and just held Him there for about 10 seconds. I was looking Him directly into His eyes. I used to be afraid of those eyes. Dark. Solemn. Demonic eyes as they were. But this time there was something shimmering in them that I hadn't saw before. *What was glistening in the corners of those eyes? I know what that is. I was familiar with that look. I've seen it in my mirror staring hopelessly back at me plenty of times as a kid. Fear! It was faint. But there it was, fear!*

"The devil is a lie! Get thee behind me Satan, not in this house! Jesse! Take ya' hands off of ya' father right this instant. Please Lord! No God! Ya'll cuts this nonsense out right now, ya hears me?" Mama shrieked in disbelief of what was going down. She was trying to wedge her body in between us but to no avail. He had fucked up this time. And unfortunately for Him I had finally noticed how weak He actually was. Which would ultimately make matters worse for all of us moving forward, especially Him. He wanted to move but I wouldn't let Him. He wanted to struggle but I wouldn't let Him. I just stood there embarrassingly holding Him in place looking Him directly in His eyes. It was the longest 10 seconds I had ever experienced. And at that time it had been the most liberating moment I ever had. It was almost as powerful as beating Grandma at checkers, but not quite. Time was standing still and I was standing on top of it. I barely noticed my mom crying, but when I did I decided to let Him go, and to let her finally get in between us.

"Let it go Joe! Let it go! Please God bless this house! In the mighty name of Jesus, let it go Joe!" Mama was holding and pleading with Him like a slave pleads to its master. Then she turned to me and said, "Honor thy father and mother so that thou days are long upon the earth boy!" *Long upon the earth? I hate this planet! And why is she begging Him to let it go? She better be thankful I'm even sticking up for her goofy ass! I should just smack the shit out of Him and prove my point some more, that He ain't shit and I'm not scared!*

"Fuck Him. He ain't honoring shit about us so I ain't honoring shit about Him. Plus He ain't none of my father anyway. He's just a stunt double in a low budget film trying to stand in for someone I could give two shits about! Jesus said turn the other cheek and I was certainly about to turn His. But I'll do ya'll one better and turn both these ass cheeks so ya'll can watch me walk the fuck right up out of here, on some real shit! Peace!" I threw two fingers up gesturing my exit and headed for the front door being careful to keep an eye out for Him trying to bum rush me, but He didn't. So I just left and didn't come back the rest of that week.

Chapter 19

Bye TDubs

I was used to being away from home now. I hated it there more and more each day, if hating it more was even possible. Us student janitors were only supposed to stay after school for work for about three hours and then we were supposed to go home. But I'd do anything to not be at home so I would just stay after school helping in anyway I could, as late as they would allow. So it would often be night the few times I decided to even go home. Sometimes instead of going home I'd go over Mook's house and stay with him for a few days. Mook stayed with his older brother so that was a lot of fun being over there with them. But whenever I thought I was wearing out my welcome I'd move on to the next spot. Sometimes I'd stay with other friends, whoever wanted my company at the time. Often I'd just climb the roof to the church, crawl through one of the upstairs bathroom windows and spend the night there. Sleeping in a huge spooky church all alone at night was certainly creepy. There'd be all kinds of squeaks and clanks that would rumble my imagination. Plus I couldn't turn on any lights inside the church in fear that someone would realize that I was there. So I would just sit there sleeping under the church pews in the sanctuary until the first signs of daylight. Most nights I could handle the solidarity. But sometimes I'd get so freaked out worrying about old church spirits wandering the halls that as soon as the hairs on my arms started pointing towards the sky, that's when I knew it was my time to get up out of there! But the times

I was there all alone would be the times I would meditate, focus and gather my thoughts. I would argue back and forth with myself on if my life was on the right track. Most times I thought it was, but I wanted the paths of my life to be much smoother than they were. I wanted more ups and less downs, more straight aheads and less curves. It was beginning to become clear to me that mostly everyone I knew was better off in life than me (except for those poor Ethiopian children, they had it the worst) and my patience was growing thin. I began to yearn for redemption. I began to thirst for a revolution to my own existence. And the greater my hunger for change, the more I began to follow Manny's lead. Manny got tired of trying to keep me at arms length. He would tell me I had a different purpose in life than running around with him but he also missed me as much as I missed him. So for the purpose of brotherhood and camaraderie him and I started hanging together more often. Sometimes I'd just skip being a janitor and roll with him after school. It seemed like every few weeks he'd pick me up in a different type of car and we'd go joy riding. Even though he knew deep down inside street life wasn't for me, he couldn't help trying to school me up on different things just to keep me safe.

"Now look nerd face, when we go in here don't touch anything. Don't say anything. And don't do anything. Got it?" I could tell whenever Manny was serious about what he was saying because his nostrils would flare out like King Kong and he'd give me a look like he was ready to slap me on queue if I didn't comply.

"Yeah, yeah, yeah I got it. Don't say nothing and don't do nothing. Sounds like what you do when handed a math test!" I laughed aloud.

Manny pulled up to some raggedy looking house. We jumped out of the car and I let him lead the way. I was expecting him to knock on the door but he just pushed the door open abruptly and went right in so I followed. There wasn't too much to the place. Right as we walked in there was an old rusty brown sofa with the stuffing coming out of it and a red, suede, worn out love seat. *Whoever the interior decorator is for this house should be fired.*

"Wait here, I'll be right back." Manny pointed at the floor as if I were a puppy who couldn't follow directions and then turned away and went upstairs.

Within five minutes I decided to take a load off and sat in the love seat. That's when I heard some footsteps coming from the kitchen. A lady came around the corner in some snagged up stockings with no shoes on her feet. Either her butt was too big to button her shorts or she was purposely wearing them that way. Her tank top was cut halfway showing off her pierced belly button which held a red ruby in it. She was too old for ponytails but still had them. They looked good on her. I remembered that we hadn't even knocked on the door so I was sure that she was going to panic when she saw me sitting there. But she didn't. She just sashayed on over and sat right on the arm rest of the chair. Had I not moved my arm she would have sat on it.

"Well hello you. And what's your name buttercup?" She said while swashing around the stick of a sucker in her mouth. She wasn't an ugly girl by any means. Her body was pretty well put together and her face was cute. At my school she'd be an 8 or a 9, but she was well past school age. I knew I was staring at her because she had shocked me with her bluntness when she sat next to me. I was trying to play it cool but was starting to get nervous.

"Jesse!" The words silently croaked out of my throat as if I were trying to tell a secret.

She laughed. "What's that now?"

"My name is Jesse but the homies call me J Dubs!" I tried to recover from the croak I let out earlier by lowering my tone.

"Oooh J Dubs. I likes that. You look just like Emmanuel, but you're just a tad bit cuter than he is. Want some?" She took the sucker out of her mouth and slid off the arm of the chair onto my lap. I instantly caught a boner. That's when Manny came down the steps and started yelling.

"Bitch get your tic tac looking ass up off of him before I crack you up side your empty head! Let's go J Dubs!" Manny signaled toward the door. The girl immediately jumped off my lap. She must have known like I did that Manny wasn't messing around. I jumped up too but tried to cool walk over to the door. Manny slapped me in the back of my head turning my cool walk into a panic. I turned back one more time to look at the girl and she gave me a wave, "Bye J Dubs!"

"Yeah, bye J Dubs!" Manny mocked her and me both and slapped me in the head once more. When we got into the car he looked at me the same way he had when we first arrived. Except this time he was disappointed.

"Nigga what did I tell you before we got out the car? Didn't I say don't touch anything, don't say anything and don't do anything? I leave you alone for 10 minutes and your friendly ass making small talk with the enemy. This is all business nigga. And we don't mix business with pleasure, ya' digs? Had I not came back downstairs that bitch would have had you sucking her asshole after she put that nasty ass sucker in your mouth! Everything that look good ain't good for you. Remember that. How you gone' watch my back and you sucking on suckers and shit?!!! A few seconds later and your ass would have caught herpes, stupid ass!" Manny was pissed and I was disappointed that I had fucked up.

"Here, put this in the glove box." He handed me a wad of money. I couldn't tell how much it was but by the weight it seemed like more than what I was used to holding. And that's yours. Put it in your sock. You fuck up again and you ain't getting shit." He gave me fifty bucks. Wow! That was double the amount of money I would have made that day had I stayed at school cleaning up the hallways. And all I did was almost catch an STD. Cool! I was pumped.

Not because I had made some money. But because I was spending time with the only person that truly knew who I was. I didn't have to adjust. I didn't have to perform. And there was no way for me to put up a wall because Manny knew everything about me. I felt totally free and I hadn't felt that way in a long time. That was just one of many stops we would make that day. Manny told me every time I fucked up and did something stupid he was going to call me "J Dubs." At first he was calling me J Dubs at every house. But by the end of the night J Dubs was gone and "nigga" was back. I had made about $300 dollars that day watching Manny's back and that was pretty cool. Of course I didn't like it that Manny was selling dope, but I did like that it was me who was watching his back. He asked me if I wanted to stay out with him, go back to his mom's house and fuck with Leslie for a little bit. But I told him just to take me home because I hadn't been there in awhile. I had been gone for most of the week and needed to check in on Mama, Lijah and Halia. There's no telling what could have transpired since I'd been gone and I couldn't let Manny know how much fun I had hanging out with him. That would have been just plain weak. When he dropped me off at home I just watched his car drive away until I couldn't see it anymore. I sat on my porch and prepared myself to enter back into a world of roaches, demons and ridiculousness. It was crazy but it was also comfortable because it was all I knew. It was hard but it was home. And there's no place like home whether you like it or not!

Chapter 20
his Middle Name's Lamont

What is life truly? Is life what happens around us or is it the substance of what is happening inside of us? Or maybe it's a combination of the two? When someone dies does their life stop? Of course life as they know it is no longer the same. But their life isn't the only one being impacted when they leave. I hear so many people say life goes on when someone goes away. But does it? Does life really just go on? Or did the person that died take some of our life with them wherever they went? When Grandma left she took a lot of my life with her. The life I knew filled with love and joy had vanished long ago. She was my strength in a world determined to weaken my spirit. She was the invaluable existence that kept my soul from being penniless. And when she died all of that died with her. Was it ever going to return? Would I ever get my true life back?

Whose dumbass idea was it anyway to make a wall of death? My friends and I stood there staring at it, but we were not in awe. And that's what made the entire moment so scary. There were more than 50 name plates hanging on it now resembling a small memorial, except these were not the names of fallen American soldiers being remembered for their virtuous sacrifices domestic and abroad. These were the names of fallen children, all high school students that had died since the beginning of the year, all homicides, all murders and all from our school. My assumption is that the school created the death wall with good intentions to discourage the students from killing one another. But what it was really doing was desensitizing any shock value that was supposed to come with people dying way ahead of their time. It just numbed our hearts and minds to the vile disgracefulness of our friends being maliciously murdered for no competent reasoning whatsoever. We were becoming used to being slaughtered and the fear of being pigs was absent from our souls. The worst thing was we knew every single name on that wall. They either grew up with us eating crayons since Preschool, complained with us about school meals at lunchtime since Jr. High or was just trying to get enough credits to graduate High School to be able to work in a factory or do something half productive with their lives other than die. And here they were, just dead! And to make matters worse, they had all been killed by the gun. So tragic. So brutal. And so normal. We tipped our arms sideways as if we were pouring out liquor in memory of our loved ones lost and kept it moving. Soon after, we stopped going up to the wall altogether because it always had a new name added to it weekly. Every now and then a real popular student landed on that wall and we'd all gather around it to pay our respects. But that would last only for a few days and we'd be right back to trying to survive our own selves. I would say a prayer to myself, *Keep me off that wall Lord...by any means necessary keep me off that got' damn wall!"*

I thought when Grandma died that was the worse tragedy of my life. And considering the aftermath of it, maybe it was. But I was only 5 years old at the time so the emotional impact was protected and censored by a lack of memory, youth and understanding. But this was considerably worse than her death. My understanding now was full and the memory of this would forever be vivid in my head. I sat on those school steps devastated, motionless and lost. Time was slowing its dance to a halt pausing in mid stride, its body perfectly aligned against the stillness of the reality that Manny was no longer here. It had not dawned on me earlier what that truly meant, but now it was pressing against my frontal lobe squeezing on me emotionally and I began to cry. This wasn't the type of cry that is accompanied by feeble whimpering and occasional gulping to catch a breath. This was a silent cry accompanied with an enormous amount of tears streaming down my face, running down my neck and dripping to the floor. Normally I'd be able to wipe away a few quick tears and move on but these tears were crippling. I could do nothing but weep and weep. And besides the obvious I didn't know why I couldn't stop or how I even got outside in the first place. It started when I was sitting in History class about to be bored to death for another hour of learning about U.S. Presidents that I could care less about. Our History teacher over the course of a year had decided that he would mainly just give out assignments and let us figure the rest out on our own. I think he made the decision to dis-engage after the first two days of the school year. I didn't mind because it allowed me to focus on the task at hand without having to be engaged in non authentic teacher rhetoric. But it also called for a more boring class, but today would not get to follow that typical pattern. Before the class could get fully underway about five guys from the neighborhood just busted into the classroom and started frantically looking around. Everyone in the class was startled even the teacher because when stuff like this happened, usually that meant someone was about to get into a fight and badly injured. But I knew what they were there for/who they were there for rather, and that was me.

"Let's go Lil' Manuel. Let's handle some G shit my nigga!" Daniel said as soon as he found me. Daniel was a distant cousin of ours but I didn't like him that much. Since we were little he was always trying to prove himself and it seemed like once again he was trying to do exactly that. But I wasn't in the mood to sit in History class that day anyway or to hear Daniel's mouth so I just grabbed my books and made my way to the door. I looked over to the teacher to see if he would make an attempt to try and stop me from leaving, but he had already put his head back into the newspaper he was reading. He didn't care not one bit about any of us, what we were doing or where we were about to go as long as it had zero to do with him.

"What's up?" I asked Daniel when we got out into the hallway. There were more people waiting out there for us. These were all peeps from the neighborhood crew that Manny ran with. I knew all of them as we all grew up in the Projects together. *What the hell were they all doing out here and what were we about to get into?* And then I realized what was going on. This was a rally, a gathering of the troops or a call to arms situation. We were assembling together to go get retribution for a grave injustice and I was excited to be a part of the team. I had only officially been running around with Manny and them for a few weeks and was proud to be even considered in whatever devious plan we were about to execute.

"They done did it this time. We bout' to put all these mother fuckers under ground today! Lil Man you ready to do this?" Stank put his arm around my shoulder and pulled me to the front of the mob. "We about to bust a cap in all these niggas' asses yo!"

"Let's gooooo! It is what it is at this point!" I screamed out. We made our way down the school hall headed for the exit. In the midst of us walking different people in the group started making comments about Manny and how close he had been to them. They started talking about how he was as a person and how much they were going to miss those things about him. Everyone was acting as if they knew him better than the guy standing next to them, as if Manny and them were related, like family. All of a sudden their comments began to take a toll on me because they had no validity to them at all. In fact, they were down right false! All I heard was comments about the fancy clothes or new shoes that Manny used to wear. Or stories about how tough or how much of a down ass nigga he was, how many bitches were on his dick or how cool of a homie/gangster he was. But none of those things were the true Manny. Those were masks that Manny would wear just to protect himself from those he believed didn't have his best interest at heart. He wasn't just some two bit, fancy pants wearing, sleazy ass drug dealer waiting for his next cracked out rat to make an appearance in that old addiction mouse trap, just so the trap could snap shut and he could collect the spoils of his victim. No sir, he was so much more than that and meant so much more to me. *Did they know that he was the greatest illustrator I had ever seen? He could draw a picture of someone and his drawing would look just as realistic as their actual photograph, only better! Did they know he'd rather not speak at all? That he was a gentle, quiet and humble soul? That when we were younger he hated me playing with his action figures so much that he would hide them under his mattress so I couldn't find them? That he looked more athletic than he actually was? That he knocked his front teeth out challenging me to a game of High/Low, had to get emergency stitches and couldn't eat solid foods for weeks? That he loved He-Man but hated The Never Ending Story? That he loved making fun of me for being a nerd but wouldn't let me not be one? That he loved being called by his first name Emmanuel, but hated it when his mama called him by his middle name Lamont? That he was only 16 years old and now was dead from living the same life he was trying to protect me from? And that he'd be gone forever, never to return, never to smile at me on this earth ever again? No! They only knew the shell of a frightened young man trying to find his way in a world that had abandoned us all long ago. And now there his precious name was plastered on that death wall as we all passionately passed by it.*

The realization crippled me to the point that I slowly began to drift from the front of the mindless herd to the back. They were too busy rambling in their false truths and plots of revenge to notice I was no longer leading the misguided pack. We made our way to the front doors of the school and pushed onward. Outside awaited three old cars, the good drive by shooting kind, like the four doored 77' Oldsmobiles or Regals. These cars always made good shootout cars because they were steel plated and if riddled with bullets you'd have a higher chance of surviving in one of those than in some plastic sports coupe or something like that. They all piled in about 6 deep a piece and pulled off. Nobody noticed I hadn't gotten into any of the cars and I didn't care. It was all hitting me now for the first time and the weight was too heavy for me to stand. So I collapsed on the middle of the school steps for what seemed an eternity and cried. Flashbacks of Emmanuel and I just ran though my mind and I cried some more. Flashbacks of Grandma, Emmanuel and I began to run through my mind as I cried even harder. I tried to stop but I couldn't. Before I knew it the crying had turned into wailing and I had no idea why. I hadn't cried this hard since the first day my mom left me to fend for myself at Pre-School. *Maybe I was crying for all the death I had seen so far? Maybe I was crying for all the death yet to come that I knew was well on its way? I had no clue but I knew I couldn't just sit there and cry, but there'd be plenty to think and cry about on my way home.* So I started walking and that's exactly what I did. Rest in Peace Emmanuel L. Axel, Rest in Peace!

How in the world did I allow myself to fail him? Manny was one of the most important people in my life and I allowed him to make a choice that eventually got him killed. The murderer shot him multiple times in his vehicle or outside his vehicle, no one was really sure. And no one was sure of who the murderer was. Or if they were sure, no one was telling me. And that bothered me more and more each day. He died alone. I wasn't there to have his back. *Me, J Dubs!* I could have done something. I would have done anything to save him. But I was probably off somewhere passing a math test or something. *Fuck me for that!* I let my brother down and would never be able to rectify that grave mistake. My heart was broken. But I refused to baby myself. Instead I decided to punish myself. I fell into a deep depression that was only internal. I would never allow anyone to see my struggles externally because Manny never used to do that. He was stronger than all of us and death still came and snatched him up before his time, and that scared me greatly. So I made Manny two promises in my heart if he'd look out for me and have my back even though I failed to have his. The first promise was to never get caught up in the drug game since he never truly wanted me to be a part of that life anyway. And the second was to never allow myself to get murdered, especially by gun shot and certainly not dying alone in a car. I was positive that I could keep up my end of the agreement if he kept up his. And the pact was made and sealed with tears from my eyes and thoughts from my head as I looked to the sky and asked Manny for his forgiveness. I could feel him in my heart agreeing to have my back, but that didn't make me feel any better about his death. My depression got deeper and I began to skip any and everything that had substance in my life. I skipped my academic classes which sent my grades spiraling into a whirlpool of unacceptable results that The Ohio State University wouldn't accept. It wasn't long before they denounced my scholarship and I lost all hopes of attending college after high school. I skipped church services which allowed the fellowship I had created with different missionaries and ministers to slowly disappear. They all assumed that the Devil had gotten ahold of me and pretty much shunned me from their church community. They hadn't truly let me into their church family anyway, since I was from The Projects and looked down on me at all times. So when I lost the love and respect of the church in general, I figured they were just giving me exactly what I had already decided to give them, which was absolutely nothing at all. I still had my friends there, but they too were oblivious to the depression I was going through because I hid it so well. The only thing I hadn't skipped was my custodial duties at the school and the constant mental and emotional struggle to stay alive between Him and I at home. He told me on several occasions that He was happy that Emmanuel had died. He said that He was just sad that someone else beat Him to the punch because sooner or later He would have killed Manny anyway. *Yeah right!*

Manny would have squashed your ass like a bug. It's easy to talk all this shit when Manny's not around. But when he was here, your ass wasn't pursuing any of this macho mumble jumbo! His comments just made me even more eager to see someone put Him in His place once and for all. That someone was most likely going to be me.

Chapter 21

Feel Froggy...Leap

They say that time flies when you're having fun. So for me it should have been standing statue still, but it wasn't. It was catapulting through thin air with the aerodynamics of a bald eagle. High School graduation was right around the corner and somehow I had managed not to screw that up, even though my academic scholarship to college was totally screwed. When it was time for me to finally walk across the stage to get my high school diploma it was a lot easier than what I thought it would be. The struggle wouldn't be in having no family members or guest at the ceremony because I was used to doing things all alone by that point. No, the biggest issue I had now was not being able to work at the school as a janitor because that program ended at graduation. *How was I going to survive now? And what was my contingency plan after losing my scholarship?* Christie's parents were pretty stern in demanding that she had a college education. They certainly wouldn't allow her to be involved with someone from The Projects especially if that someone didn't have a college degree. I hadn't even met Christie's parents yet. She said she had told them all about me and how I already had a scholarship to O.S.U. and they were still skeptical of our relationship. The worst part was I hadn't told Christie that I lost the scholarship. As far as she knew everything was business as usual and I'd be going away to college in the fall. And disappointing Christie was not an option for me. I cared about her more than anyone on earth including myself. She kept me sane while I was dealing with Manny's death. I figured I'd just get a job for the summer, save some money up and start school in the fall. Any free time in-between I'd spend making her the happiest girl in the world. The only issue with that was she stayed on the outskirts of town and I had no means of transportation to get to her. We went to different high schools in completely different school districts so any time I had spent with her over the past two years I deemed precious. However, Christie did work at a restaurant in town so I'd go there to see her whenever I could. We'd exchange love letters there that we wrote to each other when we were at our homes and then wait until we were at school to read them. Two years of exciting romance and an incredible long distance relationship had put us in a place of commitment to each other that most typical relationships dream of. So I was going to figure out how to get to college if it was the last thing I did because I couldn't lose the one person in my life that believed in me and loved me for who I was. But first I needed to find a job because meeting her at that restaurant every other day was starting to add up! However finding a pot of gold at the end of a rainbow seemed an easier task than finding work. The city was drowning in poverty since the steel mills had closed. But I knew I'd find something if I only kept trying. *In any case I'd never allow myself to be like Him and Mama. He hadn't worked a real job since I'd met Him and Mama hadn't been employed since she birthed me. That's a combination of failure that I just couldn't allow myself to comprehend.* So I was determined to find work, and work is what I found.

"Now what you have to do is make sure that your grill top stays clean so your meals don't mix, ok?" Walter scraped across the top of the grill with his spatula pushing all of the unwanted food debris into the trough. "And then you want to relayer your grill with some new grease so you can start your next order, got it?"

"Ummm, sure…if you say so." I replied. "You know

Walter I've never really cooked anything before in my entire life. Back at home the little meals that are made are made by my mom."

"No worries kid. I'm going to teach you everything you need to know about cooking. You messin' with the best in the west boy!" Walter flipped his spatula in the air and caught it behind his back.

"Most impressive!" I said in my Darth Vader voice. "Hahaha…go on head and get outta' here son. You've

done well for today. Do you still need me to pick you up for work tomorrow morning?"

"Yes Walter. I'll be ready too. Just blow the horn when you're outside my house. My bedroom window is right there so I'll hear you and come right out." I gave Walter a high five and jokingly threw my apron on top of his head and ran out.

Walter screamed out, "I ain't picking your ass up tomorrow for that dirty move right there. You better find some change and catch the bus!"

I just looked at Walter all confused as if I didn't know what he was talking about and then started laughing. Walter couldn't help but to laugh too and waved goodbye. Walter was a good man. I really liked him a lot. His shiny bald head always glistened in the heat of the kitchen and little beads of sweat would slowly roll down his face. He was a taller, slender, older gentleman in his mid 50s whose hands were rough from his years of cooking experience. But he was also the type of guy you could instantly tell within moments of being around him that he was a good person who cared about others. He had been slaving at the Route 46 Truck Stop Diner for more than 20 years now. You could look into his eyes and tell he'd seen a lot. He'd found favor in me for some reason. He'd tell me all the time that I was a special kid and that he'd look out for me. He wanted to teach me how to be a great line cook because he said that skill would always be needed no matter how the world turned. I just wanted to make a few bucks to help pay for my college education and with that being extremely high, I truly couldn't see my minimum wage at the truck stop being the solution to my tuition problems. But anything was better than nothing and at the time the truck stop was all I could get. *Beggars can't be choosy. Buckle up and make it happen. Dig deep and beat the odds. Make Grandma and Manny proud. Just do it like Nike!* The thoughts just riddled through my head as I walked along the highway. I had a long way to go, hours even before I got home. It'd be dark by the time I got there.

No worries though. This is what real men do. He'd never do something like this. He'd never fend for Himself or His family. He'd never fend for you. She'd never fend for you either. In fact, she's worse than Him because she's your flesh and blood. He's not your biological dad. He's just an imposter. But she's your mom. There's no excuse for her allowing Him to ruin your life. But she's your mom and she loves you boy. She's just in love with Him. You know what love is don't you? You know how vulnerable it makes you right? You're in love with Christie and you'd do anything for her. That's why you're out here walking home from work...because you have to go to college for her. If it wasn't for her you'd be cool with just being a line cook like Walter, wouldn't you? No, you wouldn't want to be a line cook. You can't be that and a track star at the same time dummy! You think Jesse Owens or Carl Lewis were line cooks? Man you stupid! And...fuck Him! He's the real reason you're out here walking all night. If He was a real man He'd have helped you become one. But He didn't. Fuck that! There's no excuse for Him at all. But Mama can get a pass. Just be strong and keep it moving! Just keep it moving!

By the time I got home I was super exhausted, but not too exhausted to call Christie and say good night. The conversation with her this evening would be short, sweet and to the point because I had to get up early the next day to go to work with Walter and work on my craft, my life changing skill…line cooking. *Ain't this about a bitch! No really…ain't this about a bitch! Walter was supposed to be here an hour ago and nada!*

I sat there on the edge of my bed staring at the floor. *Where in the hell was Walter? Did he forget to pick me up? Did he accidentally crash his car into a telephone pole trying to catch his spatula behind his back while bobbing his head to some Marvin Gaye classics?* I knew he hadn't blown his horn outside my house like I told him to because I'd been listening for that all morning. *Where was he?* Walter was a prompt guy. To be a great line cook you had to be prompt or all of your meals would be burnt. So him being late or forgetting to pick me up was unlikely. I walked over to my bedroom window and looked outside. I had cracked it last night to ensure I heard Walter's horn when it blew. Through the half opened window I saw someone I prayed had a heart attack and died the night before. But my prayers once again had not been answered. No surprise there. I'd been saying the same prayer of death to this man for over a decade and to no avail. He was jogging back and forth doing karate moves and half ass twist and rolls on the ground. Anyone else would have been embarrassed to be acting a fool in broad daylight like that, but not this nut! Then He looked up at me in the window and gave me a devilish smirk. I rolled my eyes in disgust and went back over to my bed. *Where the fuck is Walter? Wait a fucking minute.* Then it dawned on me. *I've seen that smirk plenty of times and knew it well. It was the same smirk He gave me years ago when He tricked me into playing football at the park just to embarrass me in front of the playground. Or the same smirk He gave Leslie when He told her that He was glad someone had killed Manny before He could do it Himself. I knew that smirk. It was pure evil, sinister and manipulating. What the fuck did you do you mangy mutt? Oh no!* I jumped off my bed and made a mad dash downstairs and grabbed the telephone. "Truck Stop Diner, how may I help you?" "Hello! Is that you Walter?" I gasped excitingly. "Yes this is Walter. Who this?"

"It's me Walter…Jesse!"

"First of all, son you're not supposed to be on the other end of this phone. You're supposed to be on the other side of this grill with me. Second of all, why in the world would you have me come all the way out to your house if you've left already? And third of all, if you've left already why ain't you here?" I could tell by Walter's tone that he was not pleased. He was speaking to me in his developmental voice which always meant he was correcting me on something I had majorly fucked up.

"Walter I'm at home. I've been waiting for you all morning and you never came by. Did you forget where I live and went to somebody else's house by mistake?"

"What??!!!" Walter starting yelling confusedly. "Your father told me as soon as I pulled up that you had already left. You ain't gotta' play games with me son. If you're not committed to being here you could have at least spared me the time of coming all that way just to pick you up. Gas ain't cheap son and time is money!"

I knew this wasn't going well and was afraid that if I didn't hurry up and explain myself that the next words out of Walter's mouth would be the kind that ended with you're fired.

"Walter, you got it all wrong man. I wouldn't tell you to come pick me up if I wasn't going to go to work with you. I have to work and I need to work. The guy that you're talking about that told you I wasn't home is not my father. He's my stepfather and He hates me. He hates me so much that He'd do anything and everything to ruin my life including but not limited to lying, cheating and fucking me out of any good thing that I have. That's why I told you to blow the horn when you arrived. I didn't hear any horn so I've been waiting for you the entire time. And all this time that bastard knew He had lied to you. He's a fucking monster and He's trying to destroy me. Please don't fire me

272

Walter over Him. This job is all I've got right now and I really, really need this job!"

There was a long pause after my rant and then Walter spoke.

"I'm sorry you're going through all of this kid. I'm not going to fire you. I know you're trying your best to be the best you can be. Don't worry about today. Take the day off and put your mind at ease. I'll be there tomorrow at the same time and this time I'll blow my horn and wait for you to come out. Deal?"

"Deal Walter! Thanks for understanding and I won't let you down, I promise!" I hung up the phone with Walter took a deep breath. I needed to compose myself before confronting the devil. I went out on the back porch and just started staring at Him.

"You feel froggy leap bitch!" He said with His hand gripping His back pocket. "You know what I'm gone do. I'm gonna split ya' and you knows it nigga!"

You can do it. Just leap off the porch and crack His dumbass right upside His bald ass head! You're stronger than Him. You're faster than Him. And He deserves to die today. Aren't you tired of being bullied? How long has it been now, thirteen years? You've been a prisoner of war for thirteen years and you still haven't found out how to escape? Escape His ass right now and break His old feeble looking neck. Come on…you know you want to!

But I didn't. I just turned around and went back to my room. *Fuck that weak ass nigga!*

Chapter 22
an Ostrich Shouldn't Have Wings

Some things in the world make sense while others don't. And I found out a long time ago that there's no rhyme or reason between the two. For example it makes sense that ducks have webbed feet because it helps them to swim. But why an ostrich has wings is completely baffling. The same goes for the life I had. Manny was engaged in street life which came with known risk. He didn't deserve to die but I wasn't surprised when he did. Therefore his death in part made sense to me. But the death I was living made no sense to me at all. Here I was trying to do the opposite of street life. I had graduated High School, found a job and was trying to make enough money to attend college to better myself. *So why was life still sticking its foot out trying to trip me up? And why was He still trying to destroy me? Wasn't He tired yet? I mean He'd only been killing me softly and loudly since I was five years old. And I'd only been hanging on by a thread since the thread was thread, so why did He care to destroy me so much?* Just when I thought He was all run out of fresh ways to torture, belittle or disgrace me, He'd always come up with something new. Him trying to make me lose this little job I had was the last and final straw for me. So I decided to move into a motel right around the corner from the restaurant. At first it felt great, not only because I was out of His sight and mind while He was out of mine, but also because I was paying my own way through life which made me feel like an accomplished adult. But that feeling was quickly short lived the day at the restaurant I couldn't remember how to scramble eggs while working the morning shift. I was so distracted that I couldn't remember to actually scramble the eggs while they were cooking on the flat grill, so after being on the grill for several minutes (and me staring at the eggs while they just cooked and cooked, pondering in my head how to get them to become scrambled) and them turning into a flat omelet, I'd take the omelet and cut it into small pieces trying to fluff them around on the plate to try and get the eggs to resemble being scrambled. It seemed to work out just fine for the first few orders, but after a while customers started to get pissed about having to pay for my new and improved version of the traditional "scrambled" egg. As soon as Walter couldn't take anymore and demoted me to dishwasher, and once I realized that my dishwasher paycheck couldn't afford to get me a motel room with a better window view than the one with the two dollar hookers hanging outside it, I had to quit my job and go right back to the place I was running away from. Summer was nearly over and it was about that time for first year college students to make their way to their dorms and introduce themselves to their new roommates. Christie was going to go to a college nearby and was putting pressure on me to tell her when my classes were starting. I still hadn't told her that I lost my scholarship, but she was starting to pick up that something fishy was going on when I couldn't show her my class schedule. And the tension at home between Him and I was at an all-time high. I literally had to sleep with one eye open (actually I would have both eyes barely closed, slitted just enough to be able to see danger if it arose) because He would sneak into my room late at night when everyone was asleep and just stand over my bed staring at me with a knife raised above His head. I always knew He was coming well before He came. After all the years of constant torture and torment my ears and instincts were well trained to wake me up whenever anyone moved throughout the house. And everyone moved differently, especially at night. When Mama moved her steps were sluggish and without haste. She never had to worry about being yelled at for being alive so her steps matched her safety and comfort of being in the home. Paul never really walked at all. Whenever he moved day or night, he always ran. Halia had more of a slide to her walk as if she was confused in whether or not she truly wanted to lift her feet. Lijah had a stomp to his walk closely mocking my own. We both were pretty confident in who we were and our walks resembled such. But none of these walks were walks I was concerned with. None of them were threatening. The walk I had to be aware of at all times was His. He had a walk that was sneaky and misleading. It was a type of tip toe that warranted He was up to no good. And late at night I had to be even more aware because now this fool for some unknown reason was up each night, coming into my room unannounced, hovering over my bed with a knife raised high above His head, just standing there at any moment ready to strike. So I'd just lay there waiting for Him to make His move and plunge down upon me so that I could roll away just in time for Him to miss me, strike His knife deep into my bed so that I could jump up and slam His forehead right into the corner of my bed frame, hopefully killing Him before He could kill me. But the entire thing would never play out because He would always eventually just leave my room and then I would be in the clear to get some rest. This had been going on every night for over a year now between one and two o'clock n the morning. Every night I'd be prepared for one of us to die and every night He'd just walk away. But after so long of being held prisoner in my own home since five years old, I just couldn't take it anymore. I couldn't breathe. The walls around me were getting smaller and smaller and the lights that ruled the sky were getting dimmer and dimmer. I knew I had to get out of there and that's exactly what I did. I would only let two people know where I was going. When I told Christie I was leaving but not to go to college she was highly disappointed. Her response to it was as if she was a dolphin and I had told her that half the earth's water supply would now be supplemented with shit and my advice to her was to swim on. Mook was a little disappointed too but understood that I had to do whatever it took to survive. From being harassed in secret to being humiliated in public. From being abused as a kid to being ridiculed as a young adult. Mook had in many ways knew just how difficult my life had been. And even though him and I were extremely close, he knew I couldn't stay…not for one more day. It was killing me on the inside to leave them. Not Him, but them…Lijah, Halia and Paul. I wanted to protect them but I knew if I wasn't my best self even I couldn't protect them from what was coming. And what was coming was a bloodbath. But I wasn't afraid to leave her…Mama. That night she chose Him over me and told the police officers to take me away had sealed our fate. And the way He disrespected Manny's death in front of her without repercussion had sealed my belief that she was no more mother to me than He was father. So early the very next morning I made sure that my walk in that house was like no other. It was a walk that was light, but sure. It was fleeting, confident and determined…determined to walk away never to be seen by Him or her ever again. The Army recruiter pulled his car up in front of my house. I had been waiting patiently outside on the front porch since 4am for his arrival. The sun had yet to rise so it almost seemed like a late night rendezvous. We had a long drive ahead of us to the airport which would give me plenty of time to reflect on my decision. And it would ring true that this decision would be one of the few to change my entire life forever.

Chapter 23
1-900 Bullsh.t

So the saying is time flies when you're having fun. And I guess I could now bear witness to that being true. It had been a year since I walked off that porch one early Sunday morning. Change can be frightening at first but nothing's more scary than remaining in a treacherous situation knowing you had the means to change it and didn't. That's complete suicide! At first I believed Drill Sergeant Moreland was an asshole that wanted to eat new recruits' hearts for breakfast. I thought he and his drill buddies were all crazed men obsessed with being in positions of power and using that power to ruin our lives. But they weren't and I was wrong. In fact they were the exact opposite of that. They were simply trying to help young men, many confused and battered, to find the light and strength deep within themselves that they had always been looking for. And though it was there, it wasn't always easy for us to find. My military career started on a base in Fort Knox, Kentucky and now it had transitioned all the way down to Fort Gordon, Georgia. I was no longer a rookie at life. I was no longer a child. I had shot guns, thrown grenades and run tactical strategies with an end game to successfully seize the enemy. I had become friends with many men I would forever respect and my life had finally taken a turn upward instead of down. I had new assignments to go to Fort Leonard Wood, Missouri. When my Sergeants found out that's where I got assigned they encouraged me to take a few compasses because the place's nickname was "Fort

Lost in the Woods." If there was anything they knew that could get under my skin, it was that. Every time we'd have to stay in the field for a few days or weeks, I'd be pissed. Fort Leonard Wood was not an adventure I was excited to have to be embarking on next so I decided to take a short vacation back home before having to report to base. As I sat on a bench waiting for a bus at the station I began to think about what I had done so far and what home was possibly like now. Not only had I not been home in a year, but I hadn't truly spoken to Mama or anyone else from there since I had left. I may have spoken to Mook a couple of times. And I had spoken to Christie about that same amount. All in all I was so busy on base that I barely had time to eat, so talking on the phone was certainly a luxury that I didn't get to experience often. *Or maybe it had nothing to do with time and had more to do with choice? Because I always saw others talking on the phones every chance they got.* There'd be long lines of people waiting at the pay phones on the weekends. I barely ever got into these lines because I just didn't have the desire to be informed of anything happening back home and didn't care to tell anyone what I was doing here either. The first few months of being away I called Mama once out of guilt. I wanted her to know that I had secretly put her on my bank account so that in case of an emergency she could go to the bank and take out money for the cause. I really wanted to help her and the family if there was ever a true need. I just requested her to let me know if she needed money by writing me a letter or telling me when I called. I never received any letters from her and the few times I did call home she had nothing to say. So I assumed all was well. And for the most part all was well with me and that's what I cared about the most. I saw my bus coming down the road and weirdly stood up in a half type stance, sorta like a stance where it's obvious one is confused on whether to stand or to remain seated. And I was confused. *Should I just go straight to Fort Leonard Wood and continue on with my life? I could have went home plenty of times between Fort Knox and Fort Gordon and decided not to. And so far everything was going just fine with me not going home. Well everything was fine for me. But everything was not fine at home. So yeah, I needed to go back even if it was just going to be this once. I needed to go back and get some closure on some things that needed closing.* So I put my duffle bag on my back and headed over to the bus. There'd be plenty of time to think about everything and get prepared for what was in store on this twelve hour bus ride back to a place I had been running from for the past year…Youngstown, Ohio.

The bus was a nice size, rather large with comfortable seating. I decided to sit at the back of the bus in an attempt to keep all of the passengers in front of me so I could keep my eyes on them. It seemed like a good idea at the time. But eventually after a few hours of travel the bumpy road and stench of the bathroom started to tap dance on my nerves. The first opportunity to move to the middle of the bus I took without question. I was happy to get a window seat because looking out the window as the world whipped by seemed soothing. The bus made a couple of stops along the way. People were getting on and off the bus accordingly in different cities, as needed as we continued along our journey. A little old lady got on the bus and sat next to me. She started knitting something that resembled either small socks or large gloves. I couldn't tell which but in either case her project seemed to be on route to a street named unsuccessful. I tried to laugh to myself but I believe she knew I was laughing at her masterpiece so she moved to another seat. *Fine by me!* I found myself once again looking out the window in a trance of corn and wheat fields quickly flashing by in sections separated by telephone poles and the occasional stop signed intersection. The combination of which immediately hypnotized my mind into thought. *What kind of a brother are you? You left them all there with Him. How could you do something like that? Was He hurting her the entire time? How could you not know? Did you know and just ignore the signs? Why didn't she say anything? Did Lijah know? His bedroom was right*

*next to hers. Paul certainly didn't know. He was too small.
But she had to know. Did she know? Yeah, she knew. He's
her husband so she had to know. But did she know? Yeah,
Mama knew! She just had to know and not do anything just
like everything else. But this time He had taken it too far.
He had crossed the line and had to pay! And all this time
I thought Halia was just extremely lazy and unmotivated.
She had dropped out of middle school complaining about
how sick she was. Every day she'd stay home. I used to
come home early from school sometimes and there she'd
be sitting there watching soap operas. I'd yell at her and
say things like "If you're so sick how come you're not too
sick to watch these wack ass soap operas...but only sick
enough to stay home from school? You're just lazy Halia.
And Mama just let's you do it!" She'd get up and run back
upstairs to her room. That's where she normally stayed.
Sometimes she wouldn't come out of there for weeks. When
she did come out we'd talk about poetry and hip hop. She
loved those things. But she was drifting further and further
away from the things she loved each day, including me. I
didn't know how to reach her. So I just started getting on
her case for disappearing all the time. I thought she just
didn't want to learn. I thought she just didn't want to exist.
I thought she just wasn't strong enough to handle what we
had been going through our entire lives. And I despised her
for that weakness. But I was wrong. He was molesting her!
What the fuck? No way! I had called back home from the
military one day to my cousin Donut who I hadn't spoken
to or told I was joining the Army. Him and I were very
close so when I did call home I thought I'd just be shooting
the breeze with him about this and that. But as soon as he
heard my voice he started telling me what had been going
on since I left. He said that Crazy Joe had lost His mind
and not the kind of lost that we already knew Him to be
familiar with. This time He had done the worst. Donut said
that my mom had confided in his mom and told her the
entire situation. Donut said my mom had even went as far
as kicking Crazy Joe out of the house! At first I told Donut*

that he had to be mistaken. But Donut insisted that it was true. Crazy Joe had been molesting Halia and no one knew for how long. I argued with him and said if that was true I would have known. If that was true I would have noticed. But then I stopped talking and dropped the phone from my ear in complete disgust. An entire flood of images slammed against the walls of my memory crashing thoughts against the banks of my brain drowning my mind in collaboration of the truth. All of a sudden I started to recognize all of the signs. He would always comment to Lijah and I in one of His rants about not having sex with our sister and what He would do if He ever caught us. I was around 10 years old at the time and Halia and Lijah had to be around 6 and 4 years of age. I never took what He said serious because Lijah and I would never want to have sex with Halia. She was our sister for crying out loud. And the idea itself was completely gross. But now it was starting to make sense why He would say things like that. He also would always walk around late at night checking to see if the doors were all locked. He claimed to be ensuring our safety in case someone tried to break in and do a home invasion. But He wouldn't just be checking the doors to our home. He'd check bedroom doors as well. I did catch Him coming out of her room late one evening. I had to use the restroom and there He was shutting her door as He was leaving. He yelled at me for being up late at night. He even said something like "Where ya' tryins' ta go nigga? To your sister's room?" But I just ignored Him because He'd say stupid shit like that all the time. But now unfortunately it was all starting to make sense. That's why He used to stand over my bed late every night with a knife ready to strike it down on me. That's why He stabbed me that one night I was talking to Christie late on the phone. And that's why He'd sneak around the house all the time like a well trained ninja. His steps were always calculated. His efforts always had purpose. And His sinisterness was blueprinted in His heart without remorse. He was a devil! He was a monster! And He had crossed a line that I'd never let Him get away with crossing. I never called Donut back. I called my mom instead. I asked her if what Donut had told me was true? She responded the same way she always did when she was trying hard not to lie but at the same time not to tell the truth either. That's how I knew what Donut had said was true. But did she kick Him out of the house? And had He molested Halia like Donut insisted? Mama wouldn't confirm or deny either so I'd have to figure the entire situation out on my own. I hung up on her but not before telling her to deliver a message to Him that I was coming home and I was coming home to do one thing. And that one thing was to kill Him!

The bus had finally arrived in Youngstown the next morning and I was eager to get off of it just as eager as I was to get on it. All I could think of was killing Him. I'd break every bone in His body. Even the bone He didn't have, His spine! And there'd be nothing He could do to stop me because I wasn't a little kid anymore. He couldn't intimidate me with His outlandish words and murderous tones. I was no longer afraid of Him like I had been throughout my childhood. I was bigger, stronger and faster than I had ever been. And He had to be every bit of the opposite. I had suffered under His tutelage for over fifteen years. He had belittled, humiliated and almost beaten my spirit into oblivion, but somehow I had survived. And now He'd have to pay for all the wrong He'd committed. I was the reaper and His time was up. I caught a taxi home from the bus station. I made the taxi driver drop me off at the top of my street and began to prepare for the battle I was about to embark. My mind was clear and calm. The Army had done a good job teaching me how to control my emotions. And even though my blood was ragingly pumping through my veins, to look at me at first glance you would have saw just another ordinary guy with no preconceived malice in his disposition. And that's exactly how I needed to be, the calm before the storm. Everyone knew I was coming home but no one knew when. And when was today. When was now! *And now I'd knock on this door and if He answered it, I'd let Him open the door and I'd walk inside right past Him as if nothing was wrong. I'd put my bag on the floor where He'd be standing behind me trying to pull rank with His hand on that popular back pocket holding all those knives. And that's when I'd turn around and break His neck before His hand had a chance to pull out one of those dull ass blades. And that would be then end of it all. That would be the conclusion to both of our lives and I couldn't care less about either of them. All I knew is that the suffering of Halia, Lijah and Paul would be over. And the world would go on just fine without the both of us.* So you can imagine my surprise when He didn't answer the door and she did, acting as if everything was peaches and cream.

"Sonny boy! Well hello there sonny boy! Come on in here and give ya' mama a big ol' hug!" I had just got there and her demeanor was already annoying me.

I just walked right past her and left her standing there with her arms stretched out. Though I had certainly changed, nothing here had changed too much. The home reeked of dirty laundry, dusty armpits and roach shit…an aroma that I had nearly forgot existed. I walked through the kitchen into the living room and dropped my bag to the floor. Mama just looked at me in disbelief that I didn't hug her. I ignored her but couldn't ignore the figure bouncing his back up against the couch in a familiar motion.

"You, you, you just get outta here Jesse. You just go back to where you, you, yooouuuu go from Jesse!" Paul stuttered his way through a ridiculous sentence as usual.

I just smiled at him because I did miss his yap, yap. He smiled back acknowledging my love for him. Then I heard the pitter patter of feet running down the stairs. I knew they weren't His because they weren't unannounced.

"Jesse! Welcome home!" Halia jumped on me and gave me a big ol' hug as if she hadn't seen me in decades. It did feel like a long time since I saw her last.

I held her in my arms tightly and then abruptly let her

go. I couldn't allow my love for her to distract me from the task at hand. I walked around her and ran up the stairs in a light trot. I looked towards Lijah's room and could easily see that no one was in there. Halia's door was open and no one was in there either. No one was in the bathroom and no one was in my old room. So that left one last room to check. All the other doors were open so they were easy to investigate. But as expected the door to His room was closed. At first I stood there expecting, anticipating it to open and for me to put my fist right through His face as soon as I saw Him. But after waiting only a few seconds the door never opened as I quickly ran out of patience and barged right in. I was expecting to have to dodge some weak ass kick or block some other futile attempt to harm me, but never had to because no one was in that room either. *Ahhhhh, the basement…hiding like a bitch in the basement are we?* I ran down to the basement but to no avail. No one was down there either. *Where could His cowardly ass be?*

"Where the fuck is He at?" I was furious at this point. I wanna know where the fuck He is!"

"Don't you comes in here with that foul language boy!" Mama was shaking a wooden spoon at me that she was using to make some goulash she was conjuring up for breakfast. "Is that what that military teachin' nowadays? How to have a potty mouth?"

"Lijah not here Jesse. He's probably over one of his friend's house. He may not have even come home last night. He's normally never here. But we didn't know what day you'd be coming home so…" I cut Halia's sentence off in a loud fit of rage!

"Ya'll know I'm not talking about Lijah! Where the fuck is He at Halia? Where's your sorry excuse for a daddy hiding?"

Mama had heard enough curse words for one day and tried to hit me in the head with the spoon. But I saw her coming a mile away and snatched the spoon out of her hand, broke it in half ad threw the pieces to the floor. The look in her eyes was pure terror. I looked around to Halia for answers and she was frightened too.

"He's not here! He doesn't live here anymore and hasn't lived here in awhile! What is wrong with you?" Halia shrieked out as if she was afraid I was going to hurt her.

I grabbed Halia by the shoulders and started shaking her and screaming, "Where does He live then? Where? Where? Where?"

"I don't know!" Halia said crying while trying to pull away from me. But I wouldn't let her go. Her tears and the fear in her voice made me start to cry.

"Why didn't you say anything? All this time He was hurting you and you couldn't tell someone? Even me? You couldn't tell even me?!!!"

Mama tried to pull me off of her but I wouldn't budge. "Don't you comes in here with all of that mess boy. You gets up outta heres with all of that foolishness. That ain't nothins' but the devil in you boy! In the name of Jesus I cast you out of here demon! You get up outta my son!"

I turned to her and looked at her with the type of eyes that burn through the soul.

"The only person in this house that has demons that need to be cast out of them is the inhuman Christian who would allow her satanic husband to not only beat and abuse her children, but also allow His evil ass to grossly molest the only daughter she has. Tell me something Mama, did you pray about it often? Did you ask Pastor what you should do? Did Pastor tell you to stick it out while He was sticking you and her?"

Once again I was in another blind rage where I could barely see anything in front of my face. I started slowly walking towards my mom as if she was now the true enemy. Though I had let go of her arms Halia just stood there frozen as if I still had hold of them watching me walk towards Mama as if I was going to kill her. My mom started slowly backing up as she had never seen me this angry before. I could see the terror flowing through her body as her arms and hands began to shake with fear.

"Did you pray to God for His soul and yours? Obey your father and mother so that your days are long upon the earth. Isn't that what the bible says? So did Halia think that she was supposed to obey Him and let Him put His filthy hands all over her? Or did she think that she was supposed to obey you and follow your weak ass until she fell into a deep depression that ruined her chances of a good education and healthy home? You and Him should burn in hell for this. But God won't let you go to hell because you've already been there. THIS IS HELL! CAN'T YOU SEE THAT? YOU'VE ALREADY BEEN TO HELL AND BACK AND YOU TOOK US ALL ALONG FOR THE RIDE WITH YOU!!!"

"Ahhhhooooooochhhhh!" Mama screamed out in pain as she backed into the hot stove and burned her hand.

Halia ran upstairs crying her eyes out. I had inadvertently torn open wounds that she was probably trying to close. Paul was sitting on the couch bouncing back and forth with his hands over his ears chanting, "Go away. Go away. Go away."

What had I done? This is not what I wanted. I didn't come home to hurt them. I came home to hurt Him! And He wasn't here! I looked at Mama one good time and turned away in disgrace to leave.

"Where's ya going son? Don't leave. Come to church with me tonights. And next week we're going on a trip to visit another church in Detroit. We're staying ats a hotel overnights and then we's coming backs in tha' mornings. It's gones' ta be blessed boy. Come on witcha' mama next week why don't ya?"

I still loved her and didn't know why. She had done so many things to break my heart but yet I still loved her. But

I needed to hurt her. Why? Because her incompetence had hurt us all.

"I wouldn't go to church with you Mama if Jesus was preaching the sermon himself and afterwards God was picking you up in a stretch limousine to drive us all to heaven. I don't know where I'm about to go right now, but I gotta' get the hell outta' here!" I walked out and slammed the door behind me.

That week was not a good week for me. I found out that Lijah was a wild child running all over the city. Mama couldn't control him so I had to have a talk with him. Come to find out he really wasn't doing anything but playing video games all night so I gave him a pass. Halia wouldn't come out of her room that much. I think I set an entire entourage of emotions off in her that she didn't know how to address. Christie was acting strange too. She had already made the mistake of not talking to me or writing me enough when I was out of state. I was disappointed and I let her know how I felt about that. But now that I was home she hadn't even made any attempts yet to call me or see me for that matter. Knowing that I would only be back for a few weeks I assumed that she would have made every attempt to hang out with me as much as possible. But instead she just had excuse after excuse as to why she couldn't. Something didn't smell right to me about the entire situation so I got upset with her and we got into a fight over the phone. It was the type of fight where you didn't have to finish it with "let's just go our separate ways" as that was already understood from the tone of the conversation. And my mom was constantly moping around the house like she had lost a new born puppy. She knew I was upset with her and she didn't know how to handle it. However, at least I was back to doing what I loved doing all the time…walking. We had walked plenty in the military however that was with pounds and pounds of gear on our backs. I didn't enjoy that type of walking like what I was doing now. I think I liked walking so much because of the freedom that came along with it. Running too. The freedom to change direction and go another way at any time made me feel alive. Waking is cool and all but I did need a vehicle. I couldn't possibly walk all the way to Missouri and I didn't want to take the bus either. Yes, it was high time for me to have my own car. Not only was there a nice car lot right up the road from the house, but my bank was there also. After cursing my mom out, day after day after day, I decided one day to go to the car lot instead. There was a beautiful little red four door Chevy that had limited miles on it that I had my eye on. At first the dealer didn't think I was serious about purchasing a car, probably because I was only 18 years old. But once he found out that I was in the Army, my birthday was in a few days and that I had enough money to make   a large down payment, he started taking me more serious. So now I was on my way to the bank to get the deposit. In fact I was contemplating taking out enough money to buy the entire car cash so that I wouldn't have to make monthly payments. Wow, I really was starting to see light at the end of my life tunnel. I was about to buy a new car and I had the money to do it. By my recollection, at a little more than one thousand dollars a month Army salary and twelve months of hard work, sweat and strict disciplined saving, I had about ten to twelve thousand dollars at my immediate disposal to make a great purchase.

"Next in line please." The bank teller was looking at me to move forward for assistance. "How can I help you today sir?"

"I don't know. Usually when I come in here it's just to cash a check for about $100.00 or so. But today is different. Today I'm going to make a withdrawal and go buy   a new car!" I was so excited my tone went to a level not conducive of typical bank chatter.

"Well that's wonderful news. Will you be withdrawing from your checking or savings account?" The teller said with a smile.

"That would be my savings account. And before you

even ask, here's some identification for you so you don't think I'm in here trying to rob the place." I handed her my military I.D. knowing that it would have all of the information on it she needed to have to find my account. "I think I'd like to withdraw either five thousand dollars or possibly ten thousand. I just can't decide!" I could barely hold back my enthusiasm to finally be in the bank and talking about real money instead of asking for an envelope to hold a measly $40.00.

Suddenly the teller began to give me a look that I had seen them give others when they're about to deliver bad news to a customer (it's an I'm confused for you, but I'm not confused myself type of look). "Sir, uhhhhh I do see that you have a savings account."

"Yes. I do." I reply as I follow her eyes as they continue to scan her computer screen in awe.

"And you can make a withdrawal…"

"Yes. I can. And will be glad to do so. So should I withdraw $5000.00 or should I withdraw twice that?" I confidently asked. "Or do you need special permission from your manager to withdraw so much money at one time? If so, I'll be happy to tell your manager why I need my money."

"Sir, you don't have ten thousand or five thousand dollars in your account. You only have fifteen hundred dollars. So would you like to withdraw fifteen hundred today?" The words fell from her lips as if she knew I could only ever afford to have fifteen hundred dollars, never ten thousand.

I just giggled because I knew she had made a mistake on her little computer screen somehow.

"You must have the wrong amount pulled up my dear. My name is Jesse W Benson. You have my military I.D. Look up my account based off my social security number, not my name. I'm sure there's another Jesse Benson somewhere with only fifteen hundred dollars in his account, but this Jesse Benson…middle initial W…has been saving his monthly salary with minimal withdrawals for an entire year. So check again please, correctly this time. My new car awaits!"

"Sir, I have the right account pulled up. It is under your social. And I do see your monthly deposits from the Army here, same time, same day, every month. But I also see a lot of withdrawals every month as well. In fact, the withdrawals are all in house from this bank." The teller was mocking my sarcastic tone now with her own.

"What, that's impossible! I haven't even been here to do any withdrawals. I've been in Georgia and have only withdrew money a few times and that was for some pizza. Georgia doesn't sell ten thousand dollar pizza, and even if they did I wouldn't buy any! There must be some kind of mistake here!" I was starting to freak out and the teller could tell.

"Sir, I'm looking here and I see in house withdrawals as early as a few weeks ago. I also see that you are not the only person with access to this account. Who is Ms. Jackson? Is that your girlfriend or something? Maybe she's the one you should be questioning, not me. So do you want to withdraw a different amount or not?"

I can't take this anymore! I'm about to kill a bitch! The question is which one? Do I kill this smart mouth teller who thinks she's smarter than me just because she has a job behind a counter that has done a poor job of protecting my money? Or do I kill my mama who I just realized (and I should have known better than to trust her knuckle headed ass to begin with) has been coming to the bank regularly withdrawing large amounts of my money without my knowledge or permission. I told this stupid chick that she could withdraw money in case of an emergency and to tell me if she had to do so. What kind of ten thousand dollar emergency could she had possibly had. Oh my God...she better not have given all of my money to that damn church! Please Baby Jesus say it ain't so. You wouldn't let her do that to me, would you? Well just to let you know if she did

I'm burning the entire church to the ground. Say it ain't so Lord! If she did I'm burning it faster than you burned Moses' bush!"

Trying to sound as civil as I could I looked at the teller with confidence and said, "Yes…withdraw one thousand dollars please and thank you."

Now what in the sevens fucks was I going to do with a thousand dollars? The dealership needed more than a thousand dollars down to give me the car I wanted because I had zero credit to my name. So now all I could afford was a car that wouldn't get me to Missouri, even if I could push it there! When I got back home me and Mama got into it big time. The good news was I found out that she hadn't withdrawn all of my money to give it to the church. The bad news was she did something even dumber than that. She had got addicted to calling 1-900 numbers trying to win millions of dollars on games where you had to answer multiple questions about new action movies that came out. If you could answer a certain amount of questions in a row correctly you'd win a million dollars. My mom was calling these hotlines multiple times a day. The cost to make the initial call was around $5.00 per call. Each additional minute after that was around $3.00 per minute. Before she new it the phone bill was thousands of dollars. You'd think she would have learned a lesson after losing the first few hundred dollars. But nope, not my mom. She would lose thousands and thousands of dollars until she had literally lost ten thousand of my hard earned money. *What a fucking moron! Who never works a job in their entire life but finds the balls to take all of their son's money and give it to the phone company? To make matters worse her excuse was that she did it to ensure that the phone didn't get cut off just in case I decided to call her, knowing at the time I wanted nothing to do with calling her. On top of that, she had allowed the phone to get cut off plenty of times for bills that were two to three hundred dollars in the past. But somehow she just couldn't stomach allowing the phone to get shut off for a ten thousand dollar bill? I knew bad teeth with more wisdom than this chick, and that was sad considering she had been praying for years for God to give her the wisdom of King Solomon. I guess he wasn't listening to her again!* But just when I thought all hope was lost for me, an old guy who lived across the street from us was selling his barely ever driven car. It had very low miles on it and he had kept it in stellar condition. It was a very clean, white and grey with white walled wheels Lincoln Continental with a limited addition fifth wheel on the back. It had leather interior, a wood grained dash and inside was power everything. What a beautiful car and it just so happened that I loved Lincolns! They were luxurious and at the time anyone driving one was considered a rather important individual. The old dude was trying to get rid of the car and happened to be selling it for a whopping

$900.00. *Bingo! What a steal! Somehow, someway my luck was finally starting to change for the positive.* I immediately started driving the car around the city. It purred like a kitten. I found myself driving all over town daily. I had a lot of ground to make up seeing old friends and such, with little time to do so because in just another week I'd have to return back to the military. I loved to play basketball so on many days I found myself doing just that with all of my friends. They were so happy to see me. I missed them a lot and they missed me. I started picking my boys up and we started playing basketball at this really nice court I found in the suburbs. Some days I would go alone because I wanted time to myself just to think things over. Christie had really broken my heart. *I mean my entire reasoning behind joining the military mainly had to do with her. Well her and the fact that I needed to get the fuck out of my entire life at that time.* But that's when I met this really cool girl at the basketball court. Her name was Carla and she was beautiful. She was also smart. She was a little skinny to my liking, but there were so many other great things about her that I quickly forgot about that. We started spending a lot of time together in a short period of time. The best part about it was that she liked me for exactly who I was. In fact she liked me more than I liked me! Even Christie didn't like me as much as she did. In just a few days Carla didn't like me anymore, she loved me. And her love for me was real. And I could tell. I liked her a lot too. I hadn't fell in love with her yet. I was actually still in love with Christie. But Carla was quickly changing that. She was well on her way to becoming the love of my life and I needed one of those! But the one thing that was about to come in between everything was the fact that I had to leave. It was time for me to report to base and I had about two days to do so. But I wasn't ready to leave. In fact I was terrified to do so. Besides really growing fond of Carla I was also waiting for the day for Him to try and come back into my family's lives. I knew one day He'd try to and I wanted to be there when He did. I still needed to desperately kill Him. I needed to know He'd never be able to hurt anyone again, especially in my family. But He hadn't come back, at least not yet. However I was still afraid that the moment I went back to the military He'd show His ugly mug back up at our house. *What the fuck you gonna' to do Jesse? Break the law and not go back to the military? You gonna' let this stupid mother fucker ruin your life even more than what He already has? I think not!*

Chapter 24
a Fickle Beast

Life is a fickle beast. There will be defining moments in yours that no matter how you react, the instances will cause catastrophic differences in how the world moves for and around you. And here lay one of mine. It was the night that my mom was scheduled to go on that bus trip to the church she was trying to visit in Detroit. She had begged me to go multiple times *(truly only because I had cut her off from my bank account and she wanted some extra spending money for the trip)* and I told her multiple times to piss off. She had been on the phone all day talking to church folks *(the same phone that she racked up a ten thousand dollar bill on)* and because it was a very old cordless phone she had either destroyed the battery life of it forever with all of her endless church gossip, or the roaches had gotten to it and eaten all of the important wires that permitted proper phone charging. In either case right before she left the phone would no longer charge. It was getting late in the evening around 10:00pm and I was supposed to go over Carla's house when she got off of work at 11:00pm. I needed to report to base in Fort Leonard Wood the next day, no particular time but well before the end of the day or I could be considered AWOL (Absent Without Official Leave) which was against military rules. I hadn't told Carla that I was planning to leave the next day. In fact I hadn't told anyone. I was just going to disappear again. I liked disappearing. It began to become very empowering to me. So since tonight would officially be my last night in town, I decided to call some of my friends just to hear their voices one last time before I was off again for another year or so. *Son of a bitch! This damn phone never works!* So I decided to jump in my car and drive around the corner to a pay phone and make some calls from it. The night was bright as the pay phone was on a main highway with lots of traffic. I pulled up to the the phone as it was one of the ones that you could talk to people from the inside of your car. I cut my car off because the power windows worked even when the car was off as long as the key was in the ignition. Most cars couldn't do that so I thought that was really cool. And there I sat. And talked. And sat. And talked. I called many different people because all it cost was a quarter a call. Before I knew it 30 minutes had shot right on by. As I was talking to this one friend of mine I noticed that a couple of guys were hanging out walking back and forth in front of my car. One of them disappeared but the other one just patiently waited near the curb. After a few more minutes he walked up to my window and knocked on the glass. Since the window was partially open from the phone cord being in the way of rolling the window all the way up, I could easily hear what he had to say without rolling it down. He asked if he could use the phone. I signaled to him ok and he walked back over to the curb near the street. I told my friend I would have to call her back another time and ended the call. I rolled the window down and hung the phone up. Instead of instantly starting the car I decided to roll the window back up first taking full advantage of the power window's off car functionality because of the "cool factor." As soon as the window was up I went to start the car and smash! The window had busted and broken glass had flown all over the place, including my face. *What the fuck? Did some wild ass dirt truck just pass and did one of its rocks just fly off the top of it and smash through my window? Great, that's all I need right now is a busted window when I'm about to have to drive out of here to Missouri tomorrow. And why is my leg hurting?*

"Give me all your money mother fucker!" The voice

sounded familiar as the culprit was the guy that had just asked me if he could use the phone.

I turned my head to see the guy and instead of seeing his face I saw the barrel of a gun sticking right into mine. *Was this little dude serious? Something told me to stay my ass in the house tonight. Why didn't I listen? Give you all of my money? Nigga please! My mama done took all of my money. I be damned if you think I'm about to give you the little shit I got left!*

"Man I ain't got no money! You got the wrong one playa!" I looked at him sarcastically as if in his hand all he had was a pencil. I hand't checked to see if I had any money on me or not. It was a regular response by habit if anyone ever asked me to borrow money, I'd always reply with I didn't have any. It was always my first response whether I had some or not.

"Nigga you think I'm playing with your bitch ass? I said give me all your money fool!" The guy pushed his gun closer to my nose. His blatant disrespect of me having any athleticism infuriated me. I hated punks anyway. (I don't know what it is about me but I just don't like punky type folks). And he was definitely a punk ass! Here I was trying to have a good last night in town and here comes this punk trying to roll me over with his pistol. But if there was one thing that rang true about me it was my speed. I wasn't a punk either. I was the type of guy that watched scary movies and if someone fell running from the monster I might just cut the film off in disgust before it was even finished. Because falling just wasn't something I believed in, period. Knowing who I was and how fast I was I just reached out to grab his gun. Unfortunately for me I grabbed it by the barrel. I caught him so off guard that I almost pulled the gun right out of his hand. But before I could pull it all the way out the gun went off. Boom! *Whoa! What the fuck was that? Now that's some hot ass shit! Mother got' damn fucker! Shit! This shit is hotter than hot! It's scalding!* In one hop I jumped from the driver seat into the passenger seat holding my wounded hand. The heat from the bullet was melting through my bones. My hand felt like someone had flipped it inside out like a glove and rested it on top of a barbecue grill! It was as if all of the nerves in my hand were soaked in lighter fluid and set aflame. It is the hottest thing I have ever felt.

"Damn my nigga, what the fuck are you doing? You done shot me in the fucking hand. You shooting already? We ain't even negotiate or nothing. Damn nigga!" I pleaded with the shooter. *All my super hero shit seeped right out of my body as soon as that bullet burned through my hand. I was no longer this confident military athlete. I was the fallen victim in the horror movies I hated so much!*

"I told you I ain't playin' wit' yo ass! Now give me all the money bitch!" The shooter was getting impatient. He had a certain look in his eye that seemed familiar. I had seen that look before in the Projects. It was the look of a desperate dope fein!

"Ok, ok I'll give you what I got!" I was shaking my hand back and forth as it was blazing with pain. That's when I realized that I may be in big trouble. If I did have any money it wasn't in the pockets of these pants because these didn't have pockets. It was so late at night I forgot I ran out the house in my pajamas. I only had some quarters that I had brought with me to use the pay phone. "Look man, I really don't have anything. Look at how I'm dressed homie! Hold up. Wait. I know. Looka' here. I've got some money right here stashed away in this here astray. This is all I got homie!" I opened my ashtray to show this ass hole what I had, and all I had was some small change mainly quarters that may have added up to about two dollars total. I guess he was disappointed in my find because it seemed to piss him off even more than what he already was.

"I'm telling you to give me all the fucking money bitch or this next shot's going in your head!" The guy was adamant, leaning all the way inside of the car now. *In my head? Oh you got me fucked up playboy! I'll be damned if*

I let some punk ass nigga like you just shoot me in the head over some quarters, dimes and a bunch of pennies. You're talking to someone that's Projects and Army bred son, not some regular Joe Schmo! There was no time to think so I just jumped across the armrest of the car reaching out with my left hand, this time ensuring not to grab the barrel of the gun. We struggled back and forth for a bit and when he and I pulled back in opposite directions, one of us had the gun and the other didn't. And the one that didn't have it was me! *Son of a bitch!* He shot at me again and this time the bullet slapped me in the neck. *Damn, this mother fucker did just try to shoot me in the head. I gotta' get the hell out of this car before this nigga ends up killing me. He done already shot me in the hand and now in the neck. I think he may have shot me in the leg too when he shot through the window to start this crazy fiasco.* I turned my back towards him to open the passenger door to get out of car. Bang! He shot me once more. The bullet slammed into my lower back. It felt like I had been kicked by a mule! But this shot was different than the others. There was an absence of pain with this one. It felt cold, not hot. And it had went into something…something strong and sturdy. *Why can't I get out of this damn car? And why can't I move? Why has my body squashed itself down into the crawl space of this damn car? What the fuck is going on here?* As my head lay rested on the seat of the car with my legs squished together like noodles, I patiently awaited for the guy to come over to my side of the car, open my door and finish me off.

You know how some people believe when you're dying your life history flashes in front of your eyes right before you go? That shit's actually true. As I lay there awaiting my fate my entire life began to flip through my mind like photographs on a rolodex. I saw Manny and I fighting over cake at my first birthday party. I saw Leslie (to no avail) trying to make us play with Barbie dolls instead of Transformers. I saw plenty of visions of my mom, Lijah, Halia and Paul trying to survive Him. My entire life was being played back to me from start to finish lightening fast.

And that's when the rolodex finally flipped to Manny's death. And in an instant I began to cry because I had promised him that I would have a better life than he did, that I would live this wonderful life for the both of us in his absence. I had promised Manny that I would never get caught up in the street life because he had already experienced that for the both of us and paid dearly for it. And I had promised him that when I died it wouldn't be at the hands of a gun and inside a vehicle. Yet, here I was. I wasn't selling drugs but this lunatic that was shooting me certainly seemed like he needed to buy some. I was dying at the hands of a gun and to make matters worse I was bleeding out right on the floor of a car...just like Manny had! And the rolodex stopped. There was nothing else left for life to show me as it had sped past all the memories I had within just a few minutes. I was about to become another young dead black kid killed way before his time and there was nothing I could do about it. And just when I closed my eyes to give up the ghost, there she was! I could hear her just as clearly as I used to hear her when she was with me.

"Is this what you gone' do? Boy, if this is what you was gonna do you might as well had not even sat down at the table." Her voice was strong. Stronger than I had ever heard it before.

"Grandma?" I was frightened to even question if that was her speaking. "What are you doing here?"

I know I'm dying now because I'm hearing dead people. Great!

"So you've forgotten my voice, did ya?" She said with a snap.

I knew I shouldn't have thought that!

"If you didn't want to play then why'd you set up the board?" She snapped at me again. "Things are going to get a lot worse for you before they get better. But you'll be ok!"

"Grandma, what in the bejesus are you talking about?!!!" I barely had the strength to reply but had just enough strength to show my frustration.

"Don't cha use that tone of voice with me son and leave Jesus outta' this here mess you done got yo' self intas'! Now I said, if ya's didn't wants to play, then why you bring out this here board and set ups all the pieces? OoooooooooooWeeeeeee! You done's forgots' what Grandma done gave ya, didn't ya? You done went to that fancy school and done learned how to plays chess and done forgots' how's to plays checkers, didn't ya? And now you's a sittin' down there feelin' all sorry for yourself and about to just give it all up? Cause you's done forgots' everythang' I taught ya!"

Her voice was stinging my heart like a deadly scorpion and what was swelling up inside of my soul was something that would never be minimized ever again. But my mind was dying. And no amount of heart is big enough to replace a dying mind.

I can't do this anymore. And I just don't want to. I tried. But ever since you left my entire life has been one long losing fight. And I just don't have the strength to try anymore Grandma. I'm ready to go. I've been ready to leave this place!

"Boy you don't thinks I can hear those negative nasty thoughts of yours? I can hear those louder than your big mouth! Now ya's listens to me and ya's listens close. You may be ready to go, but the world is not ready for you to leave yet. There's so many people that you're going to help that you haven't even met. There'll be millions and millions of them that you'll touch and influence in unimaginable ways. You don't think that all of this suffering you had to endure was for not, do you? Hahahahahaha, oh silly boy you do think that don't you? You have suffered mentally, physically and emotionally your entire life to prepare you to be worthy!"

Worthy? I loosely thought.

"Yes. You have to be worthy to have an impact in people's lives son. So in other words you have to be well trained. Certified. Tested. And approved. And there was no other way to prepare you for such a journey. That's why you had to learn how to play checkers with me, the hard way. And even though later on you learned how to play chess, life for you will always be a continuous game of checkers. There will be people in this world that only exist to try and wipe out all of the good pieces that exist on your board of life. And no matter how many of these good things disappear, you must remember that you're a king. Don't you ever forget that! Because one king can turn the entire game of life around. All he has to do is jump! So jump son! Jump up! You jump up right now and receive the life that is meant to be yours!"

And just like that, she was gone.

Chapter 25

From Him to him!

It didn't happen right away. And as always, Grandma was right. Things got a lot worse before they got better. That night I did manage to somehow jump up. The shooter just ran off. He probably figured that if he wasn't getting any money after four shots, what's the point? Either that or he heard Grandma's spooky voice too? I crawled back into the driver seat with just enough energy to drive home. I should have just used the pay phone to call 911, because when I got home our phone was still dead. Blood was everywhere. I had just enough energy to crawl myself to the back porch and collapse. I couldn't walk. Something was wrong with my legs but I didn't know what. I passed out a few times. I woke up once in the ambulance with paramedics standing on top of me and then next in the hospital with doctors doing the same. They worked on me throughout the night into the early morning. The next time I awoke   I had a patched up neck and leg, a steel plate in my hand holding my bones together accompanied by the itchiest arm cast known to man, and a bullet in my lower spine that couldn't be removed because the doctors feared that surgery could inflict further damage than what was already done and cause permanent paralysis. For the next few weeks that hospital would be my home. But even though I had tackled most things in my life solo, this time I was not alone. Carla was at my hospital bedside every single day. When I woke up, she was there. When I fell asleep, she was there. When I was sweating from the intense pain in my lower back she was screaming at the hospital staff to help me. And when I couldn't feel anything from the waist down she consoled me and told me that I'd be alright. She was just happy that I was still alive! Christie had came to the hospital once or twice for a few minutes. But I believe she only came those few times out of guilt. I was falling out of love with someone who truly didn't love me and falling into love with someone who did. It's a shame it took four gun shots and paralysis to expose that. My mom came to the hospital as well. She brought Pastor with her. Pastor I liked, but she could have just sent him to visit me alone. They both went to praying for me as if they needed to clear out the evil forces all around me that had invaded my life. I didn't even have enough energy or resolve to argue with them. I just let them pour that blessed olive oil all over my forehead and pray away. *Isn't there some after church french fries or fried chicken that could use this oil better than my face?* Besides, it wasn't like I could just get up out the bed and walk off. That was the bad thing about being paralyzed. You just couldn't walk away from whoever you thought was full of shit. You had to sit there and take it. I wasn't used to that. I was used to fighting for everything I had when I could and then running away as needed. And now I couldn't do either. That's where the depression set in. I was mentally drained and emotionally devastated. My ego was just as broken as my hand except my hand had been put in a cast. But my ego was shattered into so many pieces that there seemed to be no way to mend it. It didn't help my ego either that I was shitting all over myself randomly and didn't even know it. *That's right. The bullet in my spine had caused paralysis that wouldn't allow me to know when I needed to take a shit. So my bowel movements were coming out on their own. I only found out when I started complaining to the nurse about the terrible smell in my room all the time. I told her that I wanted to switch rooms because of it. She had to embarrassingly tell me that it was me. No wonder the nurses were always coming in and giving me baths. I thought they just wanted to see me naked all the time. What a dumbass!* But there was one person that was just as determined as Grandma had been to see me become something great and that person was Carla. She had only knew me for a few weeks but she loved me with all of her heart, unconditionally. And I had no idea why. I liked her a lot. But deep down inside I was in love with someone else, someone that was not for me. And in spite of all that Carla still loved me. It didn't matter that I couldn't walk and smelled like rotten fruit. It didn't matter that I was depressed to the point of starvation and had lost about 60 pounds in two months. It didn't matter that I was an asshole and just wanted to crawl up in a corner and die. She just kept coming back day after day because she saw something in me that only her and Grandma saw and loved. It took some time, over a year to be exact... but finally I started to believe in myself what Grandma and Carla believed in me the entire time. I got to the other side of that board, kinged myself and started to jump over every negative and pitiful thought, emotion and feeling that existed in my heart, mind and soul. And it wasn't until I conquered those things that I began to walk, feel and love again! *That's right. After a year the paralysis was over and I began to walk again. God had not forsaken me. God had not ignored all of my prayers since I was a small boy. He had just been adding them up and saving his responses for this very moment in my life. Thank you God. Thank you!*

It was a beautiful day. The sun was playing hide and seek between the clouds throwing warm shadows and dancing rays of light upon everything beneath its gaze. The city wasn't too loud today. I could hear the birds' and bees' songs of life floating over lightly honked horns and neighborly chatter. I was over my mom's house visiting Halia, Lijah and Paul. They were all doing well and that pleased me. Carla and I had gotten our own place. We were in love and trying to start a life of our own. It was going to be a struggle financially since we both had absolutely nothing in terms of money or support, but we had everything in terms of spirit. And great spirits can move mountains and cross oceans! Surprisingly…I was no longer angry at my mom. I had forgiven her for everything she had done to me/ us. I even understood from her point of view where things had went wrong in her own life. And from that understanding came great compassion accompanied with sorrowful pity. I forgave her because all the times she didn't do well, I knew deep down inside she always meant well. And in my opinion that was as good of enough place to start in rectifying our relationship as any. While I was standing out on the porch reflecting on the life I had I saw something in the distance that made all the hairs on my arms stand up. I knew that walk like I knew my own. But His had a bebop to it that I'd never forget. I could see His cocky, crooked silhouette sliding down the path toward me in those same dingy tan cargo pants He had always worn. They sagged a little to the right from the plethora of ancient cookware weaponry in His back pocket. His walk was stiff with intent as He was on a mission. And I knew exactly what that mission was. He wanted to come back to His home. A home that was no longer His to come back to. *Over my dead body! All the agony and pain He caused torturing us for all those years would never be repeated. Not with this family!* There was a rush of anger flash flooding through my body like ocean water seizing a submarine with a huge hole in its side. The fury was overwhelming. I could not contain it. He must not have saw me from a distance as He walked down the road, but as soon as He reached the corner He couldn't help but notice me. I jumped over the side of the porch like a crazed gorilla. The average man would have slipped or at least stumbled a little with a jump like that, but the animal within me would not let it be. I landed with two feet flatly planted in the dirt like a skilled acrobat. My knees were half bent in a stance leaning forward like a wild cat ready to pounce on some unfortunate prey. All He had to do was place one foot off that curb as if He were going to make an attempt to cross the street towards our home and I would have killed Him before His second foot could have joined His first. But when our eyes locked, He froze in His tracks along with time itself. Everything had stopped moving. The air between us had stiffened with the eeriness of death, as it ran away from me and chose Him. And since He was not unfamiliar with death's chill, it made Him pause dead in His tracks. And for the first time I saw something in His eyes I had never seen before. *Defeat!* And something registered in me that I had not known for a long time. *Freedom!* And from that moment on He was no longer He. He had now turned to he, the way God had always intended him to be. And I for the first time knew that to be the case. And for him I was now Me! Me…Me… ME!!! I slowly moved my foot forward as if I was about to charge him and he let out a small yelp of terror. Something came out of his mouth that sounded like "please" but I couldn't tell because of how weak it was. And as sudden as it all happened he had turned around and fled. We had not exchanged words, but the near silent conversation we did have confirmed his understanding that in him fleeing away, if I ever saw him again I would kill him on sight. And till this day our paths have never crossed again.

Chapter 26
Juliet Rose

Everything's different now. Or maybe nothing's different at all? Or maybe everything's nothing and every thing that is nothing is where it is supposed to be? Who knows? All those years of suffering I thought God wasn't listening to my pleas. I thought God had abandoned the idea of me having a purpose on the earth. But my thoughts were wrong along with everything I thought I knew. God was listening and today I have a purpose. God told me *one cannot become gold being silver!* Gold must go through the fire to become gold and I had to suffer to become me. And that suffering is now someone else's refuge. *Wow! Who knew? God did!*

Today I'm continuing to keep the promise I made my brother Manny when he was brutally murdered 25 years ago. That promise was for him to respectfully and successfully continue to live his life through me. Him and I are doing just that. And I'm keeping the promise I made to Grandma 35 years ago before she passed. That promise is to be a king and to jump over all obstacles no matter how large. Every time one of those hurdles appear, up and over I go! Last but certainly not least I'm keeping the promise that I made to myself when I was born and that promise was to always live in spite of. I am humbled to be alive today. Many people where I'm from never get to see their 16th birthday. Many of them never get to enjoy what this life and world truly have to offer. But I am fortunate to have a different fate. And I am honored to have this opportunity to share my life story with you. If you are living a life of great adversity, I am hoping that this story registers deep within your heart to encourage you to press on through the storm. Because you are here for a reason. Even if that reason has not manifested itself to you yet. If you keep pressing on, I'm sure it will. I can still hear Grandma speaking loud and clear to me every now and then. Her voice strong and true like it has always been:

"Sometimes when you close your eyes you can hear every pounding word he said grinding against your sanity and serenity, but neither has abandoned you. And even though it can get excruciatingly loud inside your head, you are never silently alone. You have a beautiful family now. You're living in a home greater than any one you and I could have possibly imagined. You're Vice President in a very successful, multimillion dollar corporation. And you're getting the opportunity to inspire and positively change the lives of many people. I would say that's impressive but you and I both know you're just getting started! Your mind is a rare jewel and your heart is a precious stone. And though the world may have believed you were worthless and pitiful, they were highly wrong and dangerously mistaken. Many have lost. Many have cried. And many have died. At any given time you could have been any of them, and in return they you. But you cannot become gold being silver. And I say that to say this. Remember where you come from and that you deserve absolutely nothing in this life. But you're worth absolutely everything. Because it was your Penniless Soul that fertilized the unforgiving soil for you to blossom into the Juliet Rose you were always meant to be. So just be!"

Jesse W. Benson

Time is the only thing that we have and do not have all at once. Thank you for taking the time to read this book and experience some excerpts from my life. As I know your time is precious, sharing it with me is highly appreciated. I hope that you enjoyed this experience as much as I enjoyed sharing it with you.

You can reach me at:
jessewbensontheauthor@gmail.com
jwbenson23@gmail.com